# Group theory for chemists

*MACMILLAN PHYSICAL SCIENCE*

**Series advisers**

Physics titles: Dr R L Havill, *University of Sheffield*
Dr A K Walton, *University of Sheffield*

Chemistry titles: Dr D M Adams, *University of Leicester*
Dr M Green, *University of York*

**Titles in the series**

Group Theory for Chemists, *G Davidson*
Chemical Kinetics, *M Robson Wright*
Cyclic Organic Chemistry, *M Gagan*
Thermal Physics, *M T Sprackling*
Low Temperature Physics, *A Kent*

MACMILLAN PHYSICAL SCIENCE SERIES

# Group theory for chemists

George Davidson
*Dept of Chemistry, University of Nottingham*

M
MACMILLAN

First edition 1991

Published by
MACMILLAN EDUCATION LTD
Houndmills, Basingstoke, Hampshire RG21 2XS
and London
Companies and representatives
throughout the world

Printed in Hong Kong

British Library Cataloguing in Publication Data
Davidson, George
Group theory for chemists.
1. Group theory
I. Title
512.2
ISBN 0–333–49298–6 pbk

# Contents

# Preface

The number of areas of chemistry where the application of simple group theoretical ideas is important for undergraduate and postgraduate students has greatly increased over recent years.

This book, written as part of the Macmillan Physical Science Series, covers the essential group theory encountered in undergraduate and postgraduate chemistry courses, with the emphasis throughout on the application of theory.

The aim has been to include a wide range of examples without unnecessarily increasing the level of difficulty for the reader. Only a very modest mathematical background is needed to be able to use this book, although an elementary knowledge of quantum mechanics and bonding theory would be helpful.

I would like to thank the series advisers for their comments on the manuscript. I am also very grateful to the many Nottingham students who have asked so many searching questions; to my colleagues, especially Professor J J Turner and Dr A H Wright, for very helpful suggestions and comments; and above all to my family, for their patience during the anti-social occupation of writing the book.

George Davidson
Nottingham, England
1990

# 1

# Symmetry elements and symmetry operations

The idea of 'symmetry' has been understood for a very long time, and the relationship of the symmetry of an object to its aesthetic appeal has been appreciated from the earliest ages. Our aim here is to make the idea of symmetry quantitative, so that we can use the symmetry properties of a molecule to simplify many of the problems concerning the structure of molecules and the bonding of their constituent atoms. We will be dealing mainly with applications that concern isolated, finite molecules, but the extension to objects that can be regarded as infinite (for example, crystal lattices) is not too difficult.

It is possible to classify the symmetry of any object in terms of the **symmetry operations** that can be carried out on that object. We will see that symmetry operations involve, for example, the rotation of the object about a certain axis. The essential property of such operations is that they bring the object into an **equivalent configuration**. Such a configuration cannot be distinguished from the original one, but it need not be identical with it, as some equivalent parts of the object may have been interchanged.

Consider, for example, any square piece of card (Figure 1.1). If this is rotated by 90° about an axis perpendicular to the plane of the card, and passing through the centre, the resulting configuration looks the same to the observer as the original. The only way in which we can show the effect of the rotation is to label the four corners, and then we see that the final configuration is not identical to the original. Further rotations by 90° about this axis can, however, be carried out, and each one is a symmetry operation for this object. When four rotations, each by 90°, have been carried out, the resulting configuration is then strictly identical to the original.

Before giving a more systematic description of all the symmetry operations that can be found in isolated molecules, it is first necessary to distinguish between two closely related, but nevertheless different, entities: *symmetry operations* and *symmetry elements*. The former are motions of an object, such as the rotations just described, which carry the object

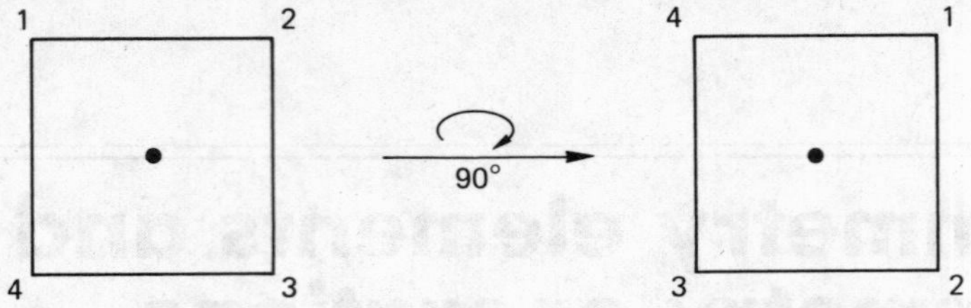


**Figure 1.1**

into an equivalent configuration – that is, an observer cannot distinguish between the initial and final states. All the symmetry operations of a finite body can be expressed in terms of rotations and reflections (see later). Such operations are intimately connected with the symmetry elements possessed by a body. Thus, a given rotation must be carried out about its symmetry *axis*, whereas any reflection is carried out with respect to a specified *plane*. These axes and planes are said to constitute the symmetry elements of a body, and they define the rotations and reflections that are its symmetry operations. Briefly, therefore, symmetry elements are geometrical constructions (lines, planes and also points – see later), whereas symmetry operations are movements of the various parts of a body (with respect to these lines, planes and points) which carry that body into indistinguishable configurations. We may note that it is the operations that are fundamental to this work, not the elements, and also that there can be more than one operation associated with a given element, as in the example of Figure 1.1, where the element is the axis about which rotation occurs.

We can now list systematically the symmetry elements, and their resultant operations, for all cases of interest.

## 1.1 Rotations: Axes of symmetry

We have already encountered the symmetry operation of rotation about an axis of symmetry. Some simple molecules can be used to illustrate various axes commonly found – for example, the water molecule (Figure 1.2). The only rotation axis, lying in the plane of the molecule, is shown by a dashed line, and rotation by 180° about this axis gives a configuration indistinguishable from the original. A different axis is illustrated by the $BF_3$ molecule (Figure 1.3). The axis here is perpendicular to the plane of the paper, passing through the boron atom, and rotation of the molecule by 120° about this axis is clearly a symmetry operation for this molecule. By convention, the rotations are shown as clockwise movements of the molecule, when looking down the axis from above.

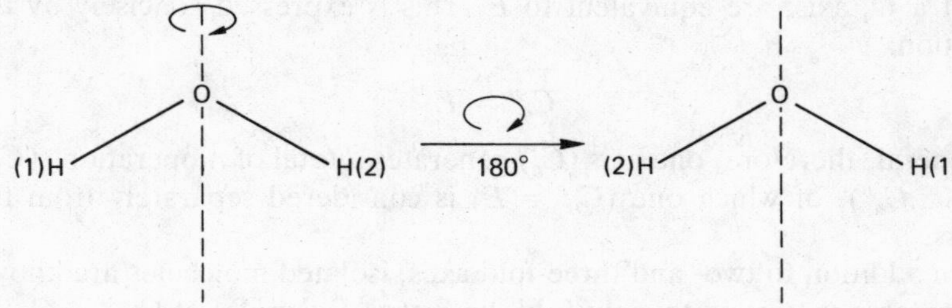


**Figure 1.2** *A two-fold axis of rotation*

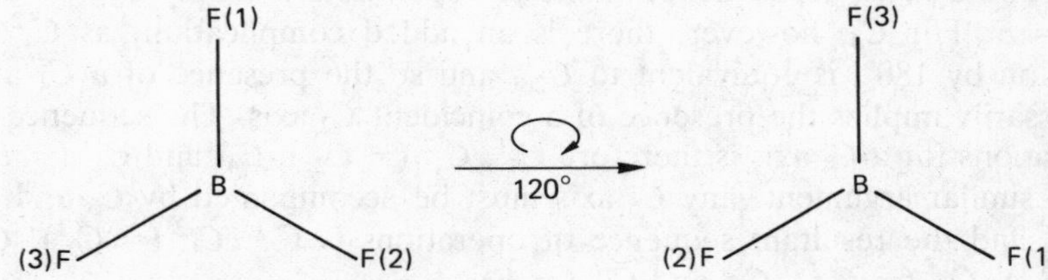


**Figure 1.3** *A three-fold axis of rotation*

It is convenient to have a shorthand representation for the symmetry elements and operations of any object. Thus, a rotation axis is given the symbol $C_n$, where $n$ is an integer, and $(360/n)°$ is the minimum rotation necessary to give an equivalent configuration (such an axis is said to be an $n$-fold axis, or an axis of order $n$). Thus, the axis of $H_2O$ is a $C_2$ (two-fold) axis of rotation, since a rotation by $(360/2)°$ is needed. Similarly, the axis shown for $BF_3$ is a $C_3$ (three-fold) axis.

The operation of rotating an object by $(360/n)°$ about a $C_n$ axis is given the symbol $C_n^1$, so care is needed to avoid confusion between the two. If we now return to the $BF_3$ molecule, we see that a rotation by 240° about the $C_3$ axis is also a symmetry operation, and this is given the symbol $C_3^2$. In general, a rotation by $m \times (360/n)°$ is given the symbol $C_n^m$, where $m$ is an integer.

We must digress briefly to describe another very important symmetry operation. If an object possesses a $C_n$ axis, then rotation about this axis by $n \times (360/n)°$ – that is, $C_n^n$ – will bring the object into exactly the original configuration. This rotation by 360° is equivalent to a rotation by 0°; that is, to the (apparently trivial) operation of 'doing nothing'. This operation is, however, very significant for reasons that will become clear later, and it is described as the **identity operation**, with the symbol $E$ (this is preferred by most chemists and physicists to the symbol $I$, which is used by many mathematicians). Therefore, we can say that $n$ rotations of $(360/n)°$, each about a $C_n$ axis, are equivalent to $E$. This is expressed concisely by the equation:

$$C_n^n = E$$

In general, therefore, one axis ($C_n$) generates a total of $n$ operations ($C_n^1$, $C_n^2$, ...,$C_n^n$), of which one ($C_n^n = E$) is considered separately from the others.

In addition to two- and three-fold axes, isolated molecules are known that possess axes of up to eight-fold symmetry. Examples of $C_4$, $C_5$, $C_6$, $C_7$ and $C_8$ axes are shown in Figure 1.4(a–e). In each case, the axis is perpendicular to the plane of the paper, passing through the central atom (in $XeF_4$) or the centre of the ring of carbon atoms, and only $C_n^1$ is shown.

For a $C_3$ axis, the sequence of allowed operations is simply $C_3^1$, $C_3^2$ and $C_3^3 = E$. For $C_4$, however, there is an added complication, as $C_4^2$, a rotation by 180°, is equivalent to $C_2^1$, and so the presence of a $C_4$ axis necessarily implies the presence of a coincident $C_2$ axis. The sequence of operations for a $C_4$ axis is therefore $C_4^1$, $C_4^2$ (= $C_2^1$), $C_4^3$ and $C_4^4$ (= $E$). By a similar argument, any $C_6$ axis must be accompanied by $C_3$ and $C_2$ axes, and the resultant sequence of operations is $C_6^1$, $C_6^2$ (= $C_3^1$), $C_6^3$ (= $C_2^1$), $C_6^4$ (= $C_3^2$), $C_6^5$ and $C_6^6$ (= $E$).

## 1.2 Reflections: Symmetry planes

The existence of reflection in a plane as a symmetry operation was mentioned briefly earlier. The water molecule again provides a very simple example (Figure 1.5). The plane is perpendicular to the plane of the paper and contains the $C_2$ axis shown in Figure 1.2. A plane of symmetry and the operation of reflection in that plane are both given the symbol $\sigma$, and if such a plane contains the highest order axis of the molecule (for example, $C_2$ for $H_2O$, $C_5$ for $C_5H_5^-$), then it is described as $\sigma_v$ ($v$ = vertical), since the molecule is by convention drawn with that axis set vertically. The $H_2O$ molecule has a further plane of symmetry, which also contains the $C_2$ axis, and which lies in the plane of the paper. To distinguish this from $\sigma_v$, it is given the symbol $\sigma_v'$. An alternative, and in this case preferable, notation uses the set of Cartesian axes shown in Figure 1.5, and by this the two planes are described as $\sigma(xz)$ and $\sigma(yz)$, respectively.

Vertical planes of symmetry are present in all of the molecules shown in Figures 1.3 and 1.4. In addition, these molecules possess a horizontal plane of symmetry, $\sigma_h$, so called because it is perpendicular to the axis of highest order.

A final type of symmetry plane is one that contains the main rotation axis, but can be distinguished from the $\sigma_v$ planes. Such planes are known as dihedral planes, $\sigma_d$, and they generally bisect the angles between the $\sigma_v$ planes. Examples of planes classified as $\sigma_v$, $\sigma_h$ and $\sigma_d$ are found in a square–planar molecule such as $XeF_4$ (Figure 1.6).

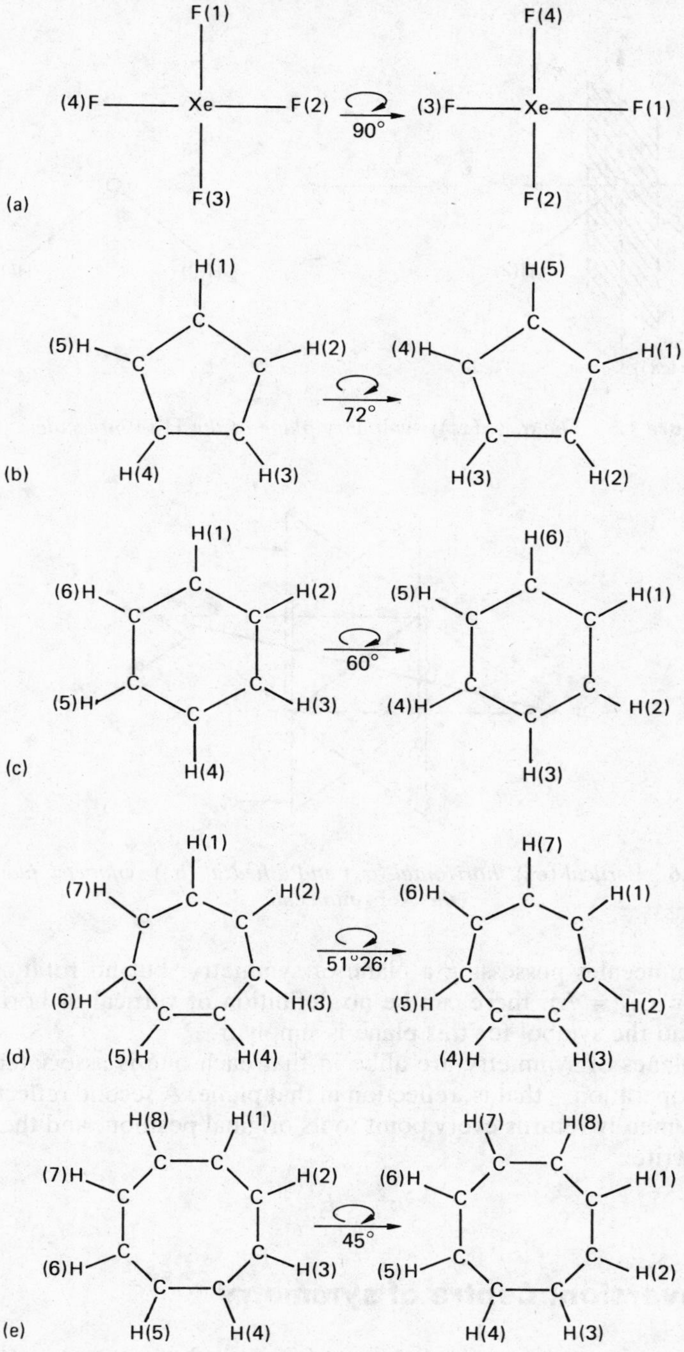

**Figure 1.4** *Some examples of rotation axes*: (a) *four-fold* ($XeF_4$); (b) *five-fold* ($C_5H_5^-$); (c) *six-fold* ($C_6H_6$); (d) *seven-fold* ($C_7H_7^+$); (e) *eight-fold* ($C_8H_8^{2-}$)

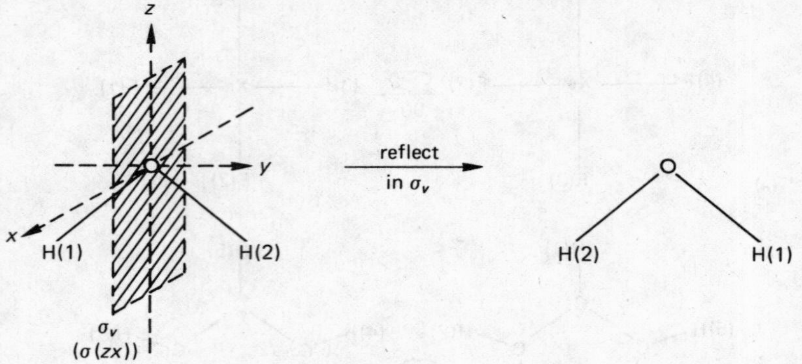


**Figure 1.5** *The* $\sigma_v$ ($\sigma(xz)$) *symmetry plane of the* $H_2O$ *molecule*

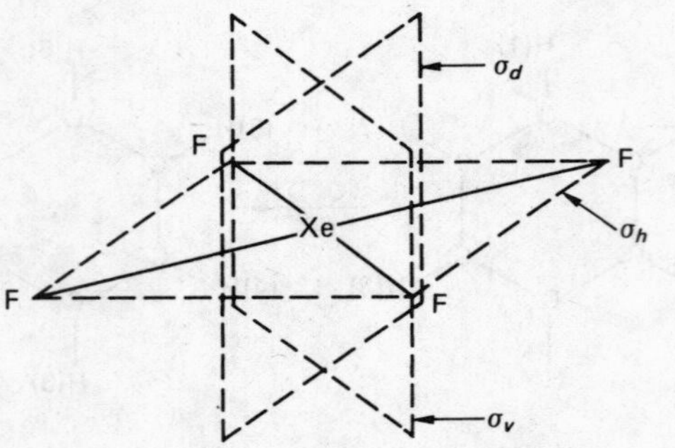


**Figure 1.6** *Vertical* ($\sigma_v$), *horizontal* ($\sigma_h$) *and dihedral* ($\sigma_d$) *symmetry planes of the* $XeF_4$ *molecule*

For molecules possessing a plane of symmetry, but no rotation axis other than $C_1$ (= $E$), there can be no definition of vertical or horizontal planes, and the symbol for this plane is simply $\sigma$.

All planes of symmetry are alike in that each one is associated with only one operation – that is, reflection in that plane. A second reflection in the plane merely returns every point to its original position, and therefore we may write:

$$\sigma^2 = E$$

## *1.3* Inversion: Centre of symmetry

The symmetry operations defined so far have been simple rotations (including the identity as a special case of rotation by 0° or 360°) or reflections. Two other types of operation are encountered which are composite operations; that is, both rotation and reflection are involved in one operation. The first is the operation of **inversion**, and the element of symmetry associated with this is a point, known as the **centre of symmetry** or **inversion centre**. The operation of inversion is shown in Figure 1.7. Consider a set of Cartesian axes with a point lying at $(x, y, z)$ relative to these axes. If the origin of the axes is taken as the inversion centre, then the operation of inversion involves carrying the point to the position $(-x, -y, -z)$. If this is done for every point in the object, and if the resulting configuration is indistinguishable from the original, then inversion is a symmetry operation for that object, which is then said to possess a centre of symmetry. The benzene molecule (Figure 1.8) is an example of a **centrosymmetric** molecule, the centre of symmetry being shown by its conventional symbol, *i*. As with the reflection plane, both the element (centre) and the operation (inversion) have the same symbol, *i*. The element gives rise to only one distinct operation since:

$$(x, y, z) \xrightarrow{i} (-x, -y, -z) \xrightarrow{i} (x, y, z)$$

That is:

$$i^2 = E$$

The operation of inversion can be regarded as a composite movement comprising rotation by 180° and reflection in a plane perpendicular to this axis. This is illustrated by the point $(x, y, z)$ in Figure 1.7. If the rotation takes place about the $z$ axis, then rotation by 180° converts $x \rightarrow -x$, $y \rightarrow -y$ and $z \rightarrow z$:

$$(x, y, z) \longrightarrow (-x, -y, z)$$

Reflection will then take place in the $xy$ plane, with the result that $-x \rightarrow -x$, $-y \rightarrow -y$ and $z \rightarrow -z$:

$$(-x, -y, z) \longrightarrow (-x, -y, -z)$$

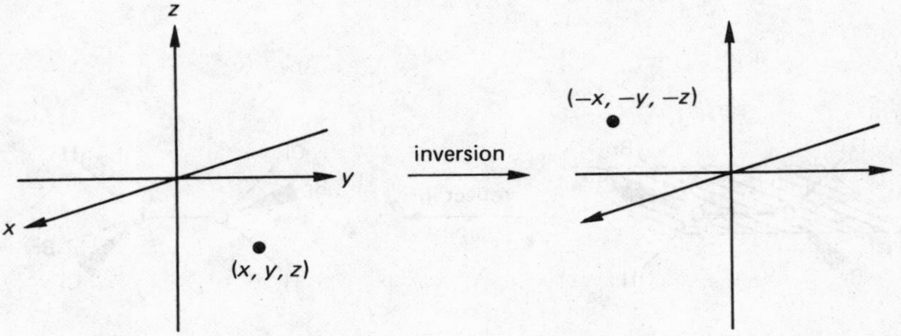


**Figure 1.7** *The inversion operation*

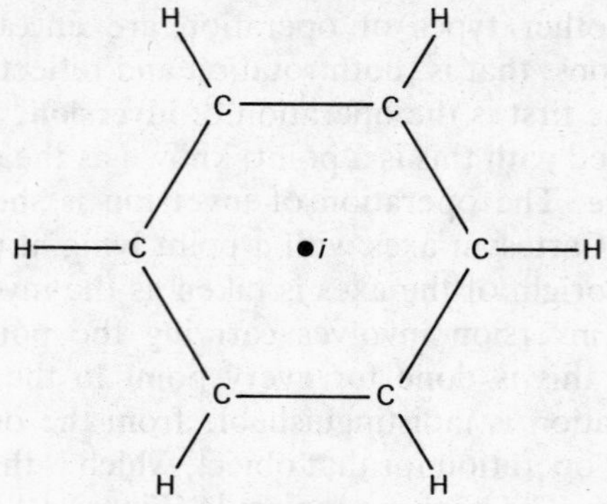


**Figure 1.8** *The centre of inversion, i, of the benzene molecule*

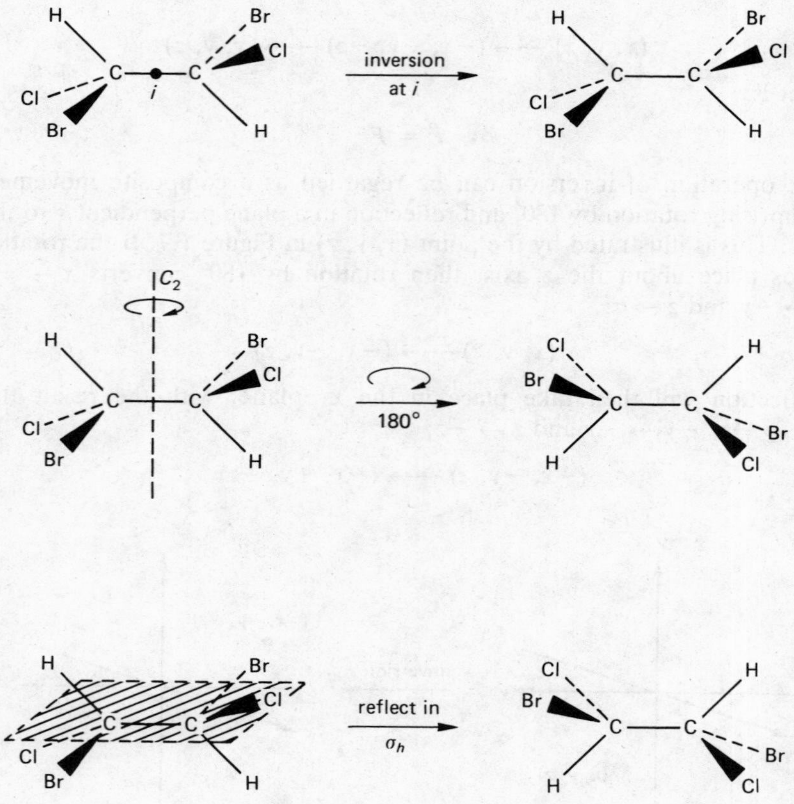


**Figure 1.9** *The effects of the operations of inversion, two-fold rotation and reflection upon the molecule* CHClBr–CHClBr *(staggered conformation)*

This produces the same overall effect as carrying out the inversion $i$ on the point $(x, y, z)$. Although the inversion can be broken down, in principle, into two other operations, it does *not* mean that the rotation by 180° and the reflection must necessarily be themselves symmetry operations of the object that possesses a centre of symmetry. In many cases they are, but as an example of a molecule that has a centre of symmetry, but no axes or planes, consider CHClBr–CHC1Br (in the staggered conformation, as shown in Figure 1.9). The figure shows the effects of inversion, rotation by 180° about the C–C axis and reflection in a plane perpendicular to that axis; only the first operation gives rise to a configuration indistinguishable from the original.

## 1.4 Improper rotations: Rotation–reflection axes

The symmetry operation of improper rotation consists of a clockwise (on looking down the axis from above) rotation about an axis, followed by reflection in a plane perpendicular to the axis. (A simple rotation is sometimes known as a proper rotation, to contrast it with the operation discussed here.) The associated symmetry element is a **rotation–reflection axis** (sometimes known as an **alternating axis of symmetry**). The symbol for such an axis is $S_n$, where the angle of rotation is $(360/n)°$, and the operation of rotation by $m \times (360/n)°$ with $m$ reflections in the perpendicular plane is given the symbol $S_n{}^m$. As an example, consider a tetrahedral molecule such as $CH_4$ (Figure 1.10). A rotation by 90° about the axis shown, followed by reflection in a perpendicular plane, gives a configuration indistinguishable from the original one. Therefore, methane possesses an $S_4$ axis.

As for the other composite operation, inversion, the individual components of the improper rotation need not be themselves symmetry operations of the molecule. This is clearly illustrated by $CH_4$, although there are examples where the individual rotation and reflection are symmetry operations, as we shall see later.

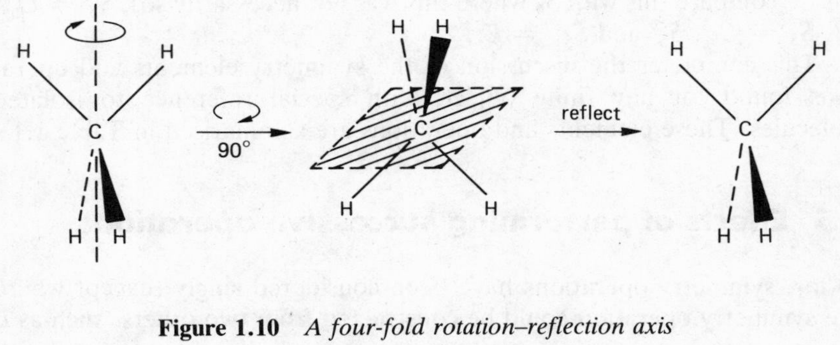


**Figure 1.10** *A four-fold rotation–reflection axis*

The following rotation–reflection axes are found in isolated molecules: $S_3$, $S_4$, $S_5$, $S_6$, $S_7$, $S_8$ and $S_{10}$. $S_4$ has been illustrated by a tetrahedral molecule (see Figure 1.10); examples of the others are given in Figure 1.11. Note that $S_1$ and $S_2$ have not been mentioned, since $S_1$ (that is, rotation by 360° followed by reflection in a perpendicular plane) is simply a reflection and $S_2$ is in fact equivalent to $i$ (that is, rotation by 180° followed by reflection in a perpendicular plane). Thus, $S_1 = \sigma$ and $S_2 = i$, and so all symmetry operations can be divided into proper ($C_n^m$, $E$) and improper ($S_n^m$, $\sigma$, $i$) rotations.

Like the ordinary rotation axis, $C_n$, the rotation–reflection axis, $S_n$, gives rise to more than one distinct symmetry operation, because successive rotation–reflections (improper rotations) about the axis do not give identical results. The number of operations generated by a rotation–reflection axis depends on whether $n$ in $S_n$ is even or odd. The lowest even number that concerns us is $S_4$ (see earlier), and all subsequent even numbers behave similarly. All give rise to $S_n^1$, $S_n^2$, ..., $S_n^n$ (= $E$). This last conclusion follows because $S_n^n$ is equivalent to $C_n^n$ combined with $\sigma_h^n$. When $n$ is even, both of these correspond to $E$. Therefore, $S_n$ generates $n$ operations when $n$ is even.

When $n$ is odd, however, $2n$ distinct operations are generated, since $S_n^n$ is now equivalent to $\sigma_h$ ($C_n^n = E$; $\sigma_h^n = \sigma_h$ when $n$ is odd), and in the series $S_n^1$, $S_n^2$, ..., the first operation equivalent to $E$ is $S_n^{2n}$ ($C_n^{2n} = E$; $\sigma_h^{2n} = E$, since $2n$ is even).

Finally, for both odd and even values of $n$, several of the operations $S_n^m$ can be expressed in terms of other operations. Consider $S_4$. $S_4^1$ and $S_4^3$ can only be expressed in that way, but $S_4^2$ is equivalent to $C_4^2$ (that is, $C_2^1$) and $\sigma_h^2$. $\sigma_h^2 = E$, and therefore $S_4^2 = C_4^2 = C_2^1$. (Note that the existence of a rotation–reflection axis $S_n$, where $n$ is even, means that a coincident rotation axis $C_{n/2}$ must also be present.) Finally, $S_4^4 = E$, and therefore the series of operations generated by $S_4$ is normally written $S_4^1$, $C_2^1$, $S_4^3$, $E$. A similar series exists for $S_5$, which must, however, be continued up to $S_5^{10}$ (= $E$). Therefore, we have $S_5^1$, $S_5^2 = C_5^2$, $S_5^3$, $S_5^4 = C_5^4$, $S_5^5 = \sigma_h$ (since $C_5^5 = E$, $\sigma_h^5 = \sigma_h$, which shows that when $n$ is odd, the presence of an $S_n$ axis implies that $C_n$ and $\sigma_h$ separately must be symmetry operations – compare this with $S_4$ where this was not necessarily so), $S_5^6 = C_5^1$, $S_5^7$, $S_5^8 = C_5^3$, $S_5^9$ and $S_5^{10} = E$.

This completes the discussion of the symmetry elements and operations found for any finite object, with special reference to isolated molecules. These elements and operations are summarised in Table 1.1

## 1.5 Effects of performing successive operations

So far, symmetry operations have been considered singly (except where one symmetry operation could be constructed from two others, such as $i$,

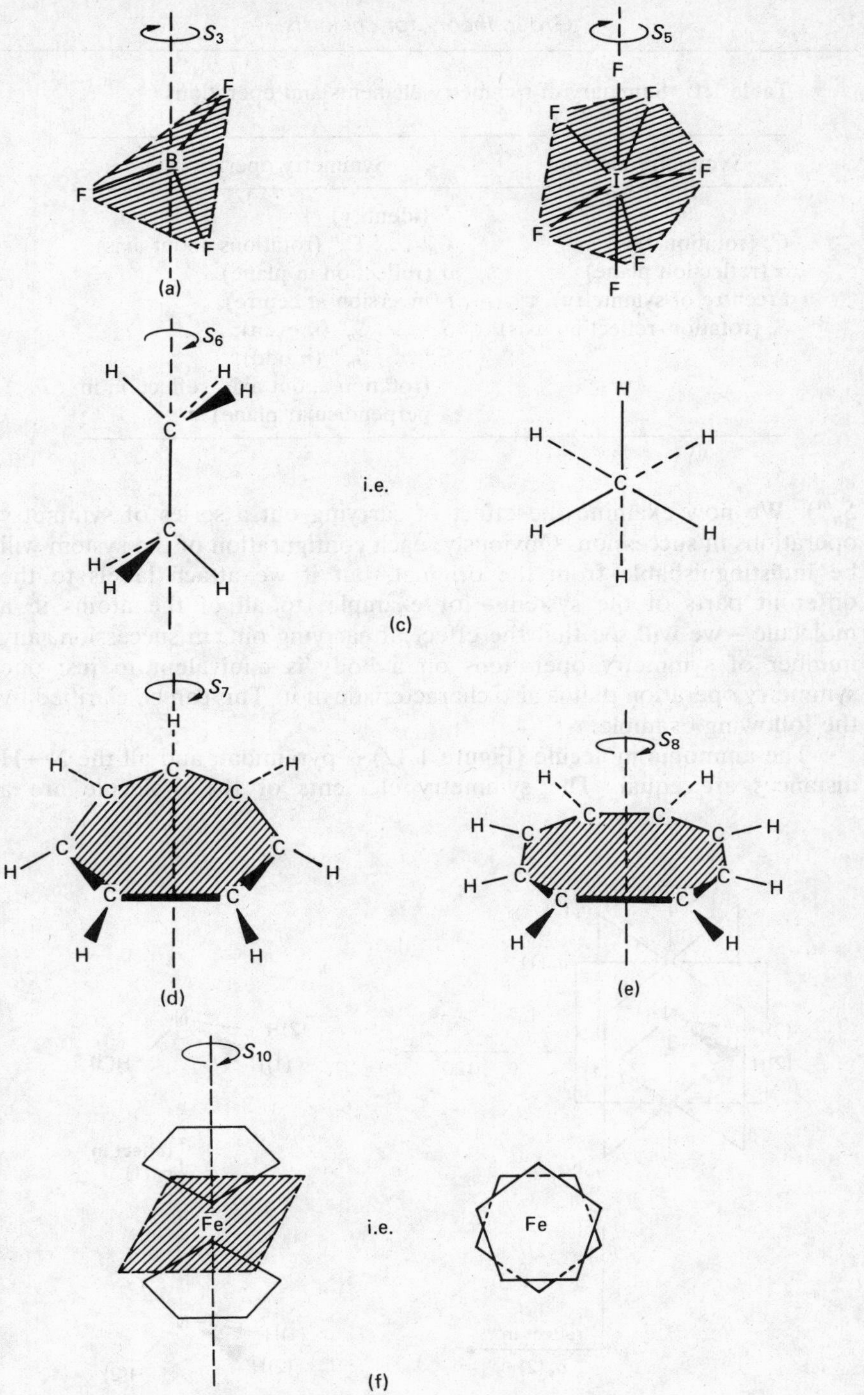


**Figure 1.11** *Examples of rotation–reflection axes*: (a) $S_3$ ($BF_3$); (b) $S_5$ ($IF_7$); (c) $S_6$ (*staggered* $C_2H_6$); (d) $S_7$ ($C_7H_7^+$); (e) $S_8$ ($C_8H_8^{2-}$); (f) $S_{10}$ (*ferrocene*, $(C_5H_5)_2Fe$)

**Table 1.1** Summary of symmetry elements and operations

| Symmetry element | Symmetry operation(s) |
|---|---|
| – | $E$ (identity) |
| $C_n$ (rotation axis) | $C_n^{\ 1} \ldots C_n^{\ n}$ (rotations about axis) |
| σ (reflection plane) | σ (reflection in plane) |
| $i$ (centre of symmetry) | $i$ (inversion at centre) |
| $S_n$ (rotation–reflection axis) | $S_n^{\ 1} \ldots S_n^{\ n}$ ($n$ even);<br>$S_n^{\ 1} \ldots S_n^{\ 2n}$ ($n$ odd);<br>(rotation about axis, reflection in perpendicular plane) |

$S_n^{\ m}$). We now examine the effect of carrying out a series of symmetry operations in succession. Obviously, each configuration of the system will be indistinguishable from the original, but if we attach labels to the different parts of the system – for example, to all of the atoms in a molecule – we will see that the effect of carrying out, in succession, any number of symmetry operations on a body is equivalent to just one symmetry operation that is also characteristic of it. This can be clarified by the following example.

The ammonia molecule (Figure 1.12) is pyramidal, and all the N—H distances are equal. The symmetry elements of the molecule are a

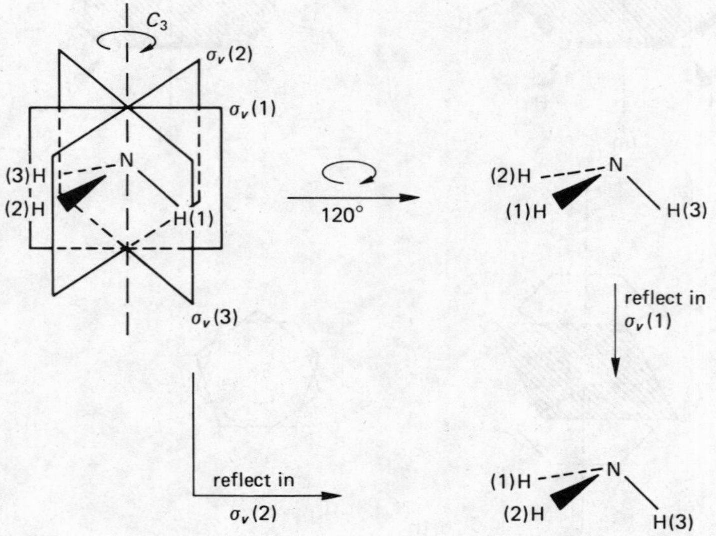


**Figure 1.12** *The symmetry elements of* $NH_3$ *and the effects of some symmetry operations*

three-fold axis, passing through the N atom, and three vertical planes of symmetry, each including the N and one of the H atoms, and bisecting the other H—N—H angle. If the H atoms are labelled as shown, we can see the effect of carrying out a rotation about the $C_3$ axis, followed by a reflection in one of the planes of symmetry, $\sigma_v(1)$. The overall result is exactly equivalent to the single operation of reflection in the plane $\sigma_v(2)$. This can be expressed as:

$$\sigma_v(1)C_3^1 = \sigma_v(2)$$

That is, carrying out two (or more) symmetry operations is represented algebraically as a multiplication. By convention, the first operation is written at the right. Exactly the same convention is used in other branches of mathematics; for example, the symbol $d/dx(d/dy)$ implies that differentiation with respect to $y$ is to be carried out first.

Any number of successive operations may be carried out and the symbolism is merely extended to the required number of terms. A further example is a trigonal–bipyramidal molecule such as $PF_5$. All of the symmetry elements of this molecule are shown in Figure 1.13: a $C_3$ axis, with three $C_2$ axes perpendicular to it, three vertical planes of symmetry, a horizontal plane of symmetry and a rotation–reflection axis $S_3$ coincident with the $C_3$ axis. A selection of the possible binary and ternary combinations of symmetry operations shows that in each case such a combination is equivalent to another single symmetry operation of the molecule:

$$\begin{aligned}
&\sigma_h C_3^1 = C_3^1\sigma_h = S_3^1 \\
&C_3^1C_2(1) = C_2(3)C_3^1 = \sigma_v(2)\sigma_h = C_2(2) \\
&C_3^1C_2(2) = C_2(1)C_3^1 = \sigma_v(3)\sigma_h = C_2(3) \\
&C_3^1C_2(3) = C_2(2)C_3^1 = \sigma_v(1)\sigma_h = C_2(1) \\
&C_2(1)\sigma_v(1) = \sigma_h = \sigma_v(1)C_2(1)
\end{aligned}$$

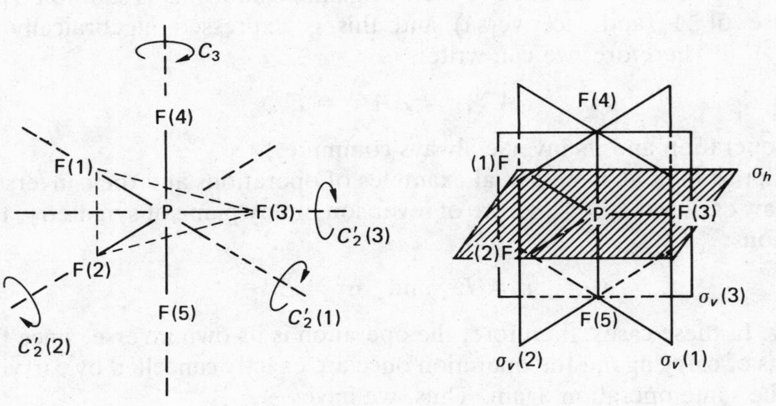


**Figure 1.13** *The symmetry elements of* $PF_5$

$$C_2(2)\sigma_v(1) = S_3^{\ 1}$$
$$\sigma_v(1)C_2(2) = S_3^{\ 5}$$
$$C_2(3)\sigma_v(1) = S_3^{\ 5}$$
$$\sigma_v(1)C_2(3) = S_3^{\ 1}$$
$$C_2(2)\sigma_v(1)C_2(1) = C_2(2)\sigma_h = \sigma_v(2)$$
$$C_3^{\ 1}\sigma_v(1)\sigma_h = C_3^{\ 1}C_2(1) = C_2(2)$$
$$\ldots$$

In some cases, the order in which two operations ($A$, $B$) are carried out is immaterial, since $AB = BA$; for example, $C_2(1)\sigma_v(1) = \sigma_v(1)C_2(1) = \sigma_h$. In this case, the multiplication is said to be **commutative**; that is, the two operations $A$ and $B$ commute. However, this is not always so, as illustrated by the example $C_3^{\ 1}C_2(1)$ $(= C_2(2)) \neq C_2(1)C_3^{\ 1}$ $(= C_2(3))$. In such a case, the multiplication is **non-commutative**; that is, the operations do not commute. In general, any two symmetry operations do *not* commute, and the order in which the operations are carried out when multiplying them together is significant, although in specific cases this is not so.

## 1.6 Inverse operations

The identity operation (that is, the operation of 'doing nothing' or rotation by 360°) has already been discussed. We find that, in all cases, when considering any symmetry operation, $A$, there exists another symmetry operation, $B$, for that object, such that the relationship:

$$BA = E = AB$$

holds. The effect of the operation $B$ is exactly the opposite to that of $A$ on the object. Thus, if $A$ is carried out on a molecule, followed by $B$, then $B$ returns all of the atoms back to their original positions. $B$ is said to be the inverse of $A$ (and vice versa) and this is expressed algebraically as $B = A^{-1}$. Therefore, we can write:

$$A^{-1}A = AA^{-1} = E$$

(An operation and its inverse always commute.)

Let us look at some actual examples of operations and their inverses. We saw earlier that for a centre of inversion or any plane of symmetry, the relations:

$$i^2 = E \quad \text{and} \quad \sigma^2 = E$$

apply. In these cases, therefore, the operation is its own inverse, since the effects of carrying out the operation once are exactly cancelled by carrying out the same operation again. Thus, we have:

$$i = i^{-1} \quad \text{and} \quad \sigma = \sigma^{-1}$$

For a rotation, simply carrying out the operation a second time does not give the original configuration (except for a $C_2$ axis), and so it is necessary to define an operation $C_n^{-1}$ which is different from $C_n^1$. The latter is defined as a clockwise rotation (about the axis $C_n$) by $(360/n)°$ and so the operation that is necessary to cancel out exactly the effects of this is clearly an anti-clockwise rotation by $(360/n)°$ about $C_n$. With this definition:

$$C_n^{-1}C_n^1 = E$$

as required. If we consider a $C_3$ axis as an example, we see that the equation:

$$C_3^2C_3^1 = E$$

is also valid ($C_3^2$ is a clockwise rotation by 240° about the $C_3$ axis), and in general:

$$C_n^{n-1}C_n^1 = E$$

and so $C_n^{-1} = C_n^{n-1}$; that is, a clockwise rotation by $[(n-1)(360/n)]°$ is equivalent to an anti-clockwise rotation by $(360/n)°$.

For a rotation–reflection axis, by analogy with the rotation axis, an operation $S_n^{-1}$ can be defined as an anti-clockwise rotation by $(360/n)°$ about the $S_n$ axis, followed by a reflection in the perpendicular plane. We can justify this definition by expanding the expressions for $S_n^1$ and $S_n^{-1}$ in terms of $C_n^1$ and $\sigma_h$:

$$S_n^{-1}S_n^1 = (C_n^{-1}\sigma_h)(C_n^1\sigma_h)$$

But $C_n^1\sigma_h = \sigma_hC_n^1$ (see the example for $PF_5$; this expression is always obeyed). Therefore:

$$S_n^{-1}S_n^1 = (C_n^{-1}\sigma_h)(C_n^1\sigma_h) = (C_n^{-1}\sigma_h)(\sigma_hC_n^1) = C_n^{-1}C_n^1 = E$$

Again, it is always possible to express the inverse operation in terms of clockwise rotations about the same axis. We saw previously that $S_n^n = E$ when $n$ is even and $S_n^{2n} = E$ when $n$ is odd. Therefore:

$$S_n^{n-1}S_n^1 = E \quad (n \text{ even}); \qquad S_n^{2n-1}S_n^1 = E \quad (n \text{ odd})$$

and so $S_n^{-1} = S_n^{n-1}$ ($n$ even) while $S_n^{-1} = S_n^{2n-1}$ ($n$ odd). Hence, the operation $S_3^5$ encountered earlier could also be written as $S_3^{-1}$, the inverse of $S_3^1$.

## EXERCISES

1 Identify the symmetry elements belonging to the following molecules:

(a) $WF_5Cl$
(b) $PtCl_4^{2-}$

(c) $SiH_3CN$
(d) 1-chloro-3,5-difluorobenzene
(e) allene, $CH_2{=}C{=}CH_2$
(f) $Ni(CO)_4$
(g) $CO_3^{2-}$
(h) $B_3N_3H_6$ (a planar, six-membered ring)

**2** List all of the symmetry operations generated by each of the following axes of symmetry:

(a) $C_5$
(b) $C_6$
(c) $S_3$
(d) $S_8$

Can any of these operations be expressed in more than one way?

**3** To which symmetry operations of $NH_3$ (see Figure 1.12) are the following combinations of operations equivalent?

(a) $C_3^2\sigma_v(2)$
(b) $\sigma_v(2)\sigma_v(3)$
(c) $\sigma_v(3)C_3^1$
(d) $\sigma_v(1)C_3^1\sigma_v(3)$

**4** To which symmetry operations of $PF_5$ (see Figure 1.13) are the following combinations of operations equivalent?

(a) $C_2(1)\sigma_h$
(b) $C_3^2C_2(2)$
(c) $S_3^1\sigma_v(1)$
(d) $\sigma_h\sigma_v(1)C_2(2)$

# 2

# Groups and their basic properties

In order to use the symmetry properties of molecules in solving problems connected with molecular structure and bonding, it is necessary to have some acquaintance with the branch of mathematics known as **group theory**. In this chapter, an introduction to the fundamental basis of group theory will be given, using only as much mathematics as we need.

A group, in the mathematical sense, is a collection of elements having certain properties in common which enable a wide variety of algebraic manipulations to be carried out on the collection. (Note that we are using the term generally, and not in relation to symmetry elements.) The elements do not need to have any physical significance, and the theory applies quite generally to abstract groups, although we will be concerned with groups that have as their elements the symmetry operations characteristic of a particular molecule.

## *2.1* Basic properties of a group

Consider a collection of elements, $A$, $B$, $C$, ..., to which no physical significance need be attached for the present. There are four properties that must be possessed by this collection, if it is to be a group in the mathematical sense. They are as follows:

**1** Any combination of two or more elements of the collection must be equivalent to one element which is also a member of the collection. The combination can be defined in a wide variety of ways, but the act of combining two or more elements is usually described as 'multiplication', even if the actual process (for example, successive performance of symmetry operations) bears no resemblance to the well-known algebraic process of that name. Thus, we can write:

$$AB = C$$

where $A$, $B$ and $C$ are all members of the collection.

It is not necessary for the multiplication, however defined, to be commutative, as, in general:

$$AB \neq BA$$

Thus, the order of writing the elements is significant. Some groups consist entirely of elements whose multiplication is commutative, but this is a special case. These groups are known as **Abelian groups**.

We can add at this point that a group may be either finite or infinite; that is, the number of elements may be finite or infinite. Nearly all of the groups with which we shall be concerned will be finite.

**2** One element in the collection must be such that it can combine with every other element in the collection and leave them unchanged. This is the **identity element**, $E$, and we can express its characteristic property thus:

$$AE = A \quad \text{(for all elements in the group)}$$

Further, the multiplication of $E$ with all of the other elements must be commutative:

$$AE = EA = A$$

**3** Although the multiplication of elements need not be commutative, it must be **associative**. This means that the following relationship must be valid:

$$A(BC) = (AB)C$$

which can be extended to any number of terms. For example, if $B$ and $C$ are multiplied together to give $BC = M$, and then the product $M$ is left-multiplied by $A$ to give $AM$, this will give the same result as the multiplication of $A$ and $B$ to give $AB = N$, followed by the right-multiplication $NC$. In general, therefore, when three or more elements are to be combined, there is no need to separate these combinations into individual pairs, as was done above; therefore:

$$A(BC) = (AB)C = ABC$$

**4** The final requirement that must be satisfied by a collection of elements is that every element in the collection must have an **inverse**, which is defined by:

$$AX = E$$

where $X$ is the inverse of $A$. Also, if $X$ is the inverse of $A$, then $A$ is the inverse of $X$ and:

$$AX = XA = E$$

This is also expressed by the equations $A = X^{-1}$, $A^{-1} = X$; that is:

$$AA^{-1} = A^{-1}A = E$$

Collections of elements having these four properties are described as **groups**, and it will be convenient to introduce some terms that are commonly used in group theory. For a finite group, the number of group elements is the **order** of the group. If the group has $n$ elements, then it is a group of order $n$. If within the group there are some elements (less than the whole group) which themselves fulfil all the necessary conditions of a group, such a collection is called a **subgroup**. All groups (except the group possessing only the identity element) contain at least one subgroup of smaller order than the group itself, even if it is only the trivial one consisting of the identity element alone. Every subgroup must, of course, include $E$.

## 2.2 Symmetry operations as group elements

In Chapter 1, we saw that a molecule can possess a variety of symmetry elements, each of which is associated with one or more symmetry operations. We will now show that the collection of symmetry operations for any molecule constitutes a group, in the sense we have just defined. In order to do so, it will be necessary to show that the collections of symmetry operations possess the four defining characteristics of a group:

**1** A definition of multiplication for symmetry operations was given in Chapter 1; that is, the successive performance of the operations. An example (the $PF_5$ molecule) showed that the 'product', so defined, was equivalent to *one* symmetry operation characteristic of the molecule. A similar treatment for all other cases leads to the same conclusion, and thus the first requirement is fulfilled. The fact that the multiplication need not be commutative was illustrated by the same example.

**2** The inclusion of the apparently trivial identity operation is now seen to be necessary for fulfilling the second characteristic of a group. The operation of 'leaving the molecule alone' can clearly be combined with any other symmetry operation of a molecule, leaving it unchanged.

**3** The multiplication of group elements must be associative, as defined earlier. A symmetry operation multiplication *is* associative, as we can see by the following example using the symmetry operations of $PF_5$ (see Figure 1.13):

$$C_3^{\,1}(\sigma_v(1)\sigma_h) = C_3^{\,1}C_2'(1) = C_2'(2)$$
$$(C_3^{\,1}\sigma_v(1))\sigma_h = \sigma_v(2)\sigma_h = C_2'(2)$$

No brackets are needed, therefore, in the definition of ternary (or higher-order) products.

**4** The inverse operations defined in Chapter 1 clearly correspond to the inverse elements required by any collection of elements which is to be a group.

All the properties of a group are possessed by the collection of symmetry operations characteristic of any molecule, and hence these operations define the **point group** for that molecule. What is the significance of the word 'point'? It is found that all of the symmetry operations for any finite molecule leave at least one point in the molecule unshifted in space – this point need not be situated at an atom. This follows from the requirement that the molecule as a whole must not be shifted in space by carrying out any symmetry operation, since the new configuration would be distinguishable from the old one at a new position in space; that is, symmetry operations involving *translation* are not allowed. As we will only be concerned with finite molecules, all the molecular symmetry groups that we will meet will be point groups. There are important fields where (effectively) *infinite* arrays of ions or molecules must be considered (for example, crystallography; the vibrational spectra of crystals or polymers), and in such cases translational symmetry is allowed. New symmetry operations are possible, but because of restrictions on the orders of axes that can be present in an infinite system, there is still a finite number (230 in three-dimensional systems) of groups. These groups are described as **space groups**, but they will not be described further here.

## 2.3 Classes of symmetry operations

A new concept, that of a **class** of group elements, requires a little discussion. This is a subdivision of the group that has a different basis from the division into subgroups. Consider two elements of a group, $A$ and $B$. If the product $B^{-1}AB$ is formed, then we know that this must be equivalent to one other element of the group, $C$; that is:

$$B^{-1}AB = C$$

This relationship is described by saying that $A$ is converted to $C$ by a **similarity transformation**; or that $C$ is the **similarity transform** of $A$ by $B$ or, most commonly, that $A$ and $C$ are **conjugate**.

Suppose that when the element $A$ is subjected to a similarity transformation by every element of the group, including $E$ and $A$ itself, it is transformed in every case into, for example, $A$ or $B$ or $C$, but no other elements. Then $A$, $B$ and $C$ are said to constitute a class of elements. A similarity transformation on $B$ or $C$, likewise, will only give rise to $A$ or $B$ or $C$. In this way, by working systematically through the elements, they will be divided into several classes such that no element belongs to more than one class. Furthermore, if the group has $n$ elements (if it is a group of order $n$), then the number of elements (necessarily an integer) in each class is $n/m$, where $m$ is an integer ($m \leqslant n$). Thus, if a group contains 10 elements, then the classes can only have 1, 2 or 5 elements (although all of these possibilities need not necessarily be realised). The identity element commutes with every other element, by definition, and we can use this fact to show that $E$ is always in a class by itself. Because of the commutative property of $E$, we can always rearrange the similarity transformations; thus:

$$A^{-1}EA = A^{-1}AE = E$$
$$B^{-1}EB = B^{-1}BE = E$$

and so on for every other element including $E$ itself. Therefore, $E$ is always the only element in its class.

Since symmetry operations are themselves group elements, they can be collected into classes by means of similarity transformations; for example, for the $NH_3$ molecule (see Figure 1.12) carrying out a similarity transformation on the identity using any symmetry operation always gives the identity. Hence, the identity is in a class by itself. Consider now the operation $C_3^1$. The following transformations can be carried out (it is suggested that the reader should check these multiplications):

$$EC_3^1E = EEC_3^1 = C_3^1$$
$$C_3^1C_3^1C_3^{-1} = C_3^1C_3^1C_3^2 = C_3^1E = C_3^1$$
$$C_3^2C_3^1C_3^{-2} = C_3^2C_3^1C_3^1 = EC_3^1 = C_3^1$$
$$\sigma_v(1)C_3^1\sigma_v(1) = \sigma_v(1)\sigma_v(3) = C_3^2$$
$$\sigma_v(2)C_3^1\sigma_v(2) = \sigma_v(2)\sigma_v(1) = C_3^2$$
$$\sigma_v(3)C_3^1\sigma_v(3) = \sigma_v(3)\sigma_v(2) = C_3^2$$

As can be seen, the transformations always give $C_3^1$ or $C_3^2$; hence, these two operations are in the same class. Carrying out similarity transformations on $C_3^2$ confirms this.

We find that $\sigma_v(1)$, $\sigma_v(2)$ and $\sigma_v(3)$ are also in one class, and so the six symmetry operations of $NH_3$ are divided into three classes: ($E$), ($C_3^1$, $C_3^2$) and ($\sigma_v(1)$, $\sigma_v(2)$, $\sigma_v(3)$), which are usually written as $E$, $2C_3$ and $3\sigma_v$. A similar division is found in all the point groups with which we shall deal.

The members of any one class can be converted into one another by carrying out one of the symmetry operations of the molecule (not necessarily in the same class) on them. Thus, $\sigma_v(1)$ can be converted into $\sigma_v(2)$ and $\sigma_v(3)$ by the action of the rotations $C_3^1$ and $C_3^2$, respectively ($\sigma_v(1)C_3^1 = \sigma_v(2)$). Conversely, no symmetry operation can be converted into an operation belonging to a different class by carrying out any one symmetry operation on it.

## 2.4 Infinite groups

Before dealing with the systematic classification of molecules into point groups and their nomenclature, it will be necessary to consider two infinite groups (that is, groups having an infinite number of elements) that are met with. These are the point groups of linear systems, with and without, respectively, a centre of symmetry. Rotation by any arbitrary angle about the molecular axis is a symmetry operation for both of these, as is reflection in any plane containing the molecular axis (Figure 2.1). All linear molecules therefore possess an infinite-order rotation axis, $C_\infty$, and an infinite number of vertical planes, $\infty\sigma_v$. In addition, if a centre of symmetry is present, as in $CO_2$, there will be a horizontal plane of symmetry, $\sigma_h$, and an infinite number of $C_2$ axes perpendicular to $C_\infty$ (one lying in each $\sigma_v$).

## 2.5 Systematic classification of molecules into point groups

All that we have done so far is to show that the collections of symmetry operations possessed by molecules do in fact constitute groups. It is now necessary to discuss the nomenclature for point groups and to show how a particular molecule can be assigned to one of these.

We will start with systems of very low symmetry and show how additional symmetry operations can be added to these in a systematic way. The least symmetric molecule will possess only the identity operation, $E$, which could also be regarded as rotation by 360° – that is, $C_1$. An example of such a molecule is CHFClBr (Figure 2.2), and this belongs to the point group $\mathbf{C}_1$. (The symbols for point groups used in this book are the **Schönflies** symbols; these are used in most applications of group theory,

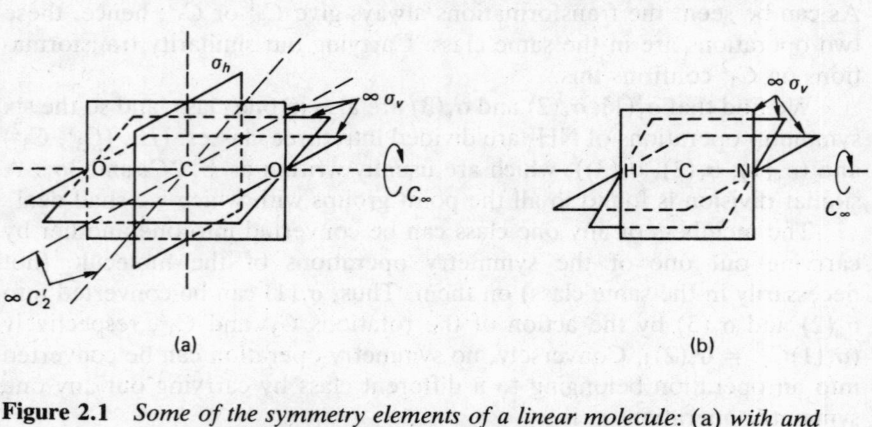


**Figure 2.1** *Some of the symmetry elements of a linear molecule*: (a) *with and* (b) *without a centre of symmetry*

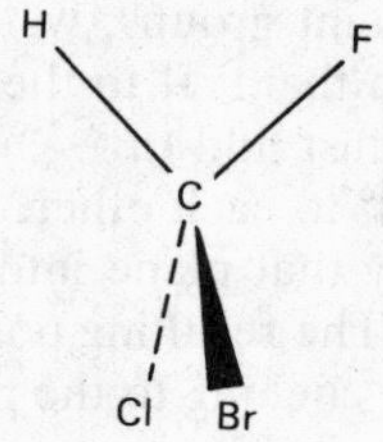


**Figure 2.2** CHFClBr: *a molecule belonging to the point group* $\mathbf{C}_1$

except crystallography, where an alternative nomenclature, the **international system**, is used.)

If a molecule possesses a $C_n$ axis in addition to the identity, it belongs to the point group $\mathbf{C}_n$. Such point groups possess a total of $n$ symmetry operations ($C_n^{\ 1}, \ldots, C_n^{\ n-1}, C_n^{\ n} = E$). Very few molecules exist that belong to the $\mathbf{C}_n$ point groups.

Two other groups exist that possess only one symmetry element besides the identity. These have, respectively, one symmetry plane (point group $\mathbf{C}_s$) or a centre of symmetry (point group $\mathbf{C}_i$). Both of these groups have just two symmetry operations, since σ and $i$, unlike $C_n$, generate only one operation each. Examples of molecules belonging to the $\mathbf{C}_s$ ($SO_2BrF$) and $\mathbf{C}_i$ (staggered CHClBr–CHClBr) point groups are shown in Figures 2.3 and 2.4, respectively.

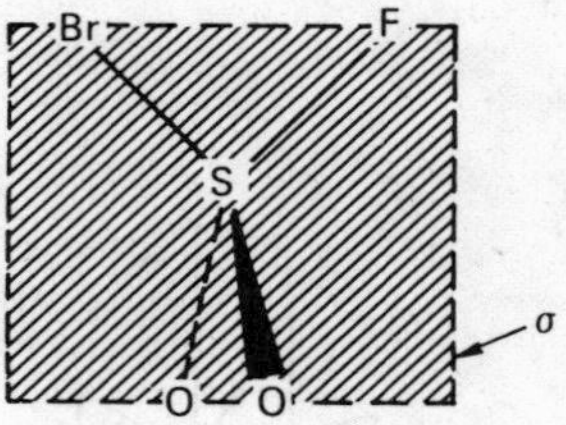


**Figure 2.3** $SO_2BrF$: *a molecule belonging to the point group* $\mathbf{C}_s$

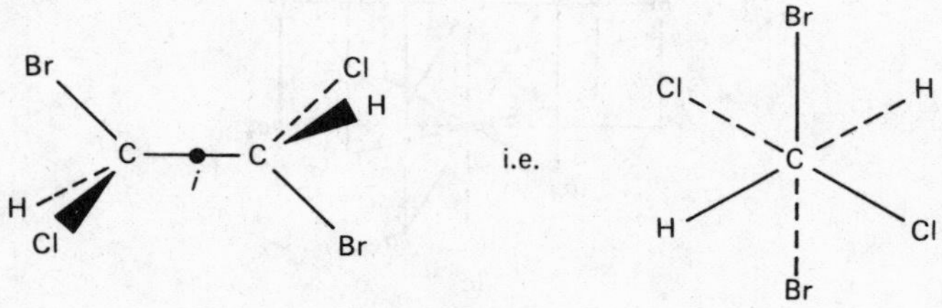


**Figure 2.4** *Staggered* CHClBr–CHClBr: *a molecule belonging to the point group* $\mathbf{C}_i$

If we return to the $\mathbf{C}_n$ point groups, we can investigate the effect of adding symmetry elements to them. If to the $C_n$ axis we add one vertical plane of symmetry, $\sigma_v$, we must add $(n - 1)$ further $\sigma_v$ planes, to give a total of $n$ at angles of $(360/n)°$ to each other. The rotation of any of these planes by $(360/n)°$ must carry that plane into an equivalent plane, hence there must be $n$ such planes. The resulting point group is given the symbol $\mathbf{C}_{nv}$. Many common molecules belong to the point groups $\mathbf{C}_{2v}$, $\mathbf{C}_{3v}$ and $\mathbf{C}_{4v}$ (Figure 2.5), and a few examples are known of $\mathbf{C}_{5v}$ and $\mathbf{C}_{6v}$

If, instead of adding a vertical plane, a horizontal plane, $\sigma_h$, is added to a $\mathbf{C}_n$ system, only one plane need be added, and the resulting point group is $\mathbf{C}_{nh}$. Molecules with this type of symmetry are rarer than $\mathbf{C}_{nv}$ systems, but examples of $\mathbf{C}_{2h}$ and $\mathbf{C}_{3h}$ molecules are illustrated in Figure 2.6.

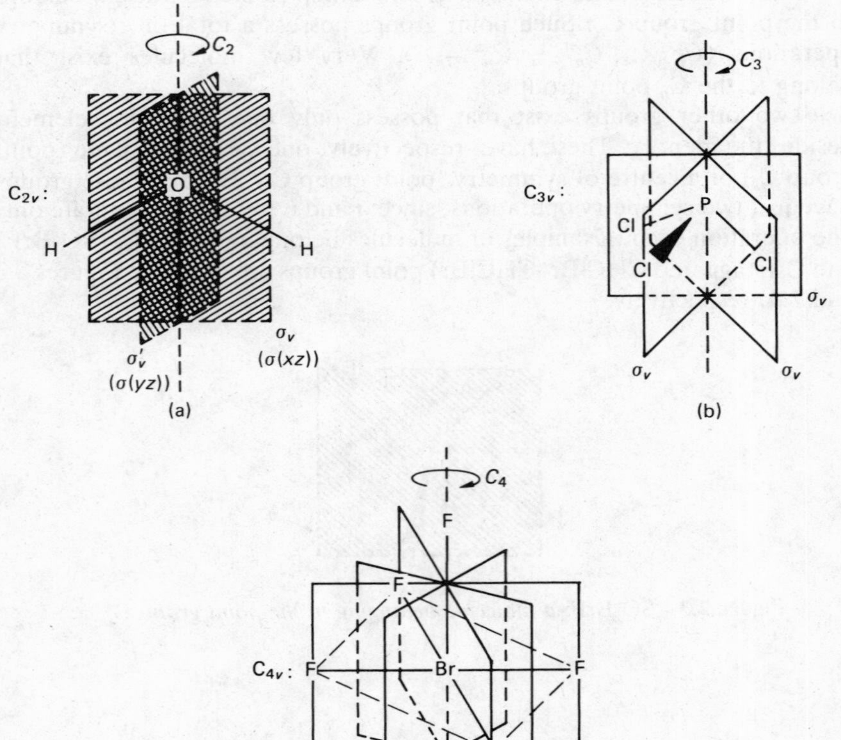


**Figure 2.5** *Molecules belonging to the point groups* $\mathbf{C}_{nv}$: (a) $H_2O$ ($\mathbf{C}_{2v}$); (b) $PCl_3$ ($\mathbf{C}_{3v}$); (c) $BrF_5$ ($\mathbf{C}_{4v}$)

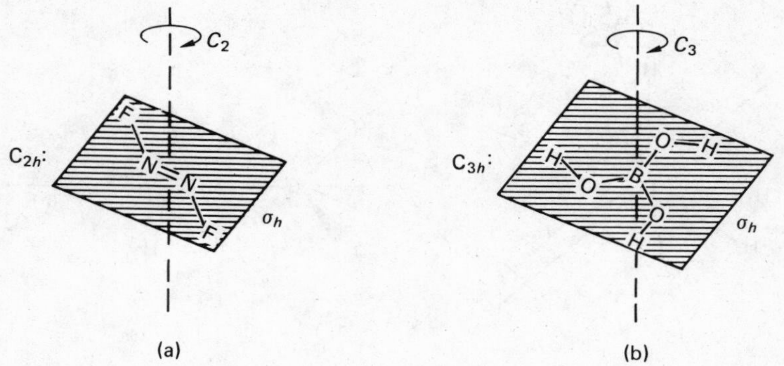


**Figure 2.6** *Molecules belonging to the point groups* $\mathbf{C}_{nh}$: (a) trans–$N_2F_2$ ($\mathbf{C}_{2h}$); (b) $B(OH)_3$ ($\mathbf{C}_{3h}$)

Another possible addition to a $\mathbf{C}_n$ system is an $S_{2n}$ axis coincident with the $C_n$ axis, giving the point group $\mathbf{S}_{2n}$. Possible examples are $\mathbf{S}_2$, $\mathbf{S}_4$ and $\mathbf{S}_6$. The first is the same as $\mathbf{C}_i$, as a rotation through 180° followed by reflection is equivalent to an inversion $i$. An example of the $\mathbf{S}_4$ point group is shown in Figure 2.7 ($(PNCl_2)_4$).

The addition of $n$ two-fold axes at right angles to the $C_n$ axis of a $\mathbf{C}_n$ system ($nC_2'$) gives rise to the point group $\mathbf{D}_n$. The reason for the presence of just $n$ two-fold axes is the same as that for the presence of $n$ $\sigma_v$ planes in $\mathbf{C}_{nv}$. The $\mathbf{D}_n$ groups are rather rare, but the *gauche* conformation of ethane possesses a $C_3$ axis, with three $C_2'$ axes perpendicular to it (Figure 2.8), and hence belongs to the point group $\mathbf{D}_3$.

From the point of view of molecular symmetry, more important groups are formed by the addition of planes of symmetry to the axes of the $\mathbf{D}_n$ groups. If $n$ such planes are present, containing the $C_n$ axis and bisecting the angles between $C_2'$ axes (these are known as dihedral planes of symmetry, $\sigma_d$), then the group so defined is $\mathbf{D}_{nd}$. In Figure 2.9, examples of the groups $\mathbf{D}_{2d}$ (allene) $\mathbf{D}_{3d}$ (ethane, in its staggered conformation) are illustrated.

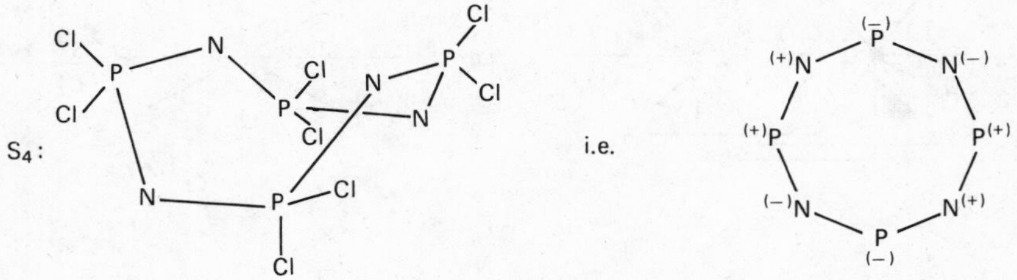


**Figure 2.7** $(PNCl_2)_4$: *a molecule belonging to the point group* $\mathbf{S}_4$

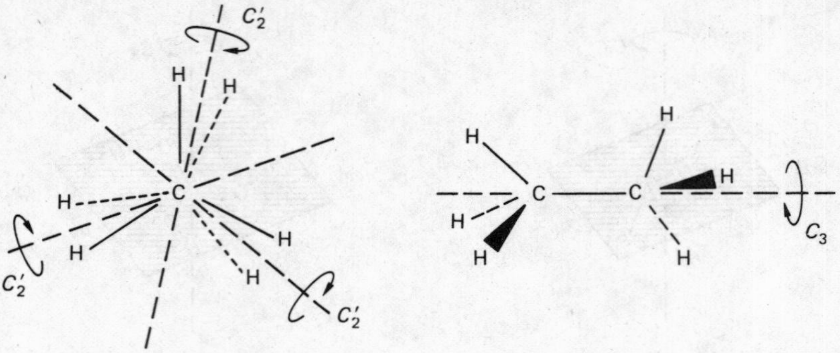


**Figure 2.8** Gauche $CH_3$–$CH_3$: *a molecule belonging to the point group* $\mathbf{D}_3$

The last of the groups that can be fitted into this scheme are those formed by adding a horizontal plane, $\sigma_h$, to the elements of $\mathbf{D}_n$, giving the groups $\mathbf{D}_{nh}$. Many examples of these are known, and molecules belonging to $\mathbf{D}_{2h}$, $\mathbf{D}_{3h}$, $\mathbf{D}_{4h}$ and $\mathbf{D}_{6h}$ are shown in Figure 2.10.

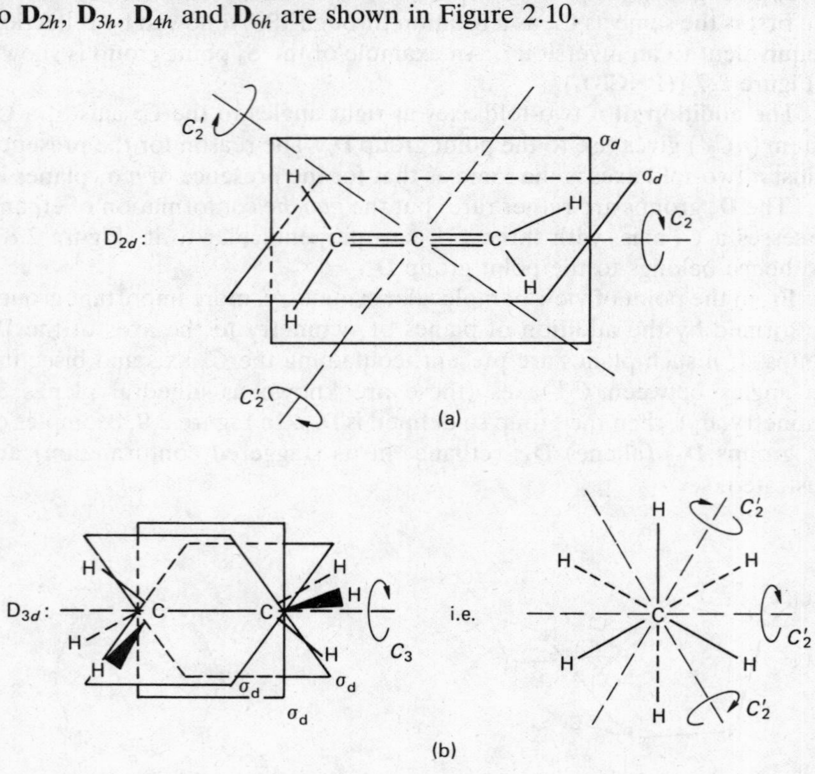


**Figure 2.9** *Molecules belonging to the point groups* $\mathbf{D}_{nd}$: (a) *allene* ($\mathbf{D}_{2d}$); (b) *staggered* $CH_3$–$CH_3$ ($\mathbf{D}_{3d}$)

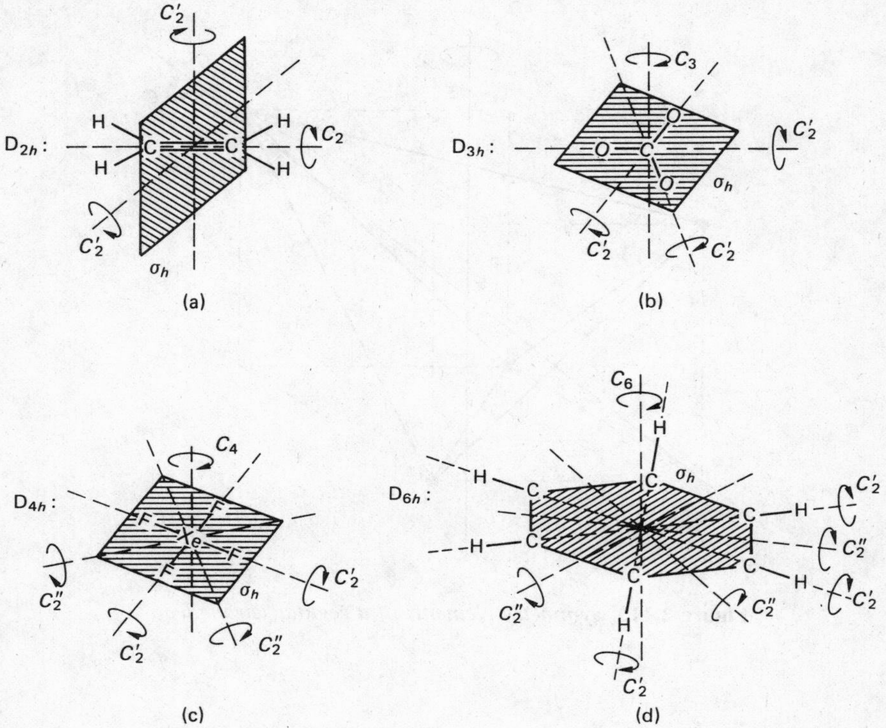


**Figure 2.10** *Molecules belonging to the point groups* $\mathbf{D}_{nh}$: (a) $CH_2{=}CH_2$ ($\mathbf{D}_{2h}$); (b) $CO_3^{2-}$ ($\mathbf{D}_{3h}$); (c) $XeF_4$ ($\mathbf{D}_{4h}$); (d) *benzene* ($\mathbf{D}_{6h}$)

The remaining groups encountered in the study of molecular symmetry cannot be fitted so easily into this simple pattern. First, there are the point groups characteristic of linear molecules. For those without a centre of symmetry, such as HCl and O═C═S, a $C_\infty$ is present, with $\infty\sigma_v$ planes containing this axis. By analogy with the finite groups, these define the point group $\mathbf{C}_{\infty v}$. In a similar way, if a centre of symmetry is present, as in H—C≡C—H and $Cl_2$, then an infinite number of $C_2'$ axes perpendicular to $C_\infty$ must be present, together with a $\sigma_h$ plane. The group is, therefore, $\mathbf{D}_{\infty h}$.

The remaining point groups of chemical significance are the **cubic** point groups – the two most frequently encountered are those characteristic of the tetrahedron and the octahedron, respectively. Both of these can be derived from the symmetry elements of the cube, and they can be visualised most easily by inscribing the tetrahedron or octahedron within a cube. The tetrahedron is shown thus in Figure 2.11. It possesses the following symmetry elements: four $C_3$ axes (one passing through each vertex and the centre of the opposite triangular face, three $C_2$ axes (each

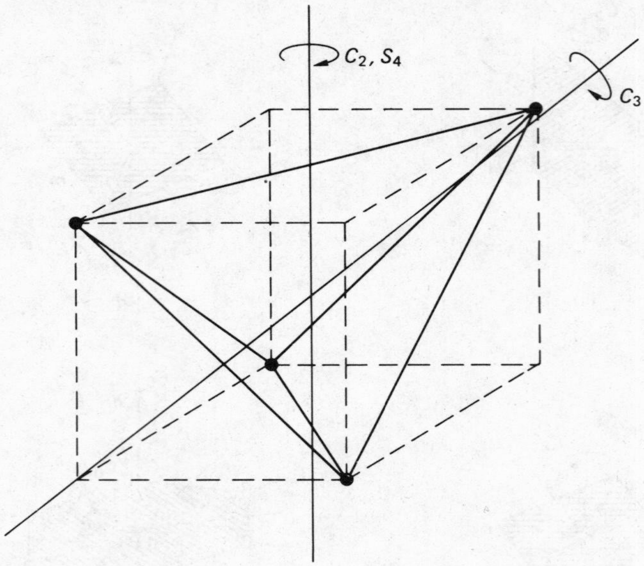


**Figure 2.11** *Symmetry elements of a regular tetrahedron*

one bisecting an opposite pair of edges), three $S_4$ axes (coincident with the $C_2$ axes, see p. 9) and six $\sigma_d$ planes (each one containing two vertices and bisecting the line joining the other two). The resulting point group is given the symbol $\mathbf{T}_d$. In a similar way, the octahedron can be inscribed within a cube, as shown in Figure 2.12. It possesses 31 symmetry elements, including $C_4$, $C_3$, $C_2$, $S_6$ and $S_4$ axes, $\sigma_h$ and $\sigma_d$ planes, a centre of symmetry and the identity, and is given the symbol $\mathbf{O}_h$.

Other cubic groups exist but are rarely encountered: **T** (containing only the rotations of $\mathbf{T}_d$ and no planes of symmetry), $\mathbf{T}_h$ (the group **T** plus a different set of planes from $\mathbf{T}_d$) and **O** (containing the rotations of $\mathbf{O}_h$). One final point group that is occasionally relevant to molecular symmetry is $\mathbf{I}_h$, possessing the symmetry of a pentagonal dodecahedron or a regular icosahedron (one example is a system having the symmetry of the ion $B_{12}H_{12}^{2-}$).

A point group of importance in atomic spectroscopy is that which possesses all possible rotations (about any axis passing through the origin of the system – for example, a sphere) and all possible reflections in any plane containing the origin as symmetry operations. This group is known as $\mathbf{R}_h(3)$, the three-dimensional, rotation–reflection group, characteristic of a single, isolated atom.

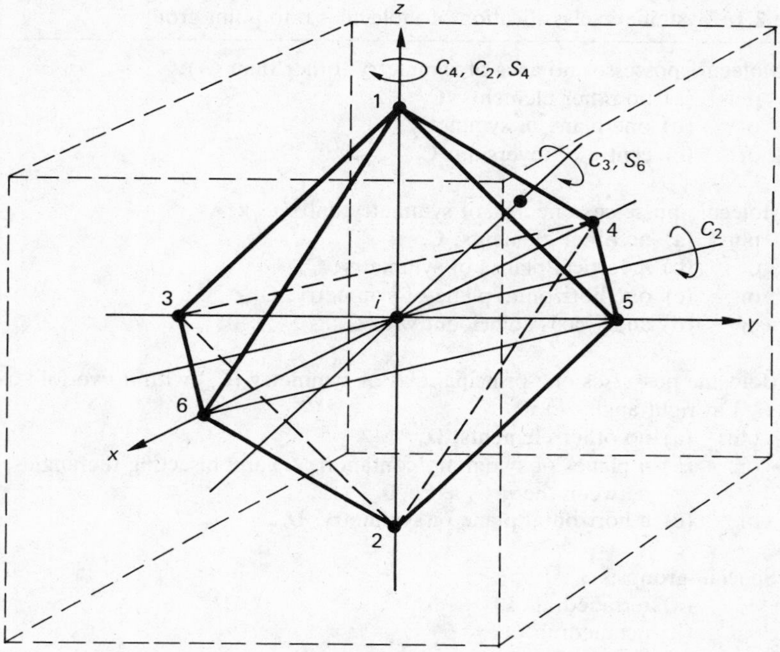


**Figure 2.12** *Symmetry elements of a regular octahedron*

This concludes the list of all the common point groups. A summary of the systematic classification is given in Table 2.1.

It must be remembered that only the minimum number of symmetry elements necessary to specify a given point group has been given. In many cases, these will not be the only symmetry elements possessed by the group – others will necessarily be present. For example, consider a molecule belonging to the point group $\mathbf{D}_{4h}$, which is defined by the symmetry elements $C_4$, with four perpendicular $C_2$ axes and a $\sigma_h$ plane. The following elements, however, must also be present: $E$, $S_4$ (coincident with $C_4$), $i$, two $\sigma_v$ planes and two $\sigma_d$ planes. These all arise because of the presence of the defining elements; for example, a $C_4$ together with a $\sigma_h$ automatically gives rise to an $S_4$ axis.

In addition, it must be stressed that while point groups have been classified in terms of the symmetry elements, as these are easier to visualise, it is the associated symmetry operations that constitute the group. In all applications of molecular symmetry, it is the operations with which we will be concerned.

**Table 2.1** Systematic classification of molecules into point groups

**1** Molecule possesses no axes of symmetry (other than $C_1$):
plus (a) no other elements: $\mathbf{C_1}$
or (b) one plane of symmetry: $\mathbf{C}_s$
or (c) centre of inversion: $\mathbf{C}_i$

**2** Molecule possesses one axis of symmetry only ($C_n$):
plus (a) no other elements: $\mathbf{C}_n$
or (b) $n$ vertical planes of symmetry: $\mathbf{C}_{nv}$
or (c) one horizontal plane of symmetry: $\mathbf{C}_{nh}$
or (d) an $S_{2n}$ axis coincident with $C_n$: $\mathbf{S}_{2n}$

**3** Molecule possesses one principal axis of symmetry ($C_n$) with $n$ two-fold axes ($C_2'$) at right angles to it:
plus (a) no other elements: $\mathbf{D}_n$
or (b) $n$ planes of symmetry containing $C_n$ and bisecting the angles between the $n$ $C_2$ axes: $\mathbf{D}_{nd}$
or (c) a horizontal plane of symmetry: $\mathbf{D}_{nh}$

**4** 'Special' groups:
(a) tetrahedral: $\mathbf{T}_d$
(b) octahedral: $\mathbf{O}_h$
(c) icosahedral: $\mathbf{I}_h$
(d) linear: (i) no centre of symmetry: $\mathbf{C}_{\infty v}$
(ii) centre of symmetry: $\mathbf{D}_{\infty h}$

## 2.6 Examples of classification into groups

Let us take a representative selection of molecules and assign them to their point groups. The procedure for doing this is outlined below:

**1** Determine whether the molecule is linear, or belongs to the highly symmetrical cubic or icosahedral point groups ($\mathbf{T}_d$, $\mathbf{O}_h$ or $\mathbf{I}_h$). If not, proceed to step 2.

**2** Find the proper rotation axis of highest order ($C_n$). In the absence of such an axis, look for (a) a plane of symmetry ($\mathbf{C}_s$), (b) a centre of symmetry ($\mathbf{C}_i$) or (c) no symmetry other than $E$ ($\mathbf{C}_1$).

**3** If an axis $C_n$ is found, look for a set of $n$ $C_2$ axes perpendicular to it. If these are present, proceed to step 4. If they are absent, look for (a) a horizontal plane ($\mathbf{C}_{nh}$), (b) $n$ vertical planes ($\mathbf{C}_{nv}$), (c) an $S_{2n}$ axis coincident with $C_n$ ($\mathbf{S}_{2n}$) or (d) no symmetry planes or other axes ($\mathbf{C}_n$).

**4** If a $C_n$ axis and $n$ $C_2$ perpendicular axes are present, check on the presence of (a) a horizontal plane ($\mathbf{D}_{nh}$), (b) $n$ vertical planes and no horizontal plane ($\mathbf{D}_{nd}$), or (c) no symmetry planes or other axes ($\mathbf{D}_n$).

Following this standard procedure, we can assign the following molecules to their respective point groups:

$H_2S$:

**1** Non-linear; does not belong to a highly symmetric group.

**2** Highest order axis is $C_2$.

**3** No $C_2$ axes perpendicular to this, but two vertical planes which contain the $C_2$ axis. Therefore, the point group is $\mathbf{C}_{2v}$.

$PCl_3$:

**1** Non-linear; does not belong to a highly symmetric group.

**2** Highest order axis is $C_3$.

**3** No $C_2$ axes perpendicular to this, but three $\sigma_v$ planes. Therefore, the point group is $\mathbf{C}_{3v}$.

*trans*–$N_2F_2$:

**1** Non-linear; does not belong to a highly symmetric group.

**2** Highest order axis is $C_2$ (passing through the midpoint of the N=N bond, perpendicular to the molecular plane).

**3** No $C_2$ axes perpendicular to this, but a $\sigma_h$ is present. Therefore, the point group is $\mathbf{C}_{2h}$.

$B_2H_6$ (Figure 2.13):

**1** Non-linear; does not belong to a highly symmetric group.

**2** Highest order axis is $C_2$. (Where there are several axes of the same order, choose one that is geometrically unique – for example, containing the B…B direction.)

**3** Two $C_2$ axes perpendicular to this.

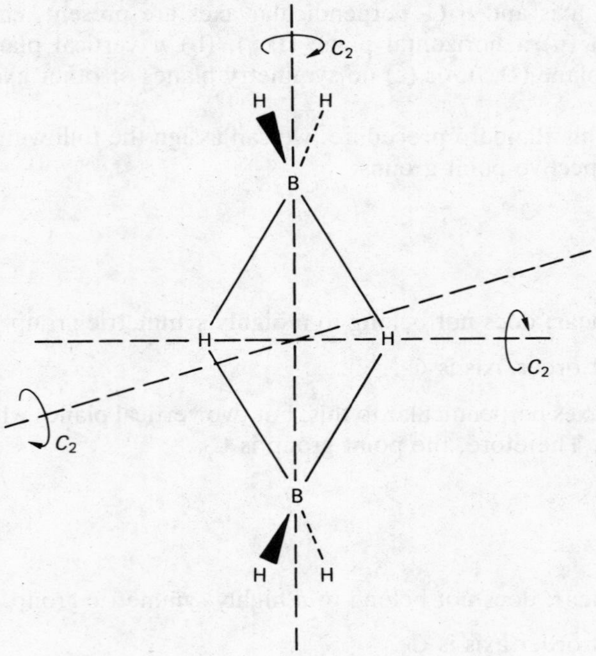


**Figure 2.13** *The molecular structure of diborane,* $B_2H_6$

**4** A horizontal plane is present. Therefore, the molecule belongs to the point group $\mathbf{D}_{2h}$.

$C_6H_6$:

**1** Non-linear; does not belong to a highly symmetric group.

**2** Highest order axis is $C_6$.

**3** Six $C_2$ axes perpendicular to this.

**4** A horizontal plane is present. Therefore, the molecule has $\mathbf{D}_{6h}$ symmetry.

$SF_6$:

**1** Non-linear; belongs to the octahedral ($\mathbf{O}_h$) point group.

H—C≡C—H:

**1** Linear, and possesses $\infty C_2$ axes perpendicular to the molecular axis and a horizontal plane. Its point group is $\mathbf{D}_{\infty h}$.

## EXERCISES

**1** For the $H_2O$ molecule (see Figure 2.5(a)), show that each of the symmetry operations ($E$, $C_2^1$, $\sigma(xz)$ and $\sigma(yz)$) belongs to a different class.

**2** Assign each of the following molecules to the correct point group:

(a) SOClF
(b) HDO
(c) $CH_3CHO$
(d) 1-chloro-3,5-difluorobenzene
(e) $SF_4$
(f) $SiH_3CN$
(g) $WF_5Cl$
(h) $PtCl_4^{2-}$
(i) $C_2(CN)_4$
(j) $SnCl_4$
(k) $NO_3^-$
(l) $C_5H_5^-$
(m) $Cr(CO)_6$
(n) $H_2$
(o) ClC≡CBr

# 3 Matrices

Before seeing how we can use the symmetry properties of molecules to help in the solution of some chemical problems, we must make a brief digression to introduce a branch of mathematics which will be extremely useful. This is matrix algebra, which, as we shall see, enables us to obtain numerical representations of the effects of symmetry operations on molecules. The mathematics introduced will be the minimum needed to appreciate the usefulness of matrices.

A matrix is a rectangular block of numbers (or symbols representing numbers) that can be written in the general form (enclosure by square brackets is characteristic of a matrix):

$$\begin{bmatrix} a_{11} & a_{12} & a_{13} & \cdots & a_{1n} \\ a_{21} & a_{22} & a_{23} & \cdots & a_{2n} \\ \cdot & \cdot & \cdot & & \cdot \\ \cdot & \cdot & \cdot & & \cdot \\ \cdot & \cdot & \cdot & & \cdot \\ a_{m1} & a_{m2} & a_{m3} & \cdots & a_{mn} \end{bmatrix}$$

Such a matrix is said to be of dimension $m \times n$; that is, it has $m$ rows and $n$ columns. A conventional shorthand for this matrix is **A** (general element $a_{ij}$). When $m = n$ the matrix is square; such matrices are particularly important in symmetry applications of matrix algebra. The elements $a_{ii}$ (that is, $a_{11}$, $a_{22}$, $a_{33}$, ..., $a_{mm}$) of a square matrix are its **diagonal elements**.

Two special examples of square matrices are the **null matrix** (all elements zero) and the **unit matrix** (all elements zero except the diagonal elements, which all have the value 1). The symbols for these are **O** and **E**, respectively; the unit matrix is particularly important.

## 3.1 Equality, addition and subtraction of matrices

All of these operations are straightforward. Two matrices (**A** and **B**) are equal only if all of the corresponding elements are identical; that is, they must have the same dimensions and $a_{ij} = b_{ij}$ (for $i = 1$ to $m$, $j = 1$ to $n$).

Addition or subtraction is only possible if the matrices concerned are of the same dimensions. If this condition is fulfilled, then addition or subtraction of two matrices consists of adding or subtracting all of the corresponding elements. Thus, if $\mathbf{A} + \mathbf{B} = \mathbf{C}$, then $a_{ij} + b_{ij} = c_{ij}$, and similarly for subtraction; for example:

$$\begin{bmatrix} 6 & 3 \\ 4 & 0 \end{bmatrix} + \begin{bmatrix} 1 & 2 \\ 1 & 1 \end{bmatrix} = \begin{bmatrix} 7 & 5 \\ 5 & 1 \end{bmatrix}$$

## 3.2 Matrix multiplication

This operation is more complicated. As an illustration, consider the multiplication of matrices in the equation:

$$\mathbf{XY} = \mathbf{Z}$$

The method of multiplication places certain restrictions on the dimensions of **X** and **Y**. It is found that the number of columns in **X** must equal the number of rows in **Y**. If **X** is $m \times p$, then **Y** must be $p \times n$, and the dimensions of **Z** will be $m \times n$. Let the individual elements of **X** and **Y** be $x_{ij}$ and $y_{jk}$; the elements of **Z** will then be $z_{ik}$, where:

$$z_{ik} = \sum_{j=1}^{p} x_{ij} y_{jk}$$

That is:

$$z_{ik} = x_{i1}y_{1k} + x_{i2}y_{2k} + \ldots + x_{ip}y_{pk}$$

These abstractions will perhaps be clarified by showing a more explicit example of matrix multiplication.

Let the matrices **X**, **Y** and **Z** be:

$$\begin{bmatrix} x_{11} & x_{12} \\ x_{21} & x_{22} \\ x_{31} & x_{32} \end{bmatrix} \begin{bmatrix} y_{11} & y_{12} & y_{13} \\ y_{21} & y_{22} & y_{23} \end{bmatrix} = \begin{bmatrix} z_{11} & z_{12} & z_{13} \\ z_{21} & z_{22} & z_{23} \\ z_{31} & z_{32} & z_{33} \end{bmatrix}$$

The elements of **Z** are obtained as follows:

$$z_{11} = x_{11}y_{11} + x_{12}y_{21}$$
$$z_{12} = x_{11}y_{12} + x_{12}y_{22}$$
$$z_{13} = x_{11}y_{13} + x_{12}y_{23}$$

$$z_{21} = x_{21}y_{11} + x_{22}y_{21}$$
$$z_{22} = x_{21}y_{12} + x_{22}y_{22}$$
$$z_{23} = x_{21}y_{13} + x_{22}y_{23}$$
$$z_{31} = x_{31}y_{11} + x_{32}y_{21}$$
$$z_{32} = x_{31}y_{12} + x_{32}y_{22}$$
$$z_{33} = x_{31}y_{13} + x_{32}y_{23}$$

In other words, the process of obtaining the element $z_{ik}$ can be described as multiplying the $i$th row of **X** by the $k$th column of **Y**. It is this that leads to the requirement that there shall be as many columns in **X** as there are rows in **Y**.

A numerical example of the process of matrix multiplication is as follows (the reader can check the evaluation of each element of the product matrix using the foregoing equations):

$$\begin{bmatrix} 1 & 4 \\ 3 & 2 \\ -1 & 0 \end{bmatrix} \begin{bmatrix} 2 & -2 & 0 \\ 1 & 1 & 3 \end{bmatrix} = \begin{bmatrix} 6 & 2 & 12 \\ 8 & -4 & 6 \\ -2 & 2 & 0 \end{bmatrix}$$

Three further points can be made concerning matrix multiplication:

**1** Multiplication of any matrix by the unit matrix **E** of appropriate dimensions leaves the matrix unchanged:

$$\mathbf{XE} = \mathbf{X} = \mathbf{EX}$$

This follows from the definition of a unit matrix and from the rules of matrix multiplication.

**2** Multiplication of matrices is, in general, non-commutative; that is, $\mathbf{XY} \neq \mathbf{YX}$. In many cases, it is not even possible to multiply two matrices 'both ways'. Two matrices are only conformable – that is, they have the correct dimensions for multiplication – both ways (**XY**, **YX**) if **X** is of dimensions $n \times p$ and **Y** is $p \times n$. Even when this general condition is fulfilled, the product matrix obtained still may depend on the order of multiplication, as in the following example:

$$\begin{bmatrix} 1 & 4 \\ 3 & 2 \end{bmatrix} \begin{bmatrix} 1 & 0 \\ 2 & 2 \end{bmatrix} = \begin{bmatrix} 9 & 8 \\ 7 & 4 \end{bmatrix}$$

while:

$$\begin{bmatrix} 1 & 0 \\ 2 & 2 \end{bmatrix} \begin{bmatrix} 1 & 4 \\ 3 & 2 \end{bmatrix} = \begin{bmatrix} 1 & 4 \\ 8 & 12 \end{bmatrix}$$

**3**  An inverse to a matrix is defined as follows: if a matrix **X** and the unit matrix are related by:

$$\mathbf{XY} = \mathbf{E}$$

then **Y** is the inverse of **X** and can be written as $\mathbf{X}^{-1}$. Note that only square matrices can have inverses. Thus:

$$\mathbf{XX}^{-1} = \mathbf{E} \qquad (=\mathbf{X}^{-1}\mathbf{X})$$

This is all that needs to be said for the present about matrices and their properties. We may just note in anticipation that some of these properties (possession of an inverse, non-commutative multiplication, and so on) are closely parallel to those of symmetry operations.

## ■ EXERCISES

**1**  Carry out the following matrix additions and subtraction:

(a)
$$\begin{bmatrix} 6 & 4 \\ 4 & -3 \\ 0 & 1 \end{bmatrix} + \begin{bmatrix} 4 & 3 \\ 0 & 1 \\ -6 & 2 \end{bmatrix} = \begin{bmatrix} 10 & 7 \\ 4 & -2 \\ -6 & 3 \end{bmatrix}$$

(b)
$$\begin{bmatrix} 7 & 4 \\ 1 & 6 \end{bmatrix} + \begin{bmatrix} 3 & 2 \\ 8 & 4 \\ 0 & 1 \end{bmatrix}$$

(c)
$$\begin{bmatrix} 2 & 1 \\ 7 & 4 \end{bmatrix} - \begin{bmatrix} 2 & -2 \\ 3 & 2 \end{bmatrix} = \begin{bmatrix} 0 & 3 \\ 4 & 2 \end{bmatrix}$$

**2**  Carry out the following matrix multiplications:

(a)
$$\begin{bmatrix} 2 & 2 \\ 1 & 0 \\ 3 & 2 \end{bmatrix} \begin{bmatrix} 1 & 2 & 1 \\ 7 & -2 & 0 \end{bmatrix} = \begin{bmatrix} 16 & 0 & 2 \\ 1 & 2 & 1 \\ 17 & 2 & 3 \end{bmatrix}$$

(b)
$$\begin{bmatrix} 6 & 4 \\ 2 & 2 \end{bmatrix} \begin{bmatrix} 1 & 1 & 2 \\ 0 & 2 & 1 \\ 3 & -2 & 0 \end{bmatrix}$$

(c)
$$\begin{bmatrix} 2 & 4 \\ 3 & 1 \end{bmatrix} \begin{bmatrix} 3 & -2 \\ -2 & 0 \end{bmatrix} = \begin{bmatrix} -2 & -4 \\ 4 & -6 \end{bmatrix}$$

(d) $\begin{bmatrix} 3 & -2 \\ -2 & 0 \end{bmatrix} \begin{bmatrix} 2 & 4 \\ 3 & 1 \end{bmatrix} = \begin{bmatrix} 0 & 12 \\ -1 & -7 \end{bmatrix}$

(e) $\begin{bmatrix} 1 & 0 \\ 0 & 2 \end{bmatrix} \begin{bmatrix} 2 & 0 \\ 0 & 1 \end{bmatrix} = \begin{bmatrix} 2 & 0 \\ 0 & 2 \end{bmatrix}$

(f) $\begin{bmatrix} 2 & 0 \\ 0 & 1 \end{bmatrix} \begin{bmatrix} 1 & 0 \\ 0 & 2 \end{bmatrix} = \begin{bmatrix} 2 & 0 \\ 0 & 2 \end{bmatrix}$

**3**    Show that the inverse of the matrix:

$$\begin{bmatrix} 0 & -1 \\ 1 & 0 \end{bmatrix} \begin{bmatrix} 1 & 0 \\ 0 & 1 \end{bmatrix} = \begin{bmatrix} 0 & -1 \\ 1 & 0 \end{bmatrix}$$

is:

$$\begin{bmatrix} 0 & 1 \\ -1 & 0 \end{bmatrix}$$

$AA^{-1} = E$

$\text{f } A = \begin{bmatrix} 0 & -1 \\ 1 & 0 \end{bmatrix}$ & $A^{-1} = \begin{bmatrix} 0 & 1 \\ -1 & 0 \end{bmatrix}$

the $\begin{bmatrix} 0 & -1 \\ 1 & 0 \end{bmatrix} \begin{bmatrix} 0 & 1 \\ -1 & 0 \end{bmatrix} = \begin{bmatrix} 0+1 & 0+0 \\ 0+0 & 1+0 \end{bmatrix}$

$= \begin{bmatrix} 1 & 0 \\ 0 & 1 \end{bmatrix}$

$AA^{-1} = E$

# 4

# Representations of groups

It is relatively straightforward to illustrate, by means of diagrams, the effects of symmetry operations on molecules. It would be much less cumbersome, however, and more convenient for mathematical analysis, if a way could be found of representing the effects of symmetry operations numerically; thus, a *representation* of the molecule's point group is required. Such a representation must reproduce exactly the relationships between the symmetry operations themselves. Thus, if multiplying two operations is equivalent to a third, then the representations of the first two, when multiplied together, must give the representation of the third.

One very convenient method for obtaining a representation of a molecular point group is to attach one or more vectors (lines of specified length *and* direction) to the molecule and to observe the effects of the symmetry operations on the vector(s). These effects can be expressed numerically, and we will show that they give a true representation of the group. The vectors used are said to form the *basis* of that representation.

## 4.1 The use of vectors

A very simple example of the use of vectors for representations is shown by any molecule of $\mathbf{C}_{2v}$ symmetry, such as $SO_2$. A set of Cartesian coordinate axes is placed on each atom (Figure 4.1 – this orientation of the axes is conventional) and a vector is drawn from each atom along its own $y$ axis, all of the vectors being of the same length. This set of vectors corresponds to a translation of the molecule in the $y$ direction; it is usually written as $\mathbf{T_y}$. The symmetry operations of the $\mathbf{C}_{2v}$ point group are $E$, $C_2$ (the axis passing through the S atom and bisecting the O—S—O angle), and $\sigma(yz)$ and $\sigma(xz)$ (these planes lie in and perpendicular to the molecular plane, respectively). Carrying out these operations on the $\mathbf{T_y}$ vector set either leaves all of the vectors completely unchanged ($E$, $\sigma(yz)$) or merely reverses their directions ($C_2$, $\sigma(xz)$). The $C_2$ operation is illustrated in Figure 4.2 and the

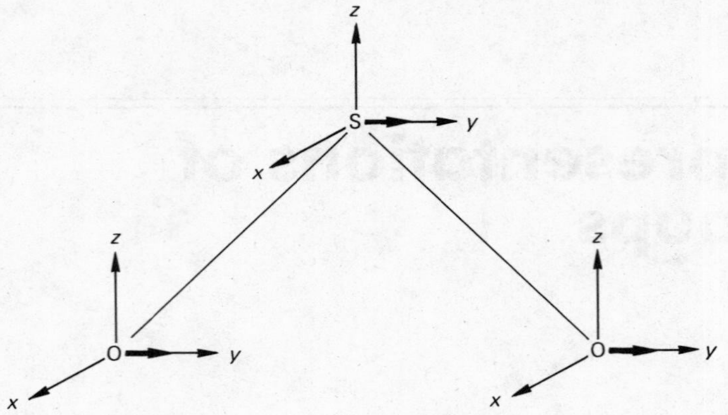


**Figure 4.1** *The translation vector,* $\mathbf{T_y}$*, of the* $SO_2$ *molecule* ($\mathbf{C_{2v}}$)

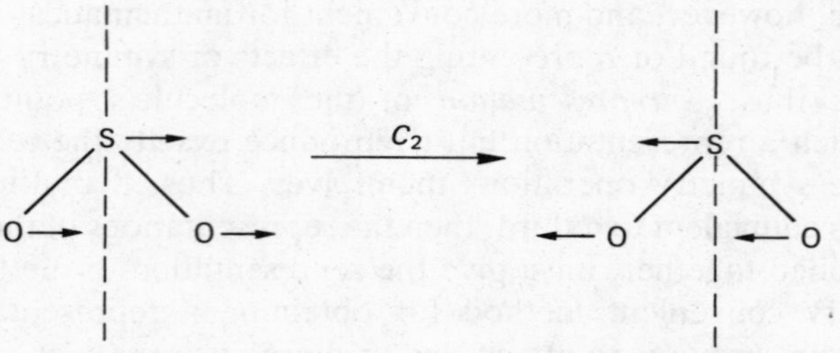


**Figure 4.2** *The effect of a* $C_2$ *rotation on the* $\mathbf{T_y}$ *vector of* $SO_2$

relationships are expressed as follows (+1 indicates that the vector is completely unchanged and −1 that the direction is reversed):

$$E(\mathbf{T_y}) = (+1)(\mathbf{T_y})$$
$$C_2(\mathbf{T_y}) = (-1)(\mathbf{T_y})$$
$$\sigma(xz)(\mathbf{T_y}) = (-1)(\mathbf{T_y})$$
$$\sigma(yz)(\mathbf{T_y}) = (+1)(\mathbf{T_y})$$

where $R(\mathbf{X})$ symbolises carrying out the symmetry operation $R$ on the vector **X**.

In a similar way, the translation vectors $\mathbf{T_x}$ and $\mathbf{T_z}$ can be attached to the molecule and the effects of the symmetry operations on them determined. Further sets of vectors, corresponding now to *rotations* of the molecule about the three Cartesian axes, can also be set up and the effects of the symmetry operations on these can be found in the same way as for

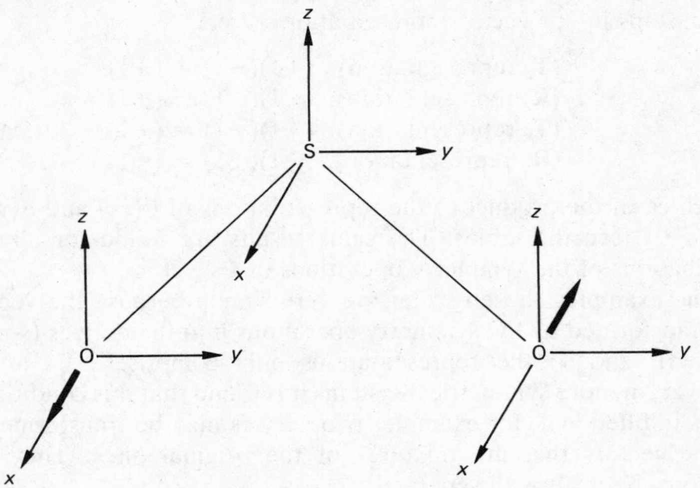


**Figure 4.3** *The rotation vector,* $\mathbf{R_z}$, *of the* $SO_2$ *molecule* ($\mathbf{C_{2v}}$)

the translations. As an example, the vector set for rotation about the *z* axis, $\mathbf{R_z}$, is shown in Figure 4.3.

For the $SO_2$ molecule, all of the translation and rotation vectors are either transformed into themselves (+1) or are merely reversed in direction (−1). The resulting representations may be summarised as follows:

| $\mathbf{C_{2v}}$ | $E$ | $C_2$ | $\sigma(xz)$ | $\sigma(yz)$ | |
|---|---|---|---|---|---|
| | +1 | +1 | +1 | +1 | $\mathbf{T_z}$ |
| | +1 | +1 | −1 | −1 | $\mathbf{R_z}$ |
| | +1 | −1 | +1 | −1 | $\mathbf{T_x}$ or $\mathbf{R_y}$ |
| | +1 | −1 | −1 | +1 | $\mathbf{T_y}$ or $\mathbf{R_x}$ |

This is a more convenient method of writing down the representations than listing all of the equations explicitly, as was done for $\mathbf{T_y}$.

It is necessary to prove that each of these is a faithful representation of the point group $\mathbf{C_{2v}}$; that is, that these sets of +1's and −1's mirror the properties of the symmetry operations of the group. To do this, we have to find the results of all possible combinations of symmetry operations and then show that, using these representations, the same answers are obtained. We will take just one example.

The following relationship holds for the operations of $\mathbf{C_{2v}}$:

$$\sigma(xz)\sigma(yz) = C_2$$

(The proof of this is left to the reader.) Now consider the equivalent relationships in our vector representations:

$$
\begin{aligned}
(\mathbf{T_z}\text{ representation}):&\ (+1)(+1) = (+1)\\
(\mathbf{R_z}\text{ representation}):&\ (-1)(-1) = (+1)\\
(\mathbf{T_x}\text{ representation}):&\ (+1)(-1) = (-1)\\
(\mathbf{R_x}\text{ representation}):&\ (-1)(+1) = (-1)
\end{aligned}
$$

In each case, the product of the representations of $\sigma(xz)$ and $\sigma(yz)$ gives that of $C_2$ (see the table). The same results are found for all possible combinations of the symmetry operations of $\mathbf{C}_{2v}$.

The examples chosen so far are very simple because the vectors are only transformed by the symmetry operations into themselves (sometimes reversed), and so the representations only comprise $+1$'s and $-1$'s. However, in more symmetrical systems it is found that this condition is not always fulfilled and, for example, two vectors may be transformed into a pair of vectors that are mixtures of the original ones. They cannot, therefore, be dealt with separately.

Consider any molecule where rotation by an angle $\theta°$ is a symmetry operation. By convention, the $z$ axis is coincident with the main rotation axis, and hence the $x$ and $y$ axes are perpendicular to it. We can set up translation vectors $\mathbf{T_x}$ and $\mathbf{T_y}$ at an atom lying on the axis (Figure 4.4 – looking down the $z$ axis). Let us now carry out a rotation by $\theta°$, which converts the original vectors into $\mathbf{T_x}'$ and $\mathbf{T_y}'$ (by convention, rotation is taken to be *clockwise* when looking down the main symmetry axis). By simple trigonometry, we can express the new vectors in terms of the original ones, showing that the original vectors have become mixed by the operation of rotation:

$$
\begin{aligned}
\mathbf{T_x}' &= (\cos\theta)\mathbf{T_x} - (\sin\theta)\mathbf{T_y}\\
\mathbf{T_y}' &= (\sin\theta)\mathbf{T_x} + (\cos\theta)\mathbf{T_y}
\end{aligned}
$$

A neater method for summarising these relationships is to use matrices:

$$
\begin{bmatrix}\mathbf{T_x}'\\ \mathbf{T_y}'\end{bmatrix} = \begin{bmatrix}\cos\theta & -\sin\theta\\ \sin\theta & \cos\theta\end{bmatrix}\begin{bmatrix}\mathbf{T_x}\\ \mathbf{T_y}\end{bmatrix}
$$

In such a case, therefore, we must use the two vectors together, and the effects of any symmetry operation on them will be represented by a **transformation matrix** (a $2 \times 2$ matrix in this case). The $\mathbf{C}_{2v}$ examples given also involved transformation matrices, but these were $1 \times 1$ matrices – that is, numbers. In general, the effects of symmetry operations on a set of $n$ vectors will be represented by $n \times n$ transformation matrices. Let us look at a specific example where such a situation arises.

Consider any $\mathbf{C}_{3v}$ molecule, such as $NF_3$. In this case, we can place a set of three Cartesian coordinates on the N atom (Figure 4.5). The F atoms are not included, since the effects of the symmetry operations on the vectors from the F atoms are not so easy to visualise. Translation vectors

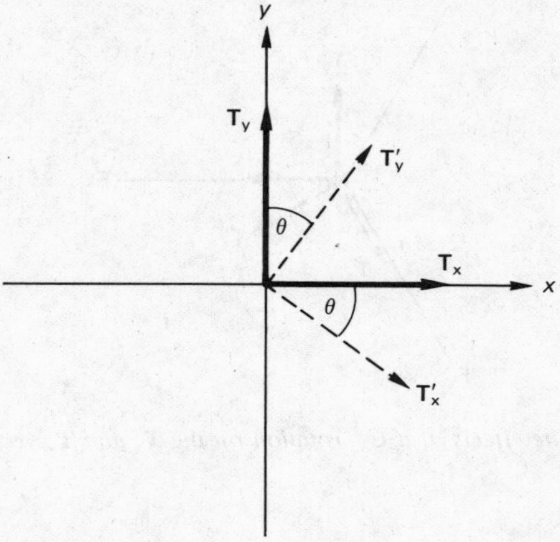


**Figure 4.4** *The effects of rotation by θ° on the* $\mathbf{T_x}$ *and* $\mathbf{T_y}$ *vectors*

along the $x$ and $y$ axes ($\mathbf{T_x}$ and $\mathbf{T_y}$) are illustrated in Figure 4.6, looking down the three-fold axis.

The effects of a $C_3^1$ rotation on the $\mathbf{T_x}$ and $\mathbf{T_y}$ vectors of $NF_3$ are also shown in Figure 4.6. $\mathbf{T_x}$ is transformed into $\mathbf{T_x}'$ and $\mathbf{T_y}$ into $\mathbf{T_y}'$. These new vectors can be expressed in terms of the original ones, using the general relationship derived earlier:

$$\mathbf{T_x}' = (\cos 120°)\mathbf{T_x} - (\sin 120°)\mathbf{T_y} = -\frac{1}{2}\mathbf{T_x} - \frac{\sqrt{3}}{2}\mathbf{T_y}$$

$$\mathbf{T_y}' = (\sin 120°)\mathbf{T_x} + (\cos 120°)\mathbf{T_y} = \frac{\sqrt{3}}{2}\mathbf{T_x} - \frac{1}{2}\mathbf{T_y}$$

for $C_3^1$.

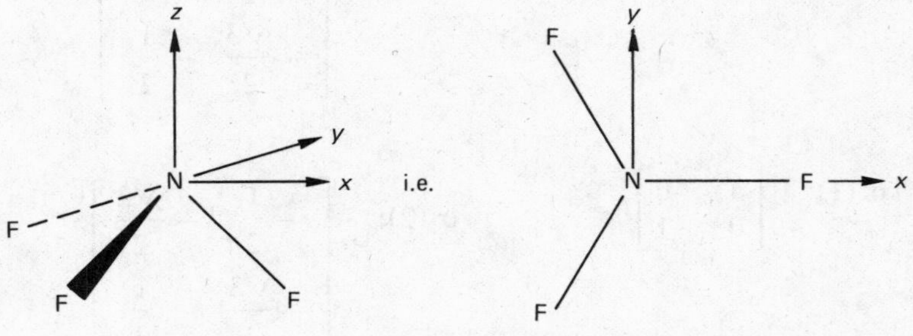


**Figure 4.5** *Cartesian axes for* $NF_3$ ($\mathbf{C_{3v}}$)

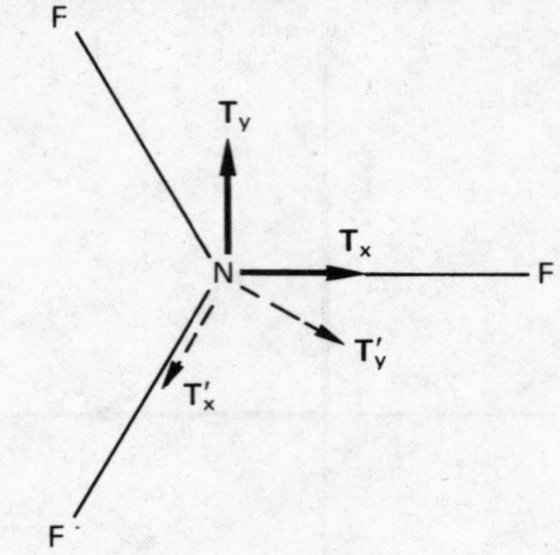


**Figure 4.6** *The effects of a $C_3^1$ rotation on the $\mathbf{T_x}$ and $\mathbf{T_y}$ vectors of* $NF_3$

The effects of a $C_3^1$ rotation on the $\mathbf{T_x}$ and $\mathbf{T_y}$ vectors of a molecule with $\mathbf{C_{3v}}$ symmetry cannot, therefore, be treated separately. In matrix form, we now have:

$$\begin{bmatrix} \mathbf{T_x}' \\ \mathbf{T_y}' \end{bmatrix} = \begin{bmatrix} -\frac{1}{2} & -\frac{\sqrt{3}}{2} \\ \frac{\sqrt{3}}{2} & -\frac{1}{2} \end{bmatrix} \begin{bmatrix} \mathbf{T_x} \\ \mathbf{T_y} \end{bmatrix}$$

for $C_3^1$.

The transformation matrices for all the other symmetry operations of $\mathbf{C_{3v}}$ using the $\mathbf{T_x}$ and $\mathbf{T_y}$ vectors as bases are as follows:

$E$: $\begin{bmatrix} 1 & 0 \\ 0 & 1 \end{bmatrix}$ $C_3^2$: $\begin{bmatrix} -\frac{1}{2} & \frac{\sqrt{3}}{2} \\ -\frac{\sqrt{3}}{2} & -\frac{1}{2} \end{bmatrix}$

$\sigma_v(1)$: $\begin{bmatrix} 1 & 0 \\ 0 & -1 \end{bmatrix}$ $\sigma_v(2)$: $\begin{bmatrix} -\frac{1}{2} & -\frac{\sqrt{3}}{2} \\ -\frac{\sqrt{3}}{2} & \frac{1}{2} \end{bmatrix}$

$$\sigma_v(3): \quad \begin{bmatrix} -\frac{1}{2} & \frac{\sqrt{3}}{2} \\ \frac{\sqrt{3}}{2} & \frac{1}{2} \end{bmatrix}$$

Once again, it is necessary to confirm that these matrices mirror the relationships between the operations themselves. In Chapter 1, we saw that:

$$\sigma_v(1)C_3^{\ 1} = \sigma_v(2)$$

Using the (2 × 2) transformation matrices, we have:

$$\begin{bmatrix} 1 & 0 \\ 0 & -1 \end{bmatrix} \begin{bmatrix} -\frac{1}{2} & -\frac{\sqrt{3}}{2} \\ \frac{\sqrt{3}}{2} & -\frac{1}{2} \end{bmatrix} = \begin{bmatrix} -\frac{1}{2} & -\frac{\sqrt{3}}{2} \\ -\frac{\sqrt{3}}{2} & \frac{1}{2} \end{bmatrix}$$

This equation is in agreement with the rules of matrix multiplication, and so we see that $\mathbf{T_x}$ and $\mathbf{T_y}$ do generate a genuine representation of $\mathbf{C}_{3v}$.

$\mathbf{R_x}$ and $\mathbf{R_y}$ can also be constructed, although they are not so easy to visualise as the $\mathbf{T_x}$ and $\mathbf{T_y}$ vectors, and they are found to behave in exactly the same way as the $\mathbf{T_x}$ and $\mathbf{T_y}$ vectors. The $\mathbf{T_z}$ and $\mathbf{R_z}$ vectors (Figure 4.7), on the other hand, are like the vectors of the $\mathbf{C}_{2v}$ system in that each one is always transformed into itself or its reverse by the symmetry operations of $\mathbf{C}_{3v}$. The representations of $\mathbf{C}_{3v}$ using the translation and rotation vectors as

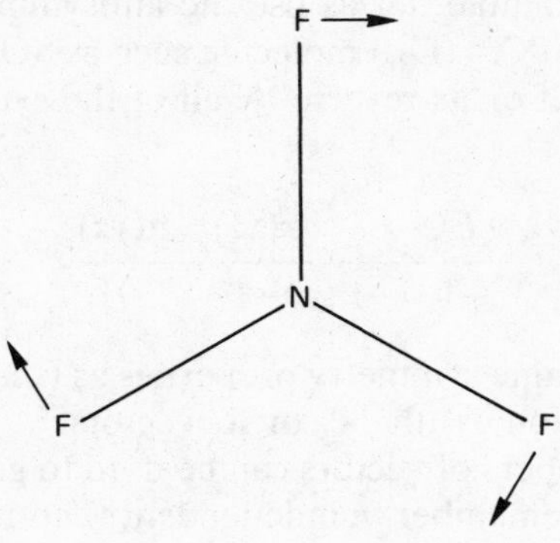


**Figure 4.7** *The rotation vector,* $\mathbf{R_z}$, *of* $NF_3$ *(viewed down the* $C_3$ *axis)*

bases are summarised thus:

| $\mathbf{C}_{3v}$ | $E$ | $C_3^1$ | $C_3^2$ | $\sigma_v(1)$ | |
|---|---|---|---|---|---|
| | $+1$ | $+1$ | $+1$ | $+1$ | $\mathbf{T_z}$ |
| | $+1$ | $+1$ | $+1$ | $-1$ | $\mathbf{R_z}$ |
| | $\begin{bmatrix} 1 & 0 \\ 0 & 1 \end{bmatrix}$ | $\begin{bmatrix} -\frac{1}{2} & -\frac{\sqrt{3}}{2} \\ \frac{\sqrt{3}}{2} & -\frac{1}{2} \end{bmatrix}$ | $\begin{bmatrix} -\frac{1}{2} & \frac{\sqrt{3}}{2} \\ -\frac{\sqrt{3}}{2} & -\frac{1}{2} \end{bmatrix}$ | $\begin{bmatrix} 1 & 0 \\ 0 & -1 \end{bmatrix}$ | $(\mathbf{T_x}, \mathbf{T_y})$ or $(\mathbf{R_x}, \mathbf{R_y})$ |

| $\mathbf{C}_{3v}$ | $\sigma_v(2)$ | $\sigma_v(3)$ | |
|---|---|---|---|
| | $+1$ | $+1$ | $\mathbf{T_z}$ |
| | $-1$ | $-1$ | $\mathbf{R_z}$ |
| | $\begin{bmatrix} -\frac{1}{2} & -\frac{\sqrt{3}}{2} \\ -\frac{\sqrt{3}}{2} & \frac{1}{2} \end{bmatrix}$ | $\begin{bmatrix} -\frac{1}{2} & \frac{\sqrt{3}}{2} \\ \frac{\sqrt{3}}{2} & \frac{1}{2} \end{bmatrix}$ | $(\mathbf{T_x}, \mathbf{T_y})$ or $(\mathbf{R_x}, \mathbf{R_y})$ |

Rotation and, especially, translation vectors are easy to visualise and draw, and hence they are useful examples to illustrate the use of vectors as bases for representations of point groups. Any other vectors could be used, however, and later in this book we shall be greatly concerned with the use of vectors corresponding to molecular vibrations as bases for representations. As a simple example, let us use the antisymmetric bond-stretching vibration vector of an $XY_2$ ($\mathbf{C}_{2v}$) molecule such as $SO_2$ (Figure 4.8). This is transformed into itself or its reverse by all of the symmetry operations of $\mathbf{C}_{2v}$; thus:

| $E$ | $C_2$ | $\sigma(xz)$ | $\sigma(yz)$ |
|---|---|---|---|
| $+1$ | $-1$ | $-1$ | $+1$ |

indicating it has the same symmetry properties as (that is, forms a basis for the same representation as) the $\mathbf{T_y}$ or $\mathbf{R_x}$ vectors.

Much larger numbers of vectors can be used to give representations of greater dimensions; remember, $n$ independent vectors give $n \times n$ transformation matrices. Examples of such representations will be given in Chapter 6.

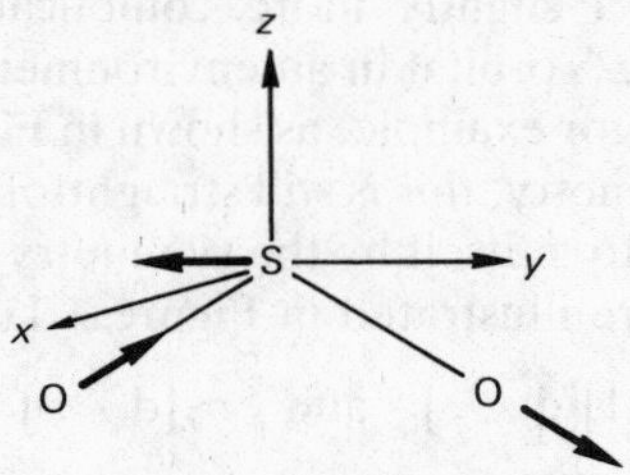


**Figure 4.8** *The antisymmetric bond-stretching vector for* $SO_2$ ($\mathbf{C}_{2v}$)

## 4.2 The use of mathematical functions

Besides using vectors, it is possible to use mathematical functions as bases for point group representations. Any function may be so used, such as one of the atomic wave functions that are particularly important to chemists. These define the various orbitals in which electrons may be placed in an atom, and the symmetry properties of these orbitals are very important in the theory of chemical bonding (see Chapter 10). One can write out the function explicitly (or at least the angular part, as only this is relevant in discussions of symmetry – the radial part is unaltered by all symmetry operations) and calculate the effect of performing any symmetry operation on the function. For our present purposes, however, it will suffice to draw the orbital and to see the effects of symmetry operations pictorially. A simple example is a $p_y$ orbital situated on the S atom of $SO_2$ (Figure 4.9).

The symmetry operations of $\mathbf{C}_{2v}$ have the following effects:

| $E$ | $C_2$ | $\sigma(xz)$ | $\sigma(yz)$ |
|---|---|---|---|
| +1 | −1 | −1 | +1 |

That is, the $p_y$ orbital gives an equivalent representation to that generated by $\mathbf{T}_y$.

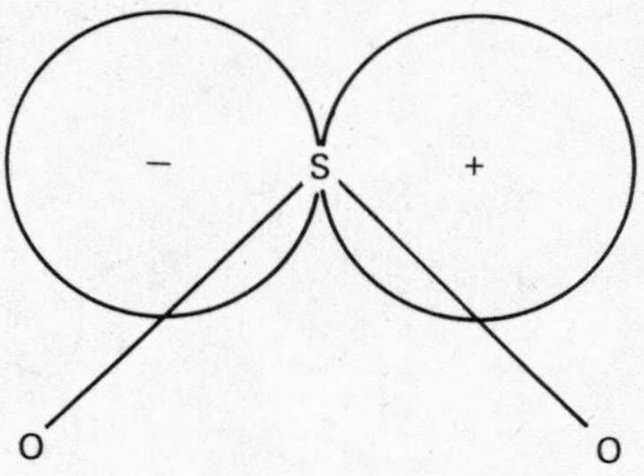


**Figure 4.9** *A* $p_y$ *orbital on the* S *atom of* $SO_2$

We can work out a slightly more complicated case as a further example, such as the $d_{x^2-y^2}$ orbital in an environment of $\mathbf{D}_{4h}$ symmetry (on the Au atom of $AuCl_4^-$, for example, as shown in Figure 4.10). As with the $p_y$ orbital under $\mathbf{C}_{2v}$ symmetry, this is still straightforward in that the orbital is always transformed into ± itself by the symmetry operations of $\mathbf{D}_{4h}$. The operations $C_4^1$ and $\sigma_h$ are illustrated in Figure 4.11, showing that:

$$C_4^1[d_{x^2-y^2}] = [-1][d_{x^2-y^2}] \quad \text{and} \quad \sigma_h[d_{x^2-y^2}] = [+1][d_{x^2-y^2}]$$

The effects of all the symmetry operations on $d_{x^2-y^2}$ can be summarised as follows:

| $E$ | $2C_4$ | $C_2$ | $2C_2'$ | $2C_2''$ | $i$ | $2S_4$ | $\sigma_h$ | $2\sigma_v$ | $2\sigma_d$ |
|---|---|---|---|---|---|---|---|---|---|
| +1 | −1 | +1 | +1 | −1 | +1 | −1 | +1 | +1 | −1 |

(The $C_4^1$ and $C_4^3$ rotations, the $S_4^1$ and $S_4^3$ improper rotations, and the $C_2'$, $C_2''$, $\sigma_v$ and $\sigma_d$ operations are grouped in pairs for brevity, as both members of each pair produce the same effect on all vectors or functions that can be used as bases for representations.)

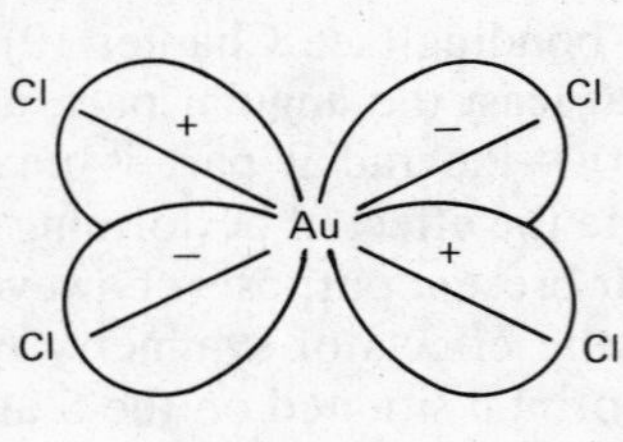


**Figure 4.10** *The* Au $d_{x^2-y^2}$ *orbital in the ion* $AuCl_4^-$ ($\mathbf{D}_{4h}$)

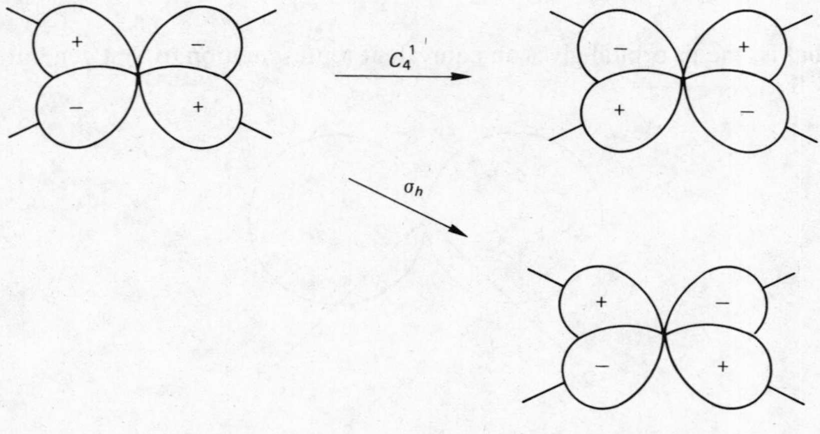


**Figure 4.11** *The effects of* $C_4^1$ *and* $\sigma_h$ *operations on a* $d_{x^2-y^2}$ *orbital*

Just as pairs of vectors can be found that are mixed by the action of symmetry operations, so two or more wave functions can be mixed in the same way; for example, the two p-orbitals $p_x$ and $p_y$ in any system possessing a $C_4$ axis (Figure 4.12). Thus:

$$p_x \longrightarrow p_x' = -p_y; \qquad p_y \longrightarrow p_y' = p_x$$

or, in matrix notation:

$$\begin{bmatrix} p_x' \\ p_y' \end{bmatrix} = \begin{bmatrix} 0 & -1 \\ 1 & 0 \end{bmatrix} \begin{bmatrix} p_x \\ p_y \end{bmatrix}$$

Such examples can be found in all systems containing a three-fold or higher-order axis.

Two more points can be made about the use of atomic wave functions as bases for representations:

**1** s-orbitals are always unchanged by the action of any symmetry operation of any point group; that is, for all symmetry operations $R$, the following relationship holds:

$$R[\mathrm{s}] = [+1][\mathrm{s}]$$

The spherically symmetrical nature of the s-orbital is responsible for this behaviour, and the s-orbital is said to be *totally symmetric* in an environment of any symmetry.

**2** In a free atom – that is, in a spherically symmetrical environment – the orbitals $np_x$, $np_y$ and $np_z$ (where $n$ is the principal quantum number) are all of the same energy; in other words, they are *degenerate*. The same is true of the five d- or the seven f-orbitals having the same principal quantum number. Such a situation does not generally apply when the atom is in an environment of lower symmetry. Consider the p-orbitals of an atom in a $C_{2v}$ environment – each one is transformed only into ± itself. There is no

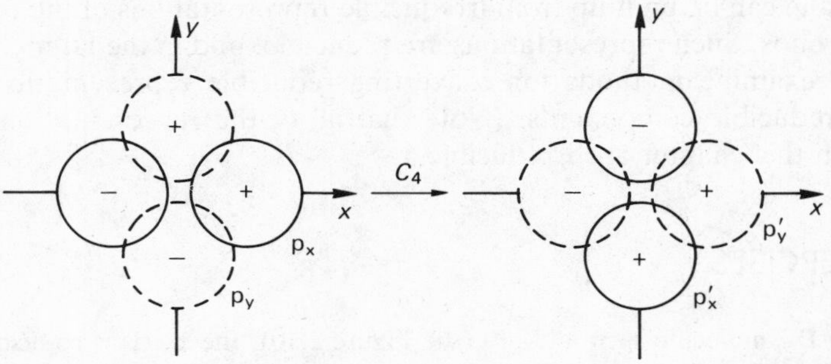


**Figure 4.12** *The effects of a $C_4^1$ rotation on $p_x$ and $p_y$ orbitals*

symmetry relationship between the different p-orbitals, and hence no reason why their energies should be the same – that is, they are now non-degenerate. The same is true of d- or f-orbitals in $\mathbf{C}_{2v}$ symmetry.

It was shown earlier that in a system having a $C_4$ axis, the $p_x$ and $p_y$ orbitals are interchanged by a $C_4^1$ rotation. Carrying out a symmetry operation on a molecule, however, must leave the energy of that molecule unchanged, since the final configuration must be indistinguishable from the original one. Therefore, since $p_x$ and $p_y$ are interchanged by $C_4^1$, they *must* have the same energy in that system (they are still degenerate). In the point group $\mathbf{C}_{4v}$, however, no symmetry relationship exists between ($p_x$, $p_y$) and $p_z$, since the latter orbital is always transformed into itself, and it need not have the same energy as $p_x$ and $p_y$.

In general, if two or more atomic wave functions (orbitals) can be transformed into each other by a symmetry operation, then they must have the same energy (be degenerate) in an environment of that symmetry. A final example of this principle is very important in the theory of transition metal complexes, which are often of $\mathbf{O}_h$ (octahedral) symmetry. Under the symmetry operations of the $\mathbf{O}_h$ point group, all three p-orbitals of the central metal can be transformed into one another and they are degenerate. Of the five d-orbitals, however, the $d_{x^2-y^2}$ and $d_{z^2}$ are degenerate, as are the $d_{xy}$, $d_{yz}$ and $d_{zx}$, but neither of the former can be transformed into any of the latter, and the two sets need not have the same energy.

We have shown a variety of examples of the use of vectors or mathematical functions as bases for the representation of point groups in this chapter. These formed a very small fraction of the possible sets of vectors or functions that could be so used. There is no limit to these, and so an infinite number of representations can be generated for any point group. Only a few of these have fundamental significance, however. These are the irreducible representations. We will define these in detail in the next chapter; all that we need to say for the moment is that these are (with very few exceptions) of order 1, 2 or 3 (that is, the transformation matrices are $1 \times 1$, $2 \times 2$ or $3 \times 3$) and that any representation that is not irreducible can be built up from irreducible representations of the relevant point groups. Such representations are reducible, and in the later chapters we will examine methods for converting reducible representations into their irreducible components. (Note that all of the representations illustrated in this chapter are irreducible.)

## EXERCISES

1 In a $\mathbf{D}_{4h}$ molecule such as $XeF_4$ (see Figure 2.10), the $z$ axis is coincident with the $C_4$ axis (see the discussion on p. 29 for the complete set of symmetry operations for this molecule).

(a) Use the $\mathbf{T_z}$ vector (placed on the Xe atom only) to generate a representation of the point group.
(b) Draw an $\mathbf{R_z}$ rotation vector for $XeF_4$ and use it to generate a representation of the point group.

2 The $\mathbf{T_x}$ and $\mathbf{T_y}$ vectors for the molecule $BrF_5$ are shown in Figure 4.13. Use these as bases for a representation of the $\mathbf{C_{4v}}$ point group (the symmetry operations are illustrated in Figure 2.5).

3 Obtain a representation of the $\mathbf{C_{4v}}$ point group using as bases:

(a) a $d_{x^2-y^2}$ orbital, and
(b) the $p_x$ and $p_y$ orbitals situated on the Br atom of $BrF_5$.

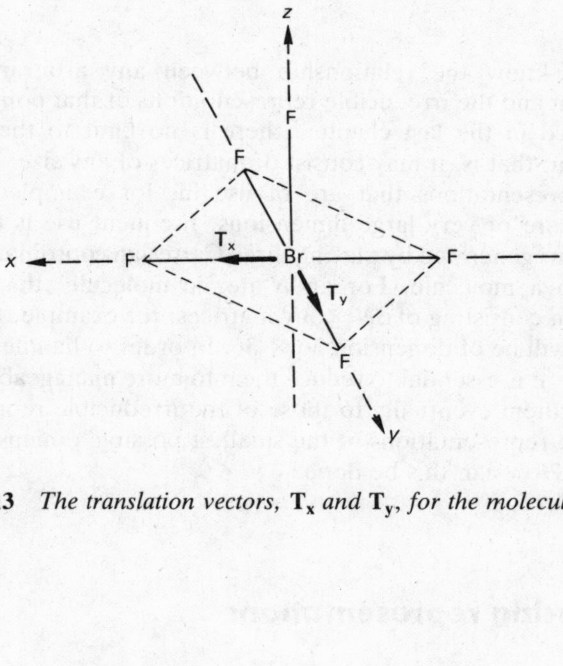


**Figure 4.13** *The translation vectors,* $\mathbf{T_x}$ *and* $\mathbf{T_y}$*, for the molecule* $BrF_5$ ($\mathbf{C_{4v}}$)

# 5

# Reducible and irreducible representations

We need to know the relationship between any arbitrary reducible representation and the irreducible representations of that point group. As was mentioned in the last chapter, there is no limit to the order of a representation; that is, it may consist of matrices of any size. Some of the reducible representations that are of use in, for example, vibrational spectroscopy are of very large dimensions. Frequent use is made of the representations generated by placing three Cartesian coordinate vectors on each atom in a molecule. For an $N$-atomic molecule, this will give a representation consisting of $3N \times 3N$ matrices; for example, for benzene, the matrices will be of dimension $36 \times 36$. In order to handle and analyse such matrices, it is essential to reduce them to more manageable sizes; that is, to reduce them eventually to those of the irreducible representations, which are the representations of the smallest possible dimensions for any point group. How can this be done?

## *5.1* Reducing representations

Consider any matrix, of dimension $n \times n$ (all transformation matrices are square, since the *number* of vectors or functions is not changed by any symmetry operation):

$$\begin{bmatrix} a_{11} & a_{12} & \cdots & a_{1n} \\ a_{21} & a_{22} & \cdots & a_{2n} \\ \cdot & \cdot & \cdots & \cdot \\ \cdot & \cdot & \cdots & \cdot \\ \cdot & \cdot & \cdots & \cdot \\ a_{n1} & a_{n2} & \cdots & a_{nn} \end{bmatrix}$$

In this matrix, the zero elements (if any) will be distributed randomly about the matrix. If, however, the matrix belongs to a reducible representation, it will be possible to rearrange the matrix so that zero elements are distributed symmetrically about the diagonal. Thus, for a 3 × 3 matrix we might have:

$$\begin{bmatrix} a_{11} & a_{12} & a_{13} \\ a_{21} & a_{22} & a_{23} \\ a_{31} & a_{32} & a_{33} \end{bmatrix} \longrightarrow \left[\begin{array}{cc|c} b_{11} & b_{12} & 0 \\ b_{21} & b_{22} & 0 \\ \hline 0 & 0 & b_{33} \end{array}\right]$$

The non-zero elements are now distributed in blocks along the diagonal – in this case, a 2 × 2 block and a 1 × 1 block. How is such a rearrangement brought about?

In Chapter 2, a method of defining classes of symmetry operations was described. This involved the application of similarity transformations, defined in terms of symmetry operations. It is found that matrix rearrangement can be accomplished by means of a similarity transformation of the original matrix. Thus, if **A** and **B** are the original and reduced matrices, respectively, then:

$$\mathbf{XAX^{-1}} = \mathbf{B}$$

**X** is a matrix of the same dimensions as **A** and **B**, and $\mathbf{X^{-1}}$ is its inverse matrix (that is, $\mathbf{XX^{-1}} = \mathbf{E}$). For any reducible representation, such a similarity transformation can be carried out on the matrix corresponding to each symmetry operation. It will be helpful to see a specific example of such a process.

Consider the set of vectors shown in Figure 5.1 – three vectors, pointing along the bonds of a pyramidal $\mathbf{C_{3v}}$ molecule such as $NH_3$. Now if we carry out the symmetry operations of $\mathbf{C_{3v}}$ on these three vectors – for example, for $C_3^1$, $\mathbf{r_1} \rightarrow \mathbf{r_3}$, $\mathbf{r_2} \rightarrow \mathbf{r_1}$ and $\mathbf{r_3} \rightarrow \mathbf{r_2}$ – we obtain the following transformation matrix:

$$\begin{bmatrix} 0 & 0 & 1 \\ 1 & 0 & 0 \\ 0 & 1 & 0 \end{bmatrix}$$

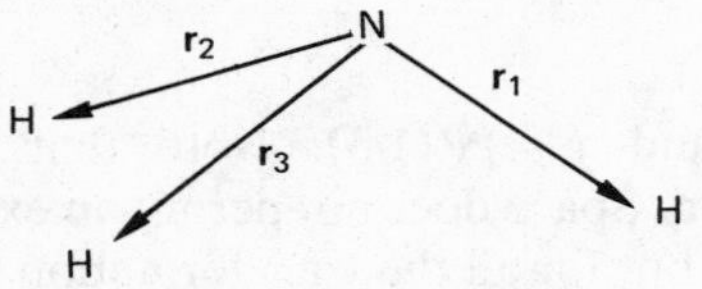


**Figure 5.1** *A set of bond vectors for a* $\mathbf{C_{3v}}$ *molecule*

For the complete set of operations, we have:

$$E: \begin{bmatrix} 1 & 0 & 0 \\ 0 & 1 & 0 \\ 0 & 0 & 1 \end{bmatrix} \qquad C_3^1: \begin{bmatrix} 0 & 0 & 1 \\ 1 & 0 & 0 \\ 0 & 1 & 0 \end{bmatrix}$$

$$C_3^2: \begin{bmatrix} 0 & 1 & 0 \\ 0 & 0 & 1 \\ 1 & 0 & 0 \end{bmatrix} \qquad \sigma_v(1): \begin{bmatrix} 1 & 0 & 0 \\ 0 & 0 & 1 \\ 0 & 1 & 0 \end{bmatrix}$$

$$\sigma_v(2): \begin{bmatrix} 0 & 0 & 1 \\ 0 & 1 & 0 \\ 1 & 0 & 0 \end{bmatrix} \qquad \sigma_v(3): \begin{bmatrix} 0 & 1 & 0 \\ 1 & 0 & 0 \\ 0 & 0 & 1 \end{bmatrix}$$

where $\sigma_v(1)$, $\sigma_v(2)$ and $\sigma_v(3)$ contain the bond vectors $\mathbf{r}_1$, $\mathbf{r}_2$ and $\mathbf{r}_3$, respectively. The non-zero elements are distributed throughout the $3 \times 3$ matrices in such a way that there are no smaller blocks of such elements present for every symmetry operation.

However, we now define a matrix $\mathbf{X}$ and its inverse $\mathbf{X}^{-1}$, as follows:

$$\mathbf{X} = \begin{bmatrix} -x & \dfrac{x}{2} & \dfrac{x}{2} \\ 0 & -\surd 3\dfrac{x}{2} & \surd 3\dfrac{x}{2} \\ -y & -y & -y \end{bmatrix} \quad \text{and}$$

$$\mathbf{X}^{-1} = \begin{bmatrix} -\dfrac{2}{3x} & 0 & -\dfrac{1}{3y} \\ \dfrac{1}{3x} & -\dfrac{1}{\surd 3x} & -\dfrac{1}{3y} \\ \dfrac{1}{3x} & \dfrac{1}{\surd 3x} & -\dfrac{1}{3y} \end{bmatrix}$$

where $x = \surd(2/3)$ and $y = \surd(1/3)$. Note that, with this definition, $\mathbf{XX}^{-1} = \mathbf{E}$, as required. Space does not permit an explanation of how these matrices are derived, but for all the transformation matrices $\mathbf{R}$ of the basis vectors $\mathbf{r}_1$, $\mathbf{r}_2$ and $\mathbf{r}_3$ we can carry out the matrix multiplications $\mathbf{XRX}^{-1} = \mathbf{S}$.

Application of the rules for matrix multiplication shows that the resultant **S** matrices are:

$$E: \begin{bmatrix} 1 & 0 & 0 \\ 0 & 1 & 0 \\ 0 & 0 & 1 \end{bmatrix} \qquad C_3^1: \begin{bmatrix} -\frac{1}{2} & -\frac{\sqrt{3}}{2} & 0 \\ \frac{\sqrt{3}}{2} & -\frac{1}{2} & 0 \\ 0 & 0 & 1 \end{bmatrix}$$

$$C_3^2: \begin{bmatrix} -\frac{1}{2} & \frac{\sqrt{3}}{2} & 0 \\ -\frac{\sqrt{3}}{2} & -\frac{1}{2} & 0 \\ 0 & 0 & 1 \end{bmatrix} \qquad \sigma_v(1): \begin{bmatrix} 1 & 0 & 0 \\ 0 & -1 & 0 \\ 0 & 0 & 1 \end{bmatrix}$$

$$\sigma_v(2): \begin{bmatrix} -\frac{1}{2} & -\frac{\sqrt{3}}{2} & 0 \\ -\frac{\sqrt{3}}{2} & \frac{1}{2} & 0 \\ 0 & 0 & 1 \end{bmatrix} \qquad \sigma_v(3): \begin{bmatrix} -\frac{1}{2} & \frac{\sqrt{3}}{2} & 0 \\ \frac{\sqrt{3}}{2} & \frac{1}{2} & 0 \\ 0 & 0 & 1 \end{bmatrix}$$

That is, they have been converted into a 2 × 2 block and a 1 × 1 block in each case, with zeros outside these blocks. Furthermore, comparison of the 2 × 2 blocks with the representation generated (in Chapter 4) by the $\mathbf{T_x}$ and $\mathbf{T_y}$ vectors for a pyramidal $\mathbf{C_{3v}}$ molecule shows that the two sets of matrices are identical. Similarly, the 1 × 1 blocks are identical to the representation generated by the $\mathbf{T_z}$ vector of such a molecule. Thus, the similarity transformation is physically equivalent to changing the set of basis vectors used for the representation – in this case, from $\mathbf{r_1}$, $\mathbf{r_2}$ and $\mathbf{r_3}$ to $\mathbf{T_x}$, $\mathbf{T_y}$ and $\mathbf{T_z}$.

Let us consider the general reduction **A** → **B**. The 3 × 3 matrices of the original representation (**A**) have been transformed into a new set of 3 × 3 matrices (**B**), each one of which can be regarded as being built up from two smaller matrices ($\mathbf{B_1}$ and $\mathbf{B_2}$). As we have just seen, the $\mathbf{B_1}$ matrices themselves form a representation of the point group (that is, the matrices mirror exactly the properties of the symmetry operations), as do the $\mathbf{B_2}$ matrices. Therefore, we have converted the 3 × 3 representation into *two* of smaller dimensions; that is, we have effected a *reduction* of the original representation. A common way of expressing the relationship between **A**, $\mathbf{B_1}$ and $\mathbf{B_2}$ is to say that **A** is the *direct sum* of $\mathbf{B_1}$ and $\mathbf{B_2}$.

Note that by the rules of matrix multiplication:

$$\begin{bmatrix} b_{11} & b_{12} & 0 \\ b_{21} & b_{22} & 0 \\ 0 & 0 & b_{33} \end{bmatrix} \begin{bmatrix} b_{11}' & b_{12}' & 0 \\ b_{21}' & b_{22}' & 0 \\ 0 & 0 & b_{33}' \end{bmatrix} = \begin{bmatrix} b_{11}'' & b_{12}'' & 0 \\ b_{21}'' & b_{22}'' & 0 \\ 0 & 0 & b_{33}'' \end{bmatrix}$$

Multiplication of two matrices 'blocked out' in the same way gives a similar matrix as product. Furthermore:

$$\begin{bmatrix} b_{11} & b_{12} \\ b_{21} & b_{22} \end{bmatrix} \begin{bmatrix} b_{11}' & b_{12}' \\ b_{11}' & b_{22}' \end{bmatrix} = \begin{bmatrix} b_{11}'' & b_{12}'' \\ b_{11}'' & b_{22}'' \end{bmatrix} \quad \text{and } [b_{33}]\,[b_{33}'] = [b_{33}'']$$

Therefore, we can combine the $\mathbf{B_1}$ matrices among themselves, independent of the $\mathbf{B_2}$ matrices (and vice versa), in order to treat the two reduced representations quite separately, as required. In our specific example, this followed from our discussion of the ($\mathbf{T_x}$, $\mathbf{T_y}$) and $\mathbf{T_z}$ representations in Chapter 4.

Such a reduction process is possible for every reducible representation, and the correct choice of similarity transformation will produce reduced representations whose matrices can be reduced in size no further. These are therefore the **irreducible representations**, and that is the derivation of the term. The overall process for every transformation matrix for any reducible representation is, therefore:

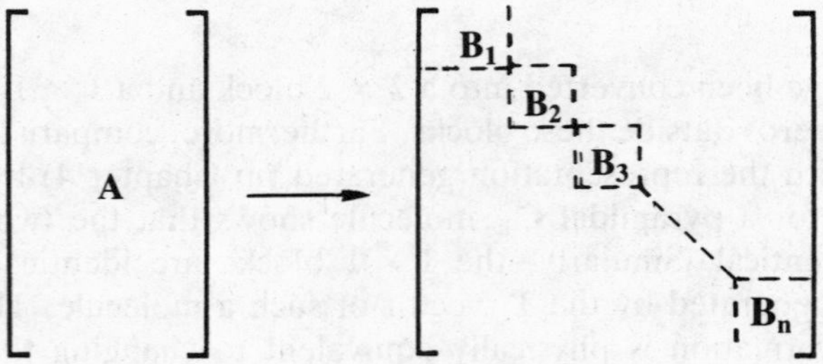


where each $\mathbf{B_i}$ is a matrix belonging to an irreducible representation, and all elements outside the $\mathbf{B_i}$ blocks are zero.

The irreducible representations are of fundamental significance, and in most of the applications of group theory to molecular problems our chief task is to determine the numbers and symmetry properties of the various irreducible representations for any given system.

There are only as many irreducible representations for any point group as there are classes of symmetry operations for the group (the proof of this statement is difficult and cannot be attempted here). Therefore, if we can always split up any representation into its constituent irreducible representations, this will provide a means of classifying and analysing the infinite possible number of reducible representations. We shall see how this may be done later in this chapter.

## 5.2 Characters of matrices

Whenever we are dealing with representations, except those with 1 × 1 constituent matrices, we face the difficulty of constructing and writing what may be very unwieldy matrices. It would be very convenient if the need for this could be removed.

It is found that all the necessary information conveyed by the matrices of any representation is contained in the *characters* of these matrices. All of the matrices comprising representations are square ($n \times n$), and for such matrices we can define the elements $a_{ii}$, for $i = 1$ to $n$, as the diagonal elements (see Chapter 3). The character of any square matrix is defined as the sum of the diagonal elements and is given the symbol $\chi$ (Greek 'chi'):

$$\chi = a_{11} + a_{22} + a_{33} + \ldots + a_{nn} = \sum_{i=1}^{n} a_{nn}$$

The character is, therefore, a number, and since we only need to record this, and not the whole matrix, a considerable saving of time and effort results. (Note that for 1 × 1 matrices, themselves pure numbers, the character and the matrix itself are identical.)

Let us return to the examples of representations given in Chapter 4 to find the characters of some of the transformation matrices listed there. For the translation and rotation vectors of a $\mathbf{C}_{2v}$ molecule, all the matrices are 1 × 1, and hence we can write out a **character table** for these representations, which is identical to the table of matrices given in Chapter 4:

| $\mathbf{C}_{2v}$ | $E$ | $C_2$ | $\sigma(xz)$ | $\sigma(yz)$ | |
|---|---|---|---|---|---|
| | +1 | +1 | +1 | +1 | $\mathbf{T_z}$ |
| | +1 | +1 | −1 | −1 | $\mathbf{R_z}$ |
| | +1 | −1 | +1 | −1 | $\mathbf{T_x}$ or $\mathbf{R_y}$ |
| | +1 | −1 | −1 | +1 | $\mathbf{T_y}$ or $\mathbf{R_x}$ |

For a $\mathbf{C}_{3v}$ system, on the other hand, one of the irreducible representations discussed in Chapter 4 (that with $\mathbf{T_x}$ and $\mathbf{T_y}$ or $\mathbf{R_x}$ and $\mathbf{R_y}$ as basis vectors) possesses a set of $2 \times 2$ matrices, and consequently the table summarising the irreducible representations was rather cumbersome. Since we are only interested in the characters of the matrices, however, we can write a character table which is much more concise:

| $\mathbf{C}_{3v}$ | $E$ | $C_3^1$ | $C_3^2$ | $\sigma_v$ | $\sigma_v$ | $\sigma_v$ | |
|---|---|---|---|---|---|---|---|
| | +1 | +1 | +1 | +1 | +1 | +1 | $\mathbf{T_z}$ |
| | +1 | +1 | +1 | −1 | −1 | −1 | $\mathbf{R_z}$ |
| | +2 | −1 | −1 | 0 | 0 | 0 | ($\mathbf{T_x}$, $\mathbf{T_y}$) or ($\mathbf{R_x}$, $\mathbf{R_y}$) |

A further condensation of the character table is possible in this case. We see that all of the operations belonging to the same class always give the *same* character in a given irreducible representation (even though the transformation matrices will be different). Hence, it is not necessary to write out the characters for all of the symmetry operations. It is sufficient to list *one* typical member of any class, together with the *number* of operations in that class. Thus, the conventional form for the character table of the $\mathbf{C}_{3v}$ point group is:

| $\mathbf{C}_{3v}$ | $E$ | $2C_3$ | $3\sigma_v$ | |
|---|---|---|---|---|
| | +1 | +1 | +1 | $\mathbf{T_z}$ |
| | +1 | +1 | −1 | $\mathbf{R_z}$ |
| | +2 | −1 | 0 | ($\mathbf{T_x}$, $\mathbf{T_y}$) or ($\mathbf{R_x}$, $\mathbf{R_y}$) |

Two points must be noted about the two character tables encountered so far: first, in $\mathbf{C}_{2v}$, all of the operations belong to separate classes, and therefore no such simplification as that for $\mathbf{C}_{3v}$ is possible; second, by chance we have already encountered all of the possible irreducible representations for $\mathbf{C}_{2v}$ and $\mathbf{C}_{3v}$.

In other cases, it would not have been possible to construct the entire character table using translation and rotation vectors as bases for the irreducible representations. When this is so, it is necessary to construct the character table using a more elaborate mathematical technique (based on the properties of the characters of irreducible representations discussed below). When this is applied to all of the point groups of interest to chemists, we obtain a set of character tables, such as that printed in Appendix A. In all cases, the table has the same general layout, being divided into six sections ((a)–(f)):

| (a) | (b) | | |
|---|---|---|---|
| (f) | (c) | (d) | (e) |

(a) gives the Schönflies symbol for the point group;

(b) lists the symmetry operations (by classes) for that group;

(c) lists the characters, for all irreducible representations, of each class of operation;

(d) shows the irreducible representations for which the six vectors $\mathbf{T_x}$, $\mathbf{T_y}$, $\mathbf{T_z}$, $\mathbf{R_x}$, $\mathbf{R_y}$ and $\mathbf{R_z}$ provide the bases;

(e) similarly shows how the functions that are binary combinations of $x$, $y$ and $z$ (for example, $xy$, $z^2$) provide bases for certain irreducible representations. This information is important in discussing the symmetries of d-orbitals (Chapters 4 and 10) and Raman spectroscopy (Chapter 8), but we do not need to consider it further at present.

(f) lists the conventional symbols for the irreducible representations.

The latter symbols are the **Mulliken symbols**. They give information in extremely concise form about the values of the characters for certain symmetry operations in that irreducible representation. Thus, all one-dimensional irreducible representations are labelled as A or B, all two-dimensional representations as E (which must not be confused with the symbol for the identity operation) and all three-dimensional representations as T (in some texts these are given the label F). Irreducible representations of higher order are denoted by G (four-dimensional), H (five-dimensional), and so on.

For 'linear' point groups, an alternative labelling system is used. Here all one-dimensional irreducible representations are given the label Σ, with two- and three-dimensional ones being given the labels Π and Δ, respectively.

In addition to the letter, most Mulliken symbols possess certain subscripts and/or superscripts. For two- (and higher-) dimensional irreducible representations, the derivation of these is not always straightforward, and they can often most conveniently be regarded merely as labels. For one-dimensional representations, however, the sub- and superscripts have simple and well-defined meanings:

**1** A one-dimensional irreducible representation is labelled A if it is symmetric with respect to rotation about the highest order axis $C_n$. (Symmetric means that $\chi = +1$ for the operation.) If it is antisymmetric with respect to that operation (that is, $\chi = -1$), then it is labelled as B.

**2** A subscript $_1$ is given if the irreducible representation is symmetric with respect to rotation about a $C_2$ axis perpendicular to $C_n$ or (in the absence of such an axis) to reflection in a $\sigma_v$ plane. An antisymmetric representation under these conditions is given a subscript $_2$. For the 'linear' point groups, symmetry with respect to $\sigma_v$ is indicated by a superscript $^+$ (symmetric) or $^-$ (antisymmetric).

**3** Subscripts $_g$ (gerade) and $_u$ (ungerade) are given to irreducible representations that are symmetric and antisymmetric, respectively, with respect to inversion at a centre of symmetry.

**4** Finally, superscripts $'$ and $''$ are given to irreducible representations that are symmetric and antisymmetric, respectively, with respect to reflection in a $\sigma_h$ plane.

Note that points 3 and 4 apply equally to one-, two- and three-dimensional representations.

Thus, the Mulliken symbol for an irreducible representation gives a good deal of information about the symmetry properties of that representation. A common usage, which follows from the characteristic symmetry properties of each of the irreducible representations, refers to each irreducible representation as defining a **symmetry species**. Any vector(s) or function(s) forming a basis for any irreducible representation is said to belong to that symmetry species.

It will be our chief task in subsequent chapters to split up a variety of reducible representations into their irreducible components, and so we must look at some of the properties of the characters that will help us in reducing representations. These will be given largely without proof, since most of the proofs are rather long and mathematically involved. Readers interested in the derivation of these properties of characters should refer to one of the more advanced texts on group theory listed in the Bibliography.

## 5.3 Some useful properties of square matrices

**1** From the definition of matrix multiplication, it can be shown that if **AB** = **C** and **BA** = **D**, then the characters of **C** and **D** are equal; that is, $\chi(\mathbf{C}) = \chi(\mathbf{D})$. This can be illustrated by an example. Let:

$$\mathbf{A} = \begin{bmatrix} 1 & 2 \\ 0 & 3 \end{bmatrix} \quad \text{and} \quad \mathbf{B} = \begin{bmatrix} 1 & 1 \\ 2 & 0 \end{bmatrix}$$

Then:

$$\mathbf{C} = \begin{bmatrix} 1 & 2 \\ 0 & 3 \end{bmatrix} \begin{bmatrix} 1 & 1 \\ 2 & 0 \end{bmatrix} = \begin{bmatrix} 5 & 1 \\ 6 & 0 \end{bmatrix} \qquad \text{i.e. } \chi(\mathbf{C}) = 5$$

and:

$$\mathbf{D} = \begin{bmatrix} 1 & 1 \\ 2 & 0 \end{bmatrix} \begin{bmatrix} 1 & 2 \\ 0 & 3 \end{bmatrix} = \begin{bmatrix} 1 & 5 \\ 2 & 4 \end{bmatrix} \quad \text{i.e. } \chi(\mathbf{D}) = 5$$

The relationship can be illustrated similarly for any other case.

**2** Using the result of 1, we can prove a most important fact; namely, that the character of a matrix is *not* changed by the performance of a similarity transformation on it. (This is detailed in Appendix B.) Consider two matrices, **A** and **B**, which are related by a similarity transformation:

$$\mathbf{CAC}^{-1} = \mathbf{B}$$

As shown in Appendix B, Section B.1, $\chi(\mathbf{A}) = \chi(\mathbf{B})$. This is a very important result, since we have seen that the reduction of a reducible representation requires the application of a similarity transformation to the matrices of that representation. Such a transformation, however, leaves the characters of the matrices unaltered, and the *sum* of the characters of the irreducible representation matrices present is equal to the character of the reducible representation matrix, for any symmetry operation. Thus, for the matrix diagram on p. 56, the following result applies:

$$\chi(\mathbf{A}) = \sum_{i=1}^{n} \chi(\mathbf{B}_i)$$

**3** The last result is of great help in deducing which irreducible representations are present in any reducible representation and how many times each one is present. In obtaining this information, however, we need to use some further properties of the characters of irreducible representation matrices. These are given in Appendix B.

The equation:

$$a_p = \left(\frac{1}{g}\right) \sum_{R} \chi(R)\chi_p(R)$$

derived in Appendix B, Section B.2 gives us the number of times, $a_p$, any irreducible representation $p$ occurs in any reducible representation, where $g$ is the number of symmetry operations in the point group, and $\chi(R)$ and $\chi_p(R)$ are the characters of the operation $R$ in the reducible and irreducible representations, respectively. This equation can be simplified slightly as the summation includes all $R$. But these will be grouped into classes (often with several $R$ in the same class), and all of the $R$'s in the same class have the same character in any representation. If, therefore, there are $n_R$

operations in the class containing $R$, we have:

$$a_p = \left(\frac{1}{g}\right) \sum n_R \chi(R) \chi_p(R) \qquad \text{(sum over classes)}$$

By working systematically through all of the irreducible representations, we can find the composition of any reducible representation, without having to carry out the necessary similarity transformations explicitly.

We will examine several examples of such analyses, relating to various molecular properties, in subsequent chapters. However, to gain practise in the method we will look at one reducible representation (having no necessary physical significance).

Consider a representation of the point group $\mathbf{C}_{4v}$:

| $\mathbf{C}_{4v}$ | $E$ | $2C_4$ | $C_2$ | $2\sigma_v$ | $2\sigma_d$ |
|---|---|---|---|---|---|
| | 6 | 0 | 2 | 0 | 0 |

(Note here that the $2C_4$ refers to the $C_4^1$ and $C_4^3$ rotations, and the $C_2$ to the $C_4^2$ rotation about the $C_4$ axis.) The irreducible representations of $\mathbf{C}_{4v}$ are as follows: $A_1$, $A_2$, $B_1$, $B_2$ and E (see the character table given in Appendix A). There are eight symmetry operations in this group ($g = 8$):

$$a(A_1) = \frac{1}{8}[(1 \times 6 \times 1) + (2 \times 0 \times 1) + (1 \times 2 \times 1) + (2 \times 0 \times 1) + (2 \times 0 \times 1)]$$

$$= \frac{1}{8}[6 + 0 + 2 + 0 + 0] = 1$$

Within each pair of round brackets, we have (number of operations in the class × character in the reducible representation × character in the irreducible representation).

$$a(A_2) = \frac{1}{8}[(1 \times 6 \times 1) + (2 \times 0 \times 1) + (1 \times 2 \times 1) + (2 \times 0 \times -1) + (2 \times 0 \times -1)]$$

$$= \frac{1}{8}[6 + 0 + 2 + 0 + 0] = 1$$

$$a(B_1) = \frac{1}{8}[6 + 0 + 2 + 0 + 0] = 1$$

$$a(B_2) = \frac{1}{8}[6 + 0 + 2 + 0 + 0] = 1$$

$$a(E) = \frac{1}{8}[12 + 0 - 4 + 0 + 0] = 1$$

The reducible representation given can, therefore, be reduced to the direct sum of one of each of the irreducible representations; that is, $A_1 + A_2 + B_1 + B_2 + E$.

## EXERCISES

1 Determine the characters of the matrices **C** (= **AB**) and **D** (= **BA**), when:

$$\mathbf{A} = \begin{bmatrix} 1 & 2 & 1 \\ 3 & 1 & 1 \\ 1 & 0 & 2 \end{bmatrix} \qquad \mathbf{B} = \begin{bmatrix} 2 & 0 & 2 \\ 1 & -2 & 1 \\ 0 & 3 & 3 \end{bmatrix}$$

2 Show that $\chi(\mathbf{A}) = \chi(\mathbf{B})$ when $\mathbf{CAC}^{-1} = \mathbf{B}$, where

$$\mathbf{C} = \begin{bmatrix} 0 & -1 \\ 1 & 0 \end{bmatrix} \quad \mathbf{A} = \begin{bmatrix} 2 & 3 \\ 3 & 5 \end{bmatrix} \quad \mathbf{C}^{-1} = \begin{bmatrix} 0 & 1 \\ -1 & 0 \end{bmatrix}$$

3 Show that the equation:

$$\sum \chi_i(R)\chi_j(R) = g\delta_{ij}$$

given in Appendix B (p. 190) applies for the following cases:

(a) Point group $\mathbf{C}_{4v}$; irreducible representations $i = j = B_2$.
(b) Point group $\mathbf{C}_{4v}$; irreducible representations $i = B_1$, $j = E$.
(c) Point group $\mathbf{D}_{3h}$; irreducible representations $i = j = E'$.
(d) Point group $\mathbf{D}_{3h}$; irreducible representations $i = E''$, $j = A_2'$.

**4** Obtain the irreducible components of the following reducible representations (use the character tables):

(a)

| $\mathbf{D}_{3d}$ | $E$ | $2C_3$ | $3C_2$ | $i$ | $2S_6$ | $3\sigma_d$ |
|---|---|---|---|---|---|---|
| | 5 | 2 | 3 | −1 | 2 | 1 |

(b)

| $\mathbf{C}_{6v}$ | $E$ | $2C_6$ | $2C_3$ | $C_2$ | $3\sigma_v$ | $3\sigma_d$ |
|---|---|---|---|---|---|---|
| | 4 | −1 | 1 | 2 | 0 | −2 |

(c)

| $\mathbf{T}_d$ | $E$ | $8C_3$ | $3C_2$ | $6S_4$ | $6\sigma_d$ |
|---|---|---|---|---|---|
| | 8 | 2 | 0 | 2 | 2 |

# 6

# Some important reducible representations

In the previous chapter, the analysis of a reducible representation into its irreducible components was discussed from a theoretical point of view. We can now illustrate the principles by reference to some types of reducible representations that are of great importance in various aspects of the study of molecular structures.

## 6.1 A useful representation

A representation that is very useful in vibrational spectroscopy (see Chapter 8) is generated by a set of 3$N$ basis vectors (for an $N$-atomic molecule). The three vectors on each atom are positioned to lie along a set of Cartesian coordinate axes with their origin at that atom. This is illustrated for the $SO_2$ molecule in Figure 6.1.

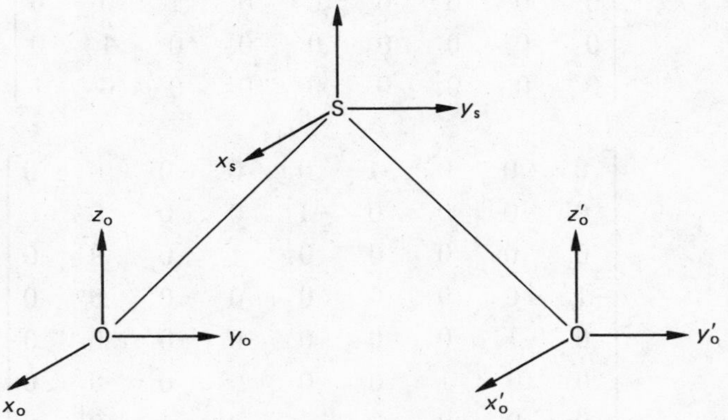


**Figure 6.1** *Cartesian coordinate system for* $SO_2$ ($\mathbf{C}_{2v}$)

To construct the representation generated by the nine vectors in Figure 6.1, we must find their transformation matrices under the symmetry operations of the $\mathbf{C}_{2v}$ point group ($E$, $C_2$, $\sigma(xz)$, $\sigma(yz)$). These will, of course, be $9 \times 9$ matrices; for example, for the $\sigma(xz)$ operation:

$$\sigma(xz)\begin{bmatrix} x_O \\ y_O \\ z_O \\ x_O' \\ y_O' \\ z_O' \\ x_S \\ y_S \\ z_S \end{bmatrix} = \begin{bmatrix} 0 & 0 & 0 & 1 & 0 & 0 & 0 & 0 & 0 \\ 0 & 0 & 0 & 0 & -1 & 0 & 0 & 0 & 0 \\ 0 & 0 & 0 & 0 & 0 & 1 & 0 & 0 & 0 \\ 1 & 0 & 0 & 0 & 0 & 0 & 0 & 0 & 0 \\ 0 & -1 & 0 & 0 & 0 & 0 & 0 & 0 & 0 \\ 0 & 0 & 1 & 0 & 0 & 0 & 0 & 0 & 0 \\ 0 & 0 & 0 & 0 & 0 & 0 & 1 & 0 & 0 \\ 0 & 0 & 0 & 0 & 0 & 0 & 0 & -1 & 0 \\ 0 & 0 & 0 & 0 & 0 & 0 & 0 & 0 & 1 \end{bmatrix} \begin{bmatrix} x_O \\ y_O \\ z_O \\ x_O' \\ y_O' \\ z_O' \\ x_S \\ y_S \\ z_S \end{bmatrix}$$

The operation $\sigma(xz)$ effects the following transformations: $x_O \rightarrow x_O'$, $y_O \rightarrow -y_O'$, $z_O \rightarrow z_O'$, $x_O' \rightarrow x_O$, $y_O' \rightarrow -y_O$, $z_O' \rightarrow z_O$, $x_S \rightarrow x_S$, $y_S \rightarrow -y_S$ and $z_S \rightarrow z_S$. Application of the usual matrix multiplication rules shows that the matrix reproduces these transformations. Similar matrices are obtained from the other symmetry operations:

$$E: \quad \begin{bmatrix} 1 & 0 & 0 & 0 & 0 & 0 & 0 & 0 & 0 \\ 0 & 1 & 0 & 0 & 0 & 0 & 0 & 0 & 0 \\ 0 & 0 & 1 & 0 & 0 & 0 & 0 & 0 & 0 \\ 0 & 0 & 0 & 1 & 0 & 0 & 0 & 0 & 0 \\ 0 & 0 & 0 & 0 & 1 & 0 & 0 & 0 & 0 \\ 0 & 0 & 0 & 0 & 0 & 1 & 0 & 0 & 0 \\ 0 & 0 & 0 & 0 & 0 & 0 & 1 & 0 & 0 \\ 0 & 0 & 0 & 0 & 0 & 0 & 0 & 1 & 0 \\ 0 & 0 & 0 & 0 & 0 & 0 & 0 & 0 & 1 \end{bmatrix}$$

$$C_2: \quad \begin{bmatrix} 0 & 0 & 0 & -1 & 0 & 0 & 0 & 0 & 0 \\ 0 & 0 & 0 & 0 & -1 & 0 & 0 & 0 & 0 \\ 0 & 0 & 0 & 0 & 0 & 1 & 0 & 0 & 0 \\ -1 & 0 & 0 & 0 & 0 & 0 & 0 & 0 & 0 \\ 0 & -1 & 0 & 0 & 0 & 0 & 0 & 0 & 0 \\ 0 & 0 & 1 & 0 & 0 & 0 & 0 & 0 & 0 \\ 0 & 0 & 0 & 0 & 0 & 0 & -1 & 0 & 0 \\ 0 & 0 & 0 & 0 & 0 & 0 & 0 & -1 & 0 \\ 0 & 0 & 0 & 0 & 0 & 0 & 0 & 0 & 1 \end{bmatrix}$$

$$\sigma(yz): \begin{bmatrix} -1 & 0 & 0 & 0 & 0 & 0 & 0 & 0 & 0 \\ 0 & 1 & 0 & 0 & 0 & 0 & 0 & 0 & 0 \\ 0 & 0 & 1 & 0 & 0 & 0 & 0 & 0 & 0 \\ 0 & 0 & 0 & -1 & 0 & 0 & 0 & 0 & 0 \\ 0 & 0 & 0 & 0 & 1 & 0 & 0 & 0 & 0 \\ 0 & 0 & 0 & 0 & 0 & 1 & 0 & 0 & 0 \\ 0 & 0 & 0 & 0 & 0 & 0 & -1 & 0 & 0 \\ 0 & 0 & 0 & 0 & 0 & 0 & 0 & 1 & 0 \\ 0 & 0 & 0 & 0 & 0 & 0 & 0 & 0 & 1 \end{bmatrix}$$

The convenience of needing to consider only the characters of the transformation matrices is now obvious. All that needs to be written down is the following set of characters:

| $\mathbf{C}_{2v}$ | $E$ | $C_2$ | $\sigma(xz)$ | $\sigma(yz)$ |
|---|---|---|---|---|
| $\Gamma_{3N}$ | 9 | −1 | 1 | 3 |

This is obtained by summing the four sets of diagonal elements. The general symbol for any representation is $\Gamma$ (apart from the specific Mulliken symbols for irreducible representations – see Chapter 5); $\Gamma_{3N}$ indicates that $3N$ vectors were used as bases.

We can now use the equation deduced in Chapter 5 to reduce $\Gamma_{3N}$ for $SO_2$ into its irreducible components. The possible irreducible representations for $\mathbf{C}_{2v}$ are $A_1$, $A_2$, $B_1$ and $B_2$ (see character table in Appendix A). The values for $a(A_1)$, etc., are given as follows:

$$a(A_1) = \frac{1}{4}[(1 \times 9 \times 1) + (1 \times -1 \times 1) + (1 \times 1 \times 1) + (1 \times 3 \times 1)]$$

$$= \frac{12}{4} = 3$$

That is, the $A_1$ representation occurs three times in $\Gamma_{3N}$ (where $g = 4$ for $\mathbf{C}_{2v}$).

$$a(A_2) = \frac{1}{4}[(1 \times 9 \times 1) + (1 \times -1 \times 1) + (1 \times 1 \times -1)$$

$$+ (1 \times 3 \times -1)] = \frac{4}{4} = 1$$

$$a(B_1) = \frac{1}{4}[(1 \times 9 \times 1) + (1 \times -1 \times -1) + (1 \times 1 \times 1)$$

$$+ (1 \times 3 \times -1)] = \frac{8}{4} = 2$$

$$a(B_2) = \frac{1}{4}[(1 \times 9 \times 1) + (1 \times -1 \times -1) + (1 \times 1 \times -1)$$
$$+ (1 \times 3 \times 1)] = \frac{12}{4} = 3$$

Therefore, we can say that:

$$\Gamma_{3N} = 3A_1 + A_2 + 2B_1 + 3B_2$$

In this case, the total number of irreducible representations equals the number of basis vectors – 9. This must always be so when only one-dimensional irreducible representations are present. In general, if *n*-dimensional irreducible representations are involved, each such representation must be multiplied by *n*, since *n* vectors constitute its basis. The sum of all the irreducible representations (with each one multiplied by the appropriate value of *n*) equals the number of basis vectors for the reducible representation. Thus, E and T representations must be multiplied by 2 and 3, respectively. Examples of this will be given later.

The process just illustrated for constructing $\Gamma_{3N}$ is very cumbersome, and as $\Gamma_{3N}$ is important for molecules much more complicated than $SO_2$, it will be worthwhile deriving a simplified method for determining $\Gamma_{3N}$. The chief difficulty lies in finding $\chi(R)$ without having to construct the whole $3N \times 3N$ transformation matrix for that symmetry operation *R*.

This is quite straightforward, however, and is related to the definition of the character as the sum of the diagonal elements of the transformation matrix. By the rules of matrix multiplication, if any atom and its associated vectors are shifted to a different position in space by any symmetry operation, then these vectors contribute *no* non-zero diagonal elements to the transformation matrix for that operation. Consequently, these vectors contribute zero to $\chi(R)$; for example, for the $\sigma(xz)$ matrix of $SO_2$, the two O atoms are shifted in space and they produce non-zero elements *off* the diagonal of the matrix; only the vectors on the unshifted S atom can give non-zero diagonal elements. In general, therefore, *only* the vectors on unshifted atoms can contribute to the character of a given symmetry operation in $\Gamma_{3N}$.

The first task in determining $\Gamma_{3N}$, therefore, is to count the number of unshifted atoms for every symmetry operation (one operation from each class is sufficient). The next process is to calculate the contribution to $\chi(R)$ for every unshifted atom in every type of symmetry operation. These contributions can be worked out for all *R*, and are always the same, in whichever point group *R* occurs. The contribution to $\chi(R)$ per unshifted atom can then be tabulated, and to deduce $\Gamma_{3N}$ from the number of unshifted atoms is a matter of simple arithmetic.

## *6.2* The contributions to $\chi(R)$ per unshifted atom

We will work systematically through the possible types of $R$:

**1** The identity ($E$). In this case, all three vectors remain unchanged for every unshifted atom, as shown in Figure 6.2, where $\mathbf{x}' = \mathbf{x}$, $\mathbf{y}' = \mathbf{y}$ and $\mathbf{z}' = \mathbf{z}$. The transformation matrix, therefore, includes the diagonal elements:

$$\begin{matrix} +1 & & \\ & +1 & \\ & & +1 \end{matrix}$$

and $\chi(\mathrm{E})$ per unshifted atom is +3.

**2** Inversion at the centre of symmetry ($i$). Figure 6.3 shows the effect for each unshifted atom, where $\mathbf{x}' = -\mathbf{x}$, $\mathbf{y}' = -\mathbf{y}$ and $\mathbf{z}' = -\mathbf{z}$. Therefore, the matrix contains the following diagonal elements:

$$\begin{matrix} -1 & & \\ & -1 & \\ & & -1 \end{matrix}$$

and $\chi(i)$ per unshifted atom is −3.

**3** Reflection in a symmetry plane ($\sigma$). The effect of any $\sigma$ on an unshifted atom is typically as shown in Figure 6.4, where $\mathbf{x}' = \mathbf{x}$, $\mathbf{y}' = -\mathbf{y}$ and $\mathbf{z}' = \mathbf{z}$. The transformation matrix, therefore, includes:

$$\begin{matrix} +1 & & \\ & -1 & \\ & & +1 \end{matrix}$$

(the order depends on the relative orientations of the plane and the axes) and $\chi(\sigma)$ per unshifted atom is +1.

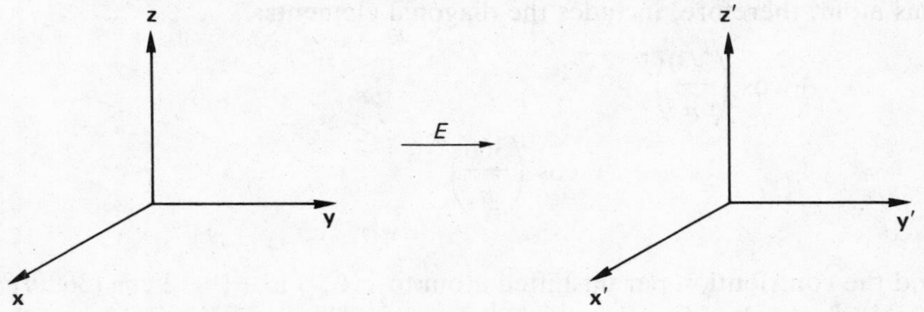


**Figure 6.2**

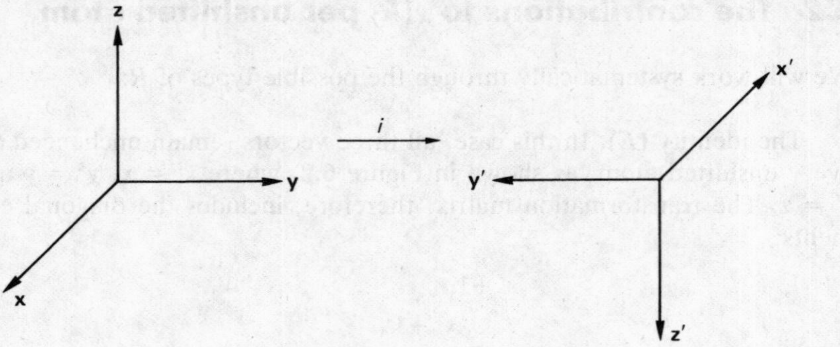


**Figure 6.3**

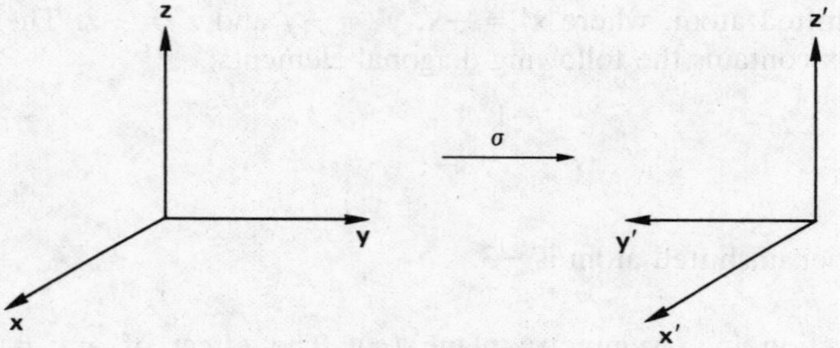


**Figure 6.4**

**4** Proper rotation ($C_n{}^1$). Rotation is by $(360/n)°$, usually about the $z$ axis. For any unshifted atom, the result is as shown in Figure 6.5, where $\theta = (360/n)°$. $\mathbf{z}' = \mathbf{z}$, contributing $+1$ to $\chi(C_n{}^1)$, and $\mathbf{x}$, $\mathbf{y}$ go to $\mathbf{x}'$, $\mathbf{y}'$, respectively. The diagonal elements of the transformation matrix are given by the component of $\mathbf{x}'$ along the $x$ direction and of $\mathbf{y}'$ along the $y$ direction – that is, $\cos(360/n)°$ in each case. The transformation matrix for this atom, therefore, includes the diagonal elements:

$$\begin{matrix} +\cos\left(\frac{360}{n}\right)^{\circ} & & \\ & +\cos\left(\frac{360}{n}\right)^{\circ} & \\ & & +1 \end{matrix}$$

and the contribution per unshifted atom to $\chi(C_n{}^1)$ is $+1 + 2\cos(360/n)°$. The same result is found for $C_n{}^{n-1}$, and a similar expression is found for any other $C_n{}^m$. Some common examples are listed in Table 6.1.

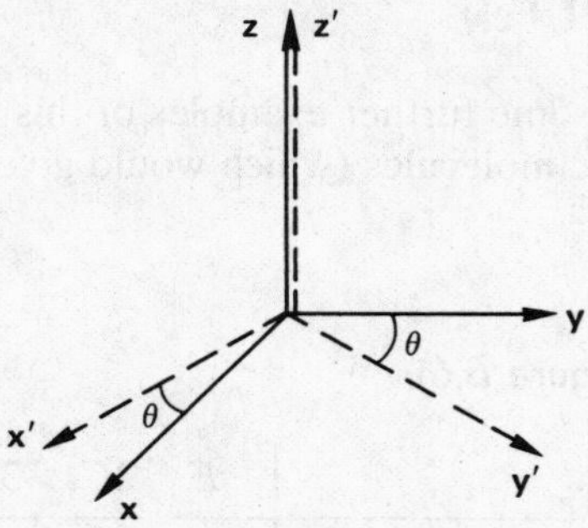


**Figure 6.5**

**Table 6.1** Contribution to character per unshifted atom in $\Gamma_{3N}$

| $R$ | $\chi(R)$ |
|---|---|
| $E$ | +3 |
| $i$ | −3 |
| $\sigma$ | +1 |
| $C_2$ | −1 |
| $C_3^1$, $C_3^2$ | 0 |
| $C_4^1$, $C_4^3$ | +1 |
| $C_6^1$, $C_6^5$ | +2 |
| $S_3^1$, $S_3^5$ | −2 |
| $S_4^1$, $S_4^3$ | −1 |
| $S_6^1$, $S_6^5$ | 0 |

**5** Improper rotation ($S_n^1$). This is exactly the same as for $C_n^1$, except that $\mathbf{z}' = -\mathbf{z}$, and so $\chi(S_n^1)$ per unshifted atom is $-1 + 2\cos(360/n)°$.

These results are perfectly general and can be applied to any point group. Let us return to $SO_2$ and deduce $\Gamma_{3N}$ by this method. All that we need to do is to determine the number of unshifted atoms for each symmetry operation and then multiply by the appropriate factors:

| $\mathbf{C}_{2v}$ | $E$ | $C_2$ | $\sigma(xz)$ | $\sigma(yz)$ |
|---|---|---|---|---|
| Unshifted atoms | 3 | 1 | 1 | 3 |
| $\Gamma_{3N}$ | 9 | −1 | 1 | 3 |

as before.

## 6.3 Examples of $\Gamma_{3N}$

We can now examine some further examples of this method for determining $\Gamma_{3N}$, using 5-atomic molecules (which would give 15 × 15 matrices) of different symmetries.

### 6.3.1 $POCl_3$ ($\mathbf{C}_{3v}$; Figure 6.6)

| $\mathbf{C}_{3v}$ | $E$ | $2C_3$ | $3\sigma_v$ |
|---|---|---|---|
| Unshifted atoms | 5 | 2 | 3 |
| $\Gamma_{3N}$ | 15 | 0 | 3 |

Rotation ($C_3^1$ or $C_3^2$) leaves P and O unshifted, while reflection in any of the $\sigma_v$ planes leaves P, O and one Cl unshifted. The irreducible representations for $\mathbf{C}_{3v}$ are $A_1$, $A_2$ and E, and application of the reduction formula gives:

$$a(A_1) = \frac{1}{6}[(1 \times 15 \times 1) + (2 \times 0 \times 1) + (3 \times 3 \times 1)] = 4$$

$$a(A_2) = \frac{1}{6}[(1 \times 15 \times 1) + (2 \times 0 \times 1) + (3 \times 3 \times -1)] = 1$$

$$a(E) = \frac{1}{6}[(1 \times 15 \times 2) + (2 \times 0 \times -1) + (3 \times 3 \times 0)] = 5$$

Therefore:

$$\Gamma_{3N} = 4A_1 + A_2 + 5E$$

(This gives the required total of 15 (=3$N$), since each E irreducible representation uses two basis vectors.)

### 6.3.2 $PtCl_4^{2-}$ ($\mathbf{D}_{4h}$; Figure 6.7)

| $\mathbf{D}_{4h}$ | $E$ | $2C_4$ | $C_2$ | $2C_2'$ | $2C_2''$ | $i$ | $2S_4$ | $\sigma_h$ | $2\sigma_v$ | $2\sigma_d$ |
|---|---|---|---|---|---|---|---|---|---|---|
| Unshifted atoms | 5 | 1 | 1 | 3 | 1 | 1 | 1 | 5 | 3 | 1 |
| $\Gamma_{3N}$ | 15 | 1 | −1 | −3 | −1 | −3 | −1 | 5 | 3 | 1 |

The $2C_4$ ($C_4^1$ and $C_4^3$) and $C_2$ ($\equiv C_4^2$) rotations only leave the Pt atom unshifted, as do the $C_2''$ rotations (bisecting the Cl—Pt—Cl angles), the $2S_4$ rotations ($S_4^1$ and $S_4^3$), the $\sigma_d$ planes (containing the $C_2''$ axes) and inversion at the centre. The $C_2'$ rotations leave the Pt and two Cl atoms

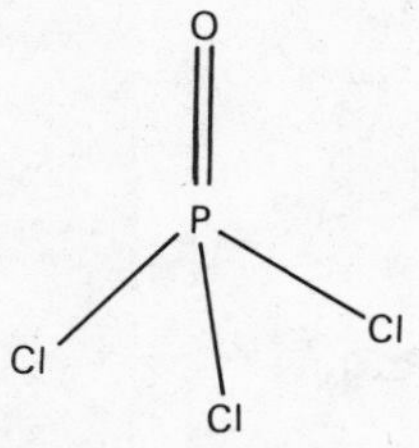


Figure 6.6

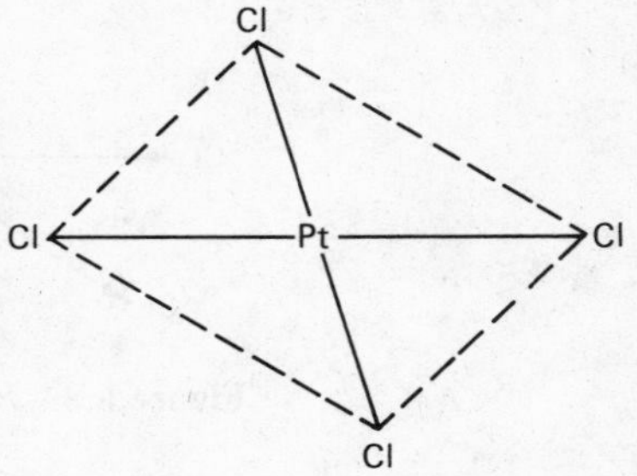


Figure 6.7

unshifted (the axes lie along the Pt—Cl bond directions), as do the $\sigma_v$ planes (containing the $C_2'$ axes), while E and $\sigma_h$ leave all five atoms unshifted. The $\mathbf{D}_{4h}$ point group has a large number of irreducible representations, but application of the reduction formula in the usual way gives:

$$\Gamma_{3N} = A_{1g} + A_{2g} + B_{1g} + B_{2g} + E_g + 2A_{2u} + B_{2u} + 3E_u$$

### 6.3.3 $RuO_4$ (a tetrahedral molecule, point group $\mathbf{T}_d$)

| $\mathbf{T}_d$ | $E$ | $8C_3$ | $3C_2$ | $6S_4$ | $6\sigma_d$ |
|---|---|---|---|---|---|
| Unshifted atoms | 5 | 2 | 1 | 1 | 3 |
| $\Gamma_{3N}$ | 15 | 0 | −1 | −1 | 3 |

This reduces to:

$$\Gamma_{3N} = A_1 + E + T_1 + 3T_2$$

As each E irreducible representation uses two basis vectors and each T uses three, this adds up to a total of 15, as required.

## 6.4 Representations generated by bond-stretching vectors

Other vectors that we will make extensive use of in later chapters are those that coincide with the bonds in a molecule, and which are used as bases to represent stretching vibrations in a molecule (see Chapter 8). Consider the square-planar ion $PtCl_4^{2-}$ and the bond vectors shown in Figure 6.8. Using

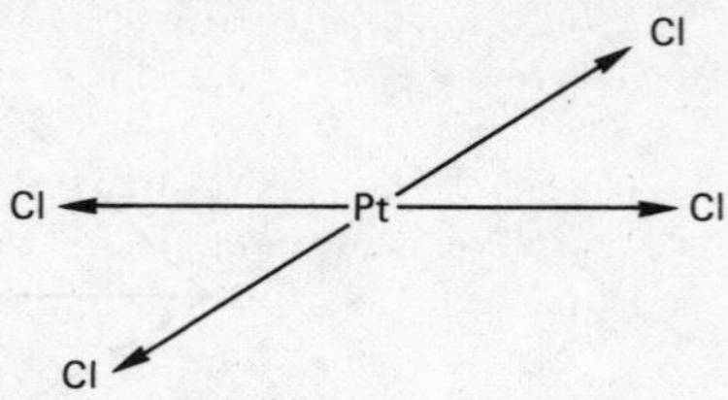


**Figure 6.8** *Bond vectors for* $PtCl_4^{2-}$

these to obtain a representation of the $\mathbf{D}_{4h}$ point group, we have:

| $\mathbf{D}_{4h}$ | $E$ | $2C_4$ | $C_2$ | $2C_2'$ | $2C_2''$ | $i$ | $2S_4$ | $\sigma_h$ | $2\sigma_v$ | $2\sigma_d$ |
|---|---|---|---|---|---|---|---|---|---|---|
| $\Gamma_{bond}$ | 4 | 0 | 0 | 2 | 0 | 0 | 0 | 4 | 2 | 0 |

That is, any vector remaining unshifted by an operation contributes +1 to $\chi(R)$, whereas any vector moved to a new position contributes zero. Use of the reduction formula for this representation shows that:

$$\Gamma_{bond} = A_{1g} + B_{1g} + E_u$$

That is, there are four possible bond-stretching vibrations for $PtCl_4^{2-}$, one of $A_{1g}$ symmetry, one of $B_{1g}$ symmetry and two (together) of $E_u$ symmetry.

A similar process for tetrahedral $RuO_4$ (bond vectors shown in Figure 6.9) gives the representation:

| $\mathbf{T}_d$ | $E$ | $8C_3$ | $3C_2$ | $6S_4$ | $6\sigma_d$ |
|---|---|---|---|---|---|
| $\Gamma_{bond}$ | 4 | 1 | 0 | 0 | 2 |

which reduces to:

$$\Gamma_{bond} = A_1 + T_2$$

That is, there is one bond-stretching vibration of $A_1$ symmetry and three (together) of $T_2$ symmetry.

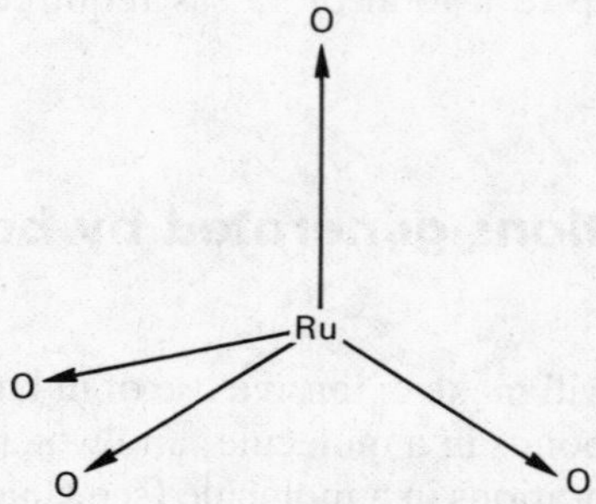


**Figure 6.9** *Bond vectors for* $RuO_4$

## 6.5 Representations generated by orbitals

So far, the reducible representations have been obtained using vectors as bases; similarly, reducible representations can be constructed using mathematical functions as bases, although in such cases the process may be not so easy to visualise. Sets of atomic orbital functions can be used as bases, and in many cases it is important to know which irreducible representations are present in the resulting representations. Only the angular part of the wave function need be considered, since the radial part is totally symmetric to all symmetry operations.

As mentioned in Chapter 4, an s-orbital always gives rise to the totally symmetric irreducible representation of any point group. For the p-orbitals, the angular functions are (omitting constant terms):

$$p_x = x$$
$$p_y = y$$
$$p_z = z$$

Consequently, they behave, from the symmetry point of view, exactly like the **x**, **y** and **z** vectors discussed in the derivation of $\Gamma_{3N}$. Thus, the p-orbitals give a representation with the following characters:

$$\chi(E) = +3; \qquad \chi(i) = -3; \qquad \chi(\sigma) = +1;$$

$$\chi(C_n^{\,1}) = +1 + 2\cos\left(\frac{360}{n}\right)^\circ; \qquad \chi(S_n^{\,1}) = -1 + 2\cos\left(\frac{360}{n}\right)^\circ$$

Using these general expressions for the characters of p-orbitals, it is quite straightforward to deduce the irreducible representations to which they give rise in an environment of any symmetry.

Consider first the p-orbitals on the O atom of $H_2O$ ($\mathbf{C}_{2v}$ point group). They will give the representation:

| $\mathbf{C}_{2v}$ | $E$ | $C_2$ | $\sigma(xz)$ | $\sigma(yz)$ |
|---|---|---|---|---|
| $\Gamma_p$ | 3 | −1 | 1 | 1 |

which reduces to:

$$\Gamma_p = A_1 + B_1 + B_2$$

These are the same irreducible representations as $\mathbf{T_x}$, $\mathbf{T_y}$ and $\mathbf{T_z}$. Inspection of the character table shows that $p_z$ gives the $A_1$ representation, $p_x$ the $B_1$ and $p_y$ the $B_2$.

Similar calculations can be made for p-orbitals on the N atom in $NF_3$ ($\mathbf{C}_{3v}$), the Xe atom on $XeF_4$ ($\mathbf{D}_{4h}$), the C atom of $CH_4$ ($\mathbf{T}_d$) and the S atom of $SF_6$ ($\mathbf{O}_h$):

| $\mathbf{C}_{3v}$ | $E$ | $2C_3$ | $3\sigma_v$ |
|---|---|---|---|
| $\Gamma_p$ | 3 | 0 | 1 |

$= A_1 (p_z) + E (p_x, p_y)$

| $\mathbf{D}_{4h}$ | $E$ | $2C_4$ | $C_2$ | $2C_2'$ | $2C_2''$ | $i$ | $2S_4$ | $\sigma_h$ | $2\sigma_v$ | $2\sigma_d$ |
|---|---|---|---|---|---|---|---|---|---|---|
| $\Gamma_p$ | 3 | 1 | −1 | −1 | −1 | −3 | −1 | 1 | 1 | 1 |

$= A_{2u} (p_z) + E_u (p_x, p_y)$

| $\mathbf{T}_d$ | $E$ | $8C_3$ | $3C_2$ | $6S_4$ | $6\sigma_d$ |
|---|---|---|---|---|---|
| $\Gamma_p$ | 3 | 0 | −1 | −1 | 1 |

$= T_2 (p_x, p_y, p_z)$

| $\mathbf{O}_h$ | $E$ | $8C_3$ | $3C_2$ | $6C_4$ | $6C_2'$ | $i$ | $6S_4$ | $8S_6$ | $3\sigma_h$ | $6\sigma_d$ |
|---|---|---|---|---|---|---|---|---|---|---|
| $\Gamma_p$ | 3 | 0 | −1 | 1 | −1 | −3 | −1 | 0 | 1 | 1 |

$= T_{1u} (p_x, p_y, p_z)$

The last two results follow from the fact that in tetrahedral and octahedral environments there are symmetry operations that can interconvert all three p-orbitals. As shown in Chapter 4, it necessarily follows that they must form an irreducible representation.

The symmetry behaviour of the set of five d-orbitals is often very important. The angular wave functions (again omitting all constant terms) are:

$$d_1 = x^2 - y^2$$
$$d_2 = xy$$
$$d_3 = zx$$
$$d_4 = yz$$
$$d_5 = 2z^2 - x^2 - y^2$$

It is possible to calculate the characters of the set of d-orbitals for any symmetry operation, although this is not so easy to visualise as for the p-orbitals:

$$\chi(E) = +5; \quad \chi(i) = +5; \quad \chi(\sigma) = +1;$$

$$\chi(C_n^{\,1}) = 4\cos^2\left(\frac{360}{n}\right)^\circ + 2\cos\left(\frac{360}{n}\right)^\circ - 1;$$

$$\chi(S_n^1) = 4\cos^2\left(\frac{360}{n}\right)^\circ - 2\cos\left(\frac{360}{n}\right)^\circ - 1$$

These functions can be used as bases for the representation of any point group. For example, the d-orbitals of the P atom in the $\mathbf{C}_{3v}$ molecule $P(=O)Cl_3$ give the following representation:

| $\mathbf{C}_{3v}$ | $E$ | $2C_3$ | $3\sigma_v$ |
|---|---|---|---|
| $\Gamma_d$ | 5 | −1 | 1 |

Reduction in the usual way shows that the irreducible representations present are:

$$\Gamma_d = A_1 + 2E$$

That is, in an environment of $\mathbf{C}_{3v}$ symmetry, the five (originally degenerate) d-orbitals can be divided into three symmetrically distinct sets. These are: $A_1$, $d_{z^2}$; E, ($d_{x^2-y^2}$, $d_{xy}$) and ($d_{zx}$, $d_{yz}$).

Similarly, in an environment of $\mathbf{O}_h$ symmetry, which is very relevant in the study of transition metal complexes, the d-orbitals are bases for the following representation:

| $\mathbf{O}_h$ | $E$ | $8C_3$ | $3C_2$ | $6C_4$ | $6C_2'$ | $i$ | $6S_4$ | $8S_6$ | $3\sigma_h$ | $6\sigma_d$ |
|---|---|---|---|---|---|---|---|---|---|---|
| $\Gamma_d$ | 5 | −1 | 1 | −1 | 1 | 5 | −1 | −1 | 1 | 1 |

$\Gamma_d$ is reducible to $E_g + T_{2g}$. The two d-orbitals that are bases for the $E_g$ representation ($d_{x^2-y^2}$ and $d_{z^2}$) can be interchanged by symmetry operations of $\mathbf{O}_h$, as can the three that are bases for $T_{2g}$ ($d_{xy}$, $d_{zx}$, $d_{yz}$), but there are no symmetry operations that will interconvert between these two groups.

Similar principles can be employed to derive the irreducible components present in the reducible representations generated by f−, g-orbitals, and so on, but these are of much less chemical significance.

The symmetries of p- and d-orbitals (s-orbitals always being totally symmetric) on the X atom in any molecule $XY_n$ are given in the character tables in Appendix A. Thus, the symmetries of the p-orbitals are the same as $x$, $y$ and $z$, respectively, which in turn are the same as the symmetries of $\mathbf{T_x}$, $\mathbf{T_y}$ and $\mathbf{T_z}$, respectively. The d-orbitals have the same symmetry as the functions $xy$, $yz$, $zx$, $x^2 - y^2$ and $2z^2 - x^2 - y^2$.

In addition to determining the symmetry of atomic orbitals for the X atom in any $XY_n$ molecule, it is also necessary (see Chapter 10) to consider the symmetries of suitable orbitals on the Y atoms to form both σ and π X—Y bonds.

For σ-bonding, it is most convenient to use s-orbitals on the Y atoms, as shown in Figure 6.10 for $H_2O$ ($XY_2$, $\mathbf{C}_{2v}$), $XeF_4$ ($XY_4$, $\mathbf{D}_{4h}$) and $SF_6$ ($XY_6$, $\mathbf{O}_h$). Note that any other orbitals with σ-symmetry with respect to the X–Y axes could be used. These generate the following reducible

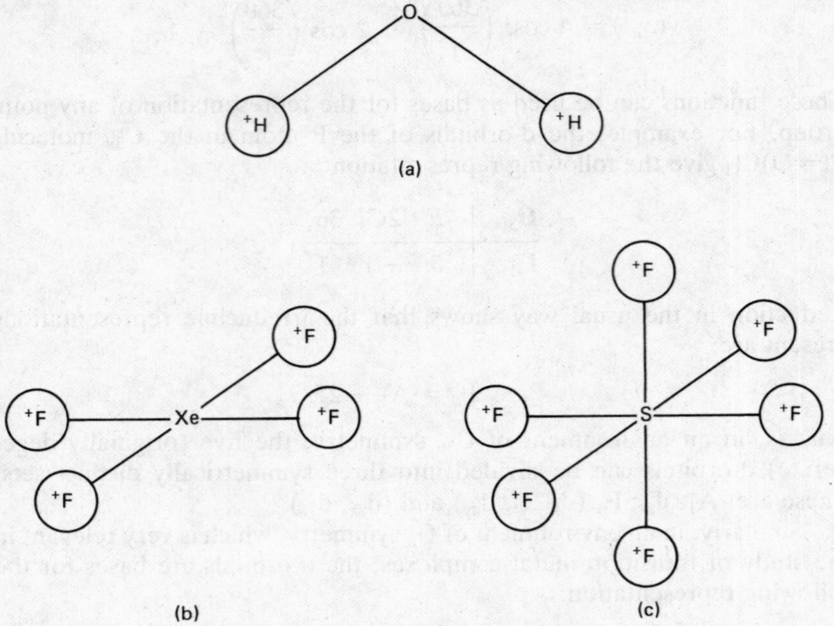


**Figure 6.10** *Sets of σ-type atomic orbitals for*: (a) $H_2O$ ($\mathbf{C}_{2v}$); (b) $XeF_4$ ($\mathbf{D}_{4h}$); (c) $SF_6$ ($\mathbf{O}_h$)

representations (unshifted orbitals contribute +1 to $\chi(R)$, whereas shifted orbitals contribute zero):

| $\mathbf{C}_{2v}$ | $E$ | $C_2$ | $\sigma(xz)$ | $\sigma(yz)$ |
|---|---|---|---|---|
| $\Gamma(\sigma)$ | 2 | 0 | 0 | 2 |

| $\mathbf{D}_{4h}$ | $E$ | $2C_4$ | $C_2$ | $2C_2'$ | $2C_2''$ | $i$ | $2S_4$ | $\sigma_h$ | $2\sigma_v$ | $2\sigma_d$ |
|---|---|---|---|---|---|---|---|---|---|---|
| $\Gamma(\sigma)$ | 4 | 0 | 0 | 2 | 0 | 0 | 0 | 4 | 2 | 0 |

| $\mathbf{T}_d$ | $E$ | $8C_3$ | $3C_2$ | $6S_4$ | $6\sigma_d$ |
|---|---|---|---|---|---|
| $\Gamma(\sigma)$ | 4 | 1 | 0 | 0 | 2 |

| $\mathbf{O}_h$ | $E$ | $8C_3$ | $3C_2$ | $6C_4$ | $6C_2'$ | $i$ | $6S_4$ | $8S_6$ | $3\sigma_h$ | $6\sigma_d$ |
|---|---|---|---|---|---|---|---|---|---|---|
| $\Gamma(\sigma)$ | 6 | 0 | 2 | 2 | 0 | 0 | 0 | 0 | 4 | 2 |

which reduce to:

$$\Gamma(\sigma) = A_1 + B_2 \qquad (\mathbf{C}_{2v})$$
$$\Gamma(\sigma) = A_{1g} + B_{1g} + E_u \qquad (\mathbf{D}_{4h})$$

$$\Gamma(\sigma) = A_1 + T_2 \qquad (\mathbf{T}_d)$$
$$\Gamma(\sigma) = A_{1g} + E_g + T_{1u} \qquad (\mathbf{O}_h)$$

These results tell us the symmetries of possible sets of $\sigma$-type atomic orbitals in these molecules.

In many molecules, it is also possible to form $\pi$-bonds, and in such cases, appropriate atomic orbital sets, with $\pi$-symmetry with respect to the X–Y axes, must be used to construct irreducible representations. Two examples are $XeF_4$ ($\mathbf{D}_{4h}$) and a transition metal complex such as $CrF_6^{3-}$ ($\mathbf{O}_h$). Sets of suitable atomic orbitals for $\pi$-bonding (that is, two p-orbitals per F atom) are shown in Figure 6.11. These generate reducible representations in the same way as for the $\sigma$-type atomic orbitals, except that on occasions an orbital may remain in the same position, but with the signs on the lobes reversed. In such a case, this orbital would give a contribution of $-1$ to $\chi(R)$.

| $\mathbf{D}_{4h}$ | $E$ | $2C_4$ | $C_2$ | $2C_2'$ | $2C_2''$ | $i$ | $2S_4$ | $\sigma_h$ | $2\sigma_v$ | $2\sigma_d$ |
|---|---|---|---|---|---|---|---|---|---|---|
| $\Gamma(\pi)$ | 8 | 0 | 0 | −4 | 0 | 0 | 0 | 0 | 0 | 0 |

| $\mathbf{O}_h$ | $E$ | $8C_3$ | $3C_2$ | $6C_4$ | $6C_2'$ | $i$ | $6S_4$ | $8S_6$ | $3\sigma_h$ | $6\sigma_d$ |
|---|---|---|---|---|---|---|---|---|---|---|
| $\Gamma(\pi)$ | 12 | 0 | −4 | 0 | 0 | 0 | 0 | 0 | 0 | 0 |

The $\mathbf{D}_{4h}$ example reduces to:

$$A_{2g} + B_{2g} + E_g + A_{2u} + B_{2u} + E_u$$

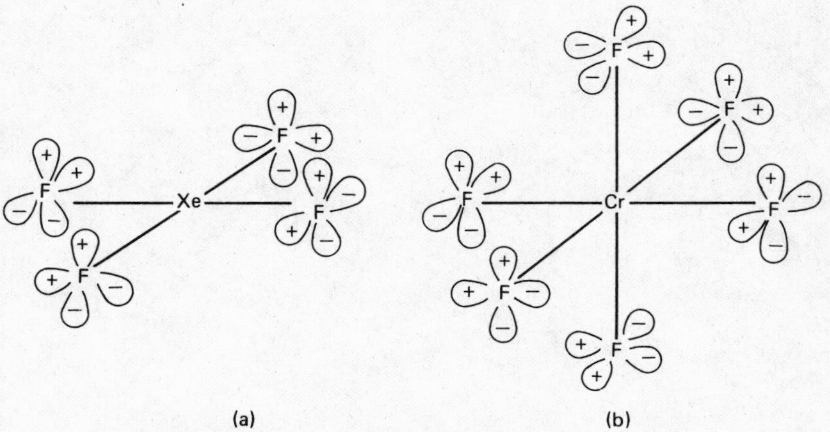


(a) (b)

**Figure 6.11** *Sets of $\pi$-type atomic orbitals for*: (a) $XeF_4$ ($\mathbf{D}_{4h}$); (b) $CrF_6^{3-}$ ($\mathbf{O}_h$)

The $\mathbf{O}_h$ case reduces to:

$$T_{1g} + T_{2g} + T_{1u} + T_{2u}$$

which summarises the symmetries of possible combinations of $\pi$-type orbitals. The significance of such results will become clear in Chapter 10.

## EXERCISES

**1** Determine $\Gamma_{3N}$ for the following molecules or ions:

(a) $NH_3$ ($\mathbf{C}_{3v}$)
(b) $WF_5Cl$ ($\mathbf{C}_{4v}$)
(c) $NO_3^-$ ($\mathbf{D}_{3h}$)
(d) $C_6H_6$ ($\mathbf{D}_{6h}$: *Note*: The $C_2'$ axes pass through two opposite C—H bonds; the $C_2''$ axes bisect the angles between the $C_2'$ axes; the $\sigma_v$ planes contain the $C_2'$ axes; and the $\sigma_d$ planes contain the $C_2''$ axes.)
(e) $NH_2NH_2$ ($\mathbf{C}_{2h}$)
(f) $Ni(CO)_4$ ($\mathbf{T}_d$)

**2** Find the irreducible components of the representations generated by a set of five d-orbitals in environments of $\mathbf{C}_{2v}$, $\mathbf{C}_{4v}$, $\mathbf{D}_{3h}$ and $\mathbf{T}_d$ symmetry.

**3** Find the irreducible components of the representations generated by a set of $\sigma$-type atomic orbitals in $XY_3$ molecules of $\mathbf{C}_{3v}$ and $\mathbf{D}_{3h}$ symmetry.

**4** Carry out the same procedure as in Exercise 3 for $\pi$-type atomic orbitals on the Y atoms of $XY_3$ ($\mathbf{D}_{3h}$ symmetry). (*Note*: Use p-orbitals on Y, perpendicular to the molecular plane.)

# 7

# Symmetry-adapted linear combinations

In Chapter 6, it was shown how to determine which irreducible representations were present in any reducible representation. For example, a set of bond vectors for a square–planar ($\mathbf{D}_{4h}$) molecule reduced to $A_{1g} + B_{1g} + E_u$. What is the physical significance of this result? It means that, for this case, the four basis vectors can be used to form four *linear combinations* (that is, sums and/or differences) such that one combination has $A_{1g}$ symmetry, one $B_{1g}$ symmetry and two (together) $E_u$ symmetry. Each of these corresponds to one vibrational mode of the molecule (see Chapter 8). Similar results are found for any set of *n* basis vectors or functions – it will be possible to form *n* **symmetry-adapted linear combination (SALCs)** of them, corresponding to the appropriate irreducible representations of the molecular point group.

In order, for example, to understand molecular vibrations or to use sets of atomic orbitals to construct molecular orbitals (see Chapter 10), it is important to know the exact form of such SALCs. In this chapter, we will introduce the principles involved by using sets of bond vectors.

The technique for determining the form of each SALC involves the use of **projection operators**. The derivation of these, and even the mathematical form in which the projection operator is expressed, appear to be very daunting. In practice, however, applying projection operators to real situations is very straightforward. No attempt will be made here to derive or explain the theory behind projection operators, but several examples will show their practical application.

## 7.1 SALCs for $C_{2v}$ systems

We will start with a very simple example – the bond-stretching vectors for a bent triatomic molecule ($\mathbf{C}_{2v}$) such as $SO_2$ (Figure 7.1). Using these two basis vectors, the following representation is obtained:

| $C_{2v}$ | $E$ | $C_2$ | $\sigma(xz)$ | $\sigma(yz)$ |
|---|---|---|---|---|
| $\Gamma_{bond}$ | 2 | 0 | 0 | 2 |

which reduces to $\Gamma_{bond} = A_1 + B_2$. We therefore need to construct two SALCs from the two bond vectors – one combination having $A_1$ and the other $B_2$ symmetry. This is where the projection operator comes in. The formula for a projection operator is:

$$[P^p]\mathbf{x} = \left[ \sum_R \{\chi_p(R) \cdot R\} \right] \mathbf{x}$$

where $P^p$ is the projection operator for the irreducible representation $p$, $\mathbf{x}$ is the generating vector or function, $R$ is the symmetry operation of the point group and $\chi_p(R)$ is the character of operation $R$ in the irreducible representation $p$. What does this mean in practice? We need to take one of the basis vectors (or functions) and carry out all of the symmetry operations of the point group on that vector (or function). Then we multiply the result for each symmetry operation by the character of that operation in the irreducible representation for which we are forming the SALC. Finally, these products are all summed, and the result gives the required SALC.

For the $SO_2$ case, let us use $\mathbf{r}_1$ as the generating vector (see Figure 7.1) and carry out all of the $C_{2v}$ symmetry operations on it:

| $C_{2v}$ | $E$ | $C_2$ | $\sigma(xz)$ | $\sigma(yz)$ |
|---|---|---|---|---|
| $\mathbf{r}_1$ | $\rightarrow \mathbf{r}_1$ | $\mathbf{r}_2$ | $\mathbf{r}_2$ | $\mathbf{r}_1$ |

This shows that the identity and reflection in the molecular plane $\sigma(yz)$ leave $\mathbf{r}_1$ unshifted, while $C_2$ and $\sigma(xz)$ move it to $\mathbf{r}_2$.

Now we multiply the results by the characters for the appropriate

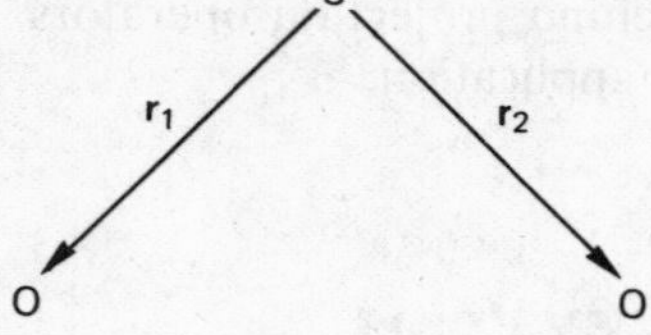


**Figure 7.1** *Bond-stretching vectors for* $SO_2$

irreducible representations and sum the results:

| $C_{2v}$ | $E$ | $C_2$ | $\sigma(xz)$ | $\sigma(yz)$ |
|---|---|---|---|---|
| $A_1$ | +1 | +1 | +1 | +1 |
| $A_2$ | +1 | +1 | −1 | −1 |
| $B_1$ | +1 | −1 | +1 | −1 |
| $B_2$ | +1 | −1 | −1 | +1 |

For $A_1$, we have:

$$(+1)\mathbf{r_1} + (+1)\mathbf{r_2} + (+1)\mathbf{r_2} + (+1)\mathbf{r_1} \qquad \text{i.e. } 2\mathbf{r_1} + 2\mathbf{r_2}$$

As we are only interested in the relative contributions of $\mathbf{r_1}$ and $\mathbf{r_2}$, we can write the $A_1$ SALC as $\mathbf{r_1} + \mathbf{r_2}$ (we will discuss the problem of normalisation later). For $B_2$, we have:

$$(+1)\mathbf{r_1} + (-1)\mathbf{r_2} + (-1)\mathbf{r_2} + (+1)\mathbf{r_1} \qquad \text{i.e. } 2\mathbf{r_1} - 2\mathbf{r_2}$$
$$\text{or (effectively) } \mathbf{r_1} - \mathbf{r_2}$$

Thus, the projection operator method has given us two SALCs, of the correct symmetries, corresponding to the $A_1$ and $B_2$ stretching vibrations of $SO_2$ (Figure 7.2).

This was a very straightforward example, but there are some further points to be made about the results before moving on to a more complicated example.

**1** It is easy to prove that the resultant SALCs do have the correct symmetry; that is, that each is the basis for the appropriate irreducible representation. Thus, we see that the $A_1$ combination is indeed left unchanged by all of the symmetry operations of $C_{2v}$, giving +1 as the character each time, as required. The $B_2$ combination is left unchanged (+1) by $E$ and $\sigma(yz)$, but reversed in sign (−1) for $C_2$ and $\sigma(xz)$; that is, it is indeed a basis for $B_2$.

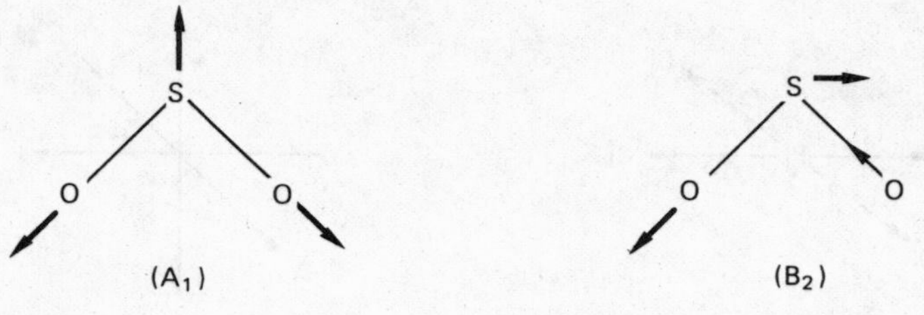


**Figure 7.2** $A_1$ *and* $B_2$ *SALCs of the bond-stretching vectors of* $SO_2$

**2** Let us attempt to generate combinations of $SO_2$ bond-stretching vectors of $A_2$ or $B_1$ symmetry. Using the irreducible representation characters listed, we have:

$$A_2: \quad (+1)\mathbf{r_1} + (+1)\mathbf{r_2} + (-1)\mathbf{r_2} + (-1)\mathbf{r_1} = 0$$
$$B_1: \quad (+1)\mathbf{r_1} + (-1)\mathbf{r_2} + (+1)\mathbf{r_2} + (-1)\mathbf{r_1} = 0$$

This is very useful confirmation of the information obtained from the reduction of the reducible bond-stretching representation. In general, applying a projection operator of the 'wrong' symmetry will always give a zero answer, confirming that no such SALC is possible.

**3** In order to be strictly accurate, each SALC must be *normalised*, which means that the sum of the squares of the coefficients in the SALC must equal one. Thus, to normalise the two SALCs for the $SO_2$ bond stretches, they must be multiplied by $(1/\sqrt{2})$; that is, $(1/\sqrt{2})$ $(\mathbf{r_1} + \mathbf{r_2})$ and $(1/\sqrt{2})$ $(\mathbf{r_1} - \mathbf{r_2})$. The required **normalisation constant** for any SALC is $(1/\sqrt{n})$, where $n$ is the sum of the squares of the individual coefficients.

The $\mathbf{C_{2v}}$ example was very straightforward, as only non-degenerate (one-dimensional) irreducible representations were involved. Examples for which degenerate (E, T or higher) irreducible representations are involved introduce new problems.

## 7.2 SALCs for $\mathbf{D_{4h}}$ systems

In Chapter 6, we saw that for $PtCl_4^{2-}$ (square–planar, $\mathbf{D_{4h}}$), $\Gamma_{bond} = A_{1g} + B_{1g} + E_u$. Let us now apply the projection operator method to this example, using the basis vectors of Figure 7.3.

Using $\mathbf{r_1}$ as the generating vector, we have the following. (Note that we must deal individually with every symmetry operation; it is not possible to group them into classes.)

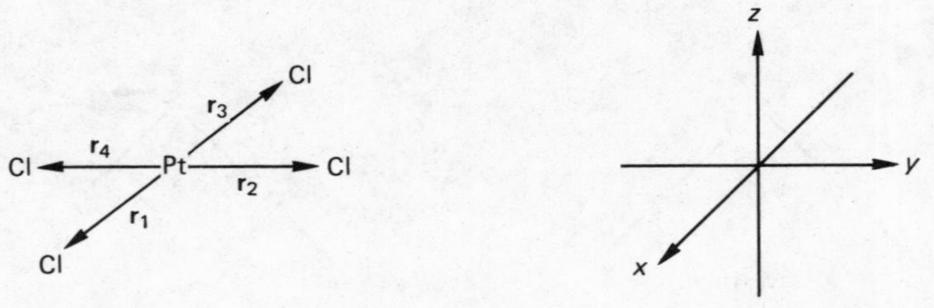


**Figure 7.3** *Bond-stretching vectors for* $PtCl_4^{2-}$ $(\mathbf{D_{4h}})$

| $\mathbf{D}_{4h}$ | $E$ | $C_4^1$ | $C_4^3$ | $C_2$ | $C_2'(x)$ | $C_2'(y)$ | $C_2''(1)$ | $C_2''(2)$ | $i$ | $S_4^1$ | $S_4^3$ |
|---|---|---|---|---|---|---|---|---|---|---|---|
| $\mathbf{r}_1$ | $\rightarrow \mathbf{r}_1$ | $\mathbf{r}_4$ | $\mathbf{r}_2$ | $\mathbf{r}_3$ | $\mathbf{r}_1$ | $\mathbf{r}_3$ | $\mathbf{r}_4$ | $\mathbf{r}_2$ | $\mathbf{r}_3$ | $\mathbf{r}_4$ | $\mathbf{r}_2$ |

| $\sigma_h$ | $\sigma_v(x)$ | $\sigma_v(y)$ | $\sigma_d(1)$ | $\sigma_d(2)$ |
|---|---|---|---|---|
| $\mathbf{r}_1$ | $\mathbf{r}_1$ | $\mathbf{r}_3$ | $\mathbf{r}_4$ | $\mathbf{r}_2$ |

(Note also that $C_2''(1)$, $\sigma_d(1)$ bisect the angle between $\mathbf{r}_1$ and $\mathbf{r}_4$ while $C_2''(2)$, $\sigma_d(2)$ bisect the angle between $\mathbf{r}_1$ and $\mathbf{r}_2$.)

From the character table for $\mathbf{D}_{4h}$, we have:

| $\mathbf{D}_{4h}$ | $E$ | $2C_4$ | $C_2$ | $2C_2'$ | $2C_2''$ | $i$ | $2S_4$ | $\sigma_h$ | $2\sigma_v$ | $2\sigma_d$ |
|---|---|---|---|---|---|---|---|---|---|---|
| $A_{1g}$ | +1 | +1 | +1 | +1 | +1 | +1 | +1 | +1 | +1 | +1 |
| $B_{1g}$ | +1 | −1 | +1 | +1 | −1 | +1 | −1 | +1 | +1 | −1 |
| $E_u$ | +2 | 0 | −2 | 0 | 0 | −2 | 0 | +2 | 0 | 0 |

Multiplying, summing and normalising therefore gives the following SALCs:

$$A_{1g}: \quad \frac{1}{2}(\mathbf{r}_1 + \mathbf{r}_2 + \mathbf{r}_3 + \mathbf{r}_4)$$

$$B_{1g}: \quad \frac{1}{2}(\mathbf{r}_1 - \mathbf{r}_2 + \mathbf{r}_3 - \mathbf{r}_4)$$

$$E_u: \quad \frac{1}{\sqrt{2}}(\mathbf{r}_1 - \mathbf{r}_3)$$

For the non-degenerate SALCs, this is the end of the story (Figure 7.4), and carrying out the $\mathbf{D}_{4h}$ symmetry operations on them generates the $A_{1g}$ and $B_{1g}$ irreducible representations. For the doubly-degenerate $E_u$ repre-

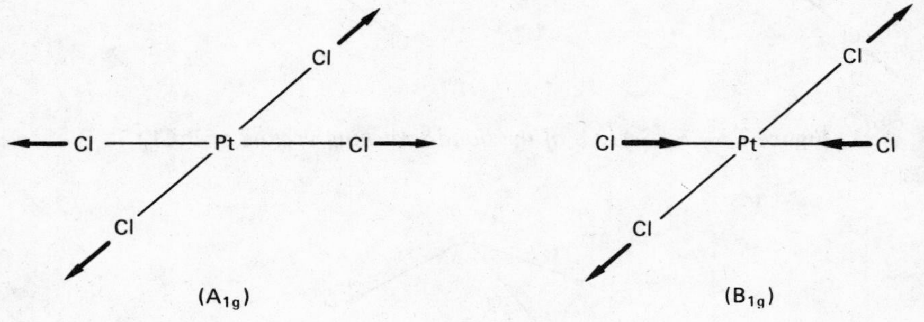


**Figure 7.4** $A_{1g}$ *and* $B_{1g}$ *SALCs of the bond-stretching vectors of* $PtCl_4^{2-}$

sentation, however, we only have half of the answer, as a second SALC is needed, independent of the first. For all systems with four-fold symmetry, there is a simple solution to this problem. You will note that for the $E_u$ SALC obtained so far, $\mathbf{r}_1$ generates a combination of $\mathbf{r}_1$ and $\mathbf{r}_3$ only. It is easy to prove that $\mathbf{r}_2$, as a generating vector, gives the SALC $(1/\sqrt{2})(\mathbf{r}_2 - \mathbf{r}_4)$. In all such systems, therefore, use of two generating vectors, related by a $C_4^1$ rotation, gives the required pair of SALCs for a doubly-degenerate representation. Figure 7.5 shows the two $E_u$ bond-stretching SALCs for $PtCl_4^{2-}$; they will give rise to a set of $(2 \times 2)$ transformation matrices under $\mathbf{D}_{4h}$ symmetry, and these have the characters for the $E_u$ irreducible representation.

## 7.3 SALCs for $C_{3v}$ systems

If we move on to an example with three-fold symmetry, there will again be doubly-degenerate irreducible representations, but this time it is more difficult to generate correct pairs of SALCs for them.

Consider the ammonia molecule, of $\mathbf{C}_{3v}$ symmetry, the bond vectors for which are shown in Figure 7.6. Using these to obtain a reducible representation gives $\Gamma_{bond} = A_1 + E$. If we now take $\mathbf{r}_1$ as the generating vector, this is transformed as follows by the symmetry operations of $\mathbf{C}_{3v}$ ($\sigma_v(1)$, $\sigma_v(2)$ and $\sigma_v(3)$ contain $\mathbf{r}_1$, $\mathbf{r}_2$ and $\mathbf{r}_3$, respectively):

| $\mathbf{C}_{3v}$ | $E$ | $C_3^1$ | $C_3^2$ | $\sigma_v(1)$ | $\sigma_v(2)$ | $\sigma_v(3)$ |
|---|---|---|---|---|---|---|
| $\mathbf{r}_1 \rightarrow$ | $\mathbf{r}_1$ | $\mathbf{r}_3$ | $\mathbf{r}_2$ | $\mathbf{r}_1$ | $\mathbf{r}_3$ | $\mathbf{r}_2$ |

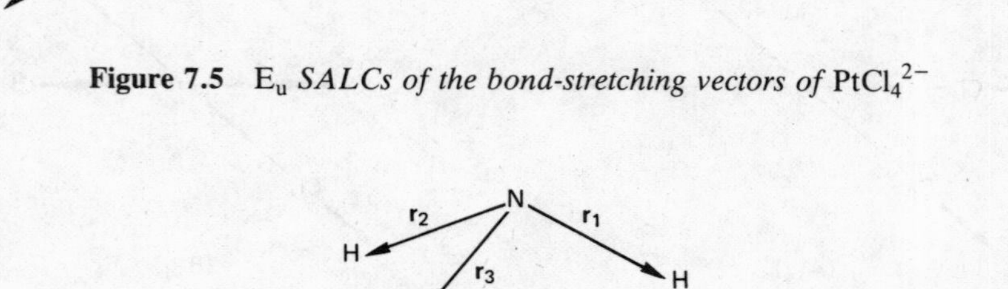

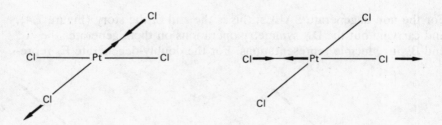

**Figure 7.5** $E_u$ *SALCs of the bond-stretching vectors of* $PtCl_4^{2-}$

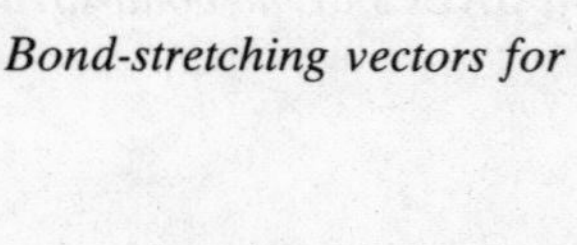


**Figure 7.6** *Bond-stretching vectors for* $NH_3$ ($\mathbf{C}_{3v}$)

Using the characters for $A_1$ and E:

| $\mathbf{C_{3v}}$ | $E$ | $2C_3$ | $3\sigma_v$ |
|---|---|---|---|
| $A_1$ | +1 | +1 | +1 |
| E | +2 | −1 | 0 |

then gives the following SALCs:

$$A_1: \quad \frac{1}{\sqrt{3}}(\mathbf{r}_1 + \mathbf{r}_2 + \mathbf{r}_3)$$

$$E: \quad \frac{1}{\sqrt{6}}(2\mathbf{r}_1 - \mathbf{r}_2 - \mathbf{r}_3)$$

As for the $\mathbf{D}_{4h}$ case, it is necessary to generate another SALC to give a pair which together have E symmetry. For $\mathbf{C}_{3v}$, however, simply using a different single generating vector will not do. Suppose that we use $\mathbf{r}_2$ or $\mathbf{r}_3$: these would give $-\mathbf{r}_1 + 2\mathbf{r}_2 - \mathbf{r}_3$ and $-\mathbf{r}_1 - \mathbf{r}_2 + 2\mathbf{r}_3$, respectively. Why are neither of these combinations acceptable? They are not acceptable because they do not fulfil a criterion that is necessary for all sets of SALCs. They are not *orthogonal* to the other SALCs so far obtained, and it is an absolute requirement that each member of any set of SALCs must be orthogonal to all the other members of that set.

How do we define orthogonality? The requirement is that if we take any two SALCs, they are orthogonal if the sum of the products of the corresponding coefficients is zero. Consider the $A_1$ and E SALCs so far obtained for the $\mathbf{C}_{3v}$ example. The coefficients for $\mathbf{r}_1$ are +1 and +2, respectively, while for both $\mathbf{r}_2$ and $\mathbf{r}_3$ they are +1 and −1, respectively. The sum of the products is, therefore, $(+1)(+2) + (+1)(-1) + (+1)(-1) = 0$, and so these two SALCs are orthogonal.

Now consider $2\mathbf{r}_1 - \mathbf{r}_2 - \mathbf{r}_3$ and $-\mathbf{r}_1 + 2\mathbf{r}_2 - \mathbf{r}_3$. Here the sum is $(+2)(-1) + (-1)(+2) + (-1)(-1) = -3$, and so they are not orthogonal. It is not possible in the space at our disposal to give a rigorous explanation of how to generate the second E SALC for a system with three-fold symmetry. It is clear that no single generating vector can give the right answer, so let us try the combination $\mathbf{r}_2 - \mathbf{r}_3$. As can be seen from the $\mathbf{C}_{3v}$ character table, $\chi(\sigma_v) = 0$ for the E representation, so we only need to consider the operations $E$, $C_3^1$ and $C_3^2$. What are the effects of these symmetry operations on $\mathbf{r}_2 - \mathbf{r}_3$?

| $\mathbf{C_{3v}}$ | $E$ | $C_3^1$ | $C_3^2$ |
|---|---|---|---|
| $\mathbf{r}_2 - \mathbf{r}_3 \rightarrow$ | $\mathbf{r}_2 - \mathbf{r}_3$ | $\mathbf{r}_1 - \mathbf{r}_2$ | $\mathbf{r}_3 - \mathbf{r}_1$ |

Multiplying by +2 for $E$, and −1 for $C_3^1$ and $C_3^2$, and summing gives us $2\mathbf{r}_2 - 2\mathbf{r}_3 - \mathbf{r}_1 + \mathbf{r}_2 - \mathbf{r}_3 + \mathbf{r}_1 = 3\mathbf{r}_2 - 3\mathbf{r}_3$. The required (normalised) SALC is, therefore, $(1/\sqrt{2})\,(\mathbf{r}_2 - \mathbf{r}_3)$.

Is this orthogonal to the other E SALC? The required sum is $(+2)(0) + (-1)(+1) + (-1)(-1) = 0$, and so the answer is yes. This method for calculating pairs of doubly-degenerate SALCs for molecules with three-fold symmetry always works.

The complete set of bond-stretching SALCs for $NH_3$ is, therefore (Figure 7.7):

$$A_1: \quad \frac{1}{\sqrt{3}}(\mathbf{r}_1 + \mathbf{r}_2 + \mathbf{r}_3)$$

$$E: \quad \frac{1}{\sqrt{6}}(2\mathbf{r}_1 - \mathbf{r}_2 - \mathbf{r}_3) \quad \text{and} \quad \frac{1}{\sqrt{2}}(\mathbf{r}_2 - \mathbf{r}_3)$$

## 7.4 SALCs for $\mathbf{T}_d$ and $\mathbf{O}_h$ *systems*

We can now calculate SALCs for singly- and doubly-degenerate irreducible representations in most chemically significant cases. For triply-degenerate irreducible representations, which are important for studies on regular tetrahedral and octahedral molecules, it again will not be possible to give an explanation as to how the SALCs are derived, but because of their importance the results are worth noting.

Using the bond vectors for a $\mathbf{T}_d$ molecule such as $CH_4$ (Figure 7.8), we can show that $\Gamma_{bond} = A_1 + T_2$. The (un-normalised) SALCs are as follows, with the generating vectors shown in brackets:

| | | |
|---|---|---|
| $A_1$: | $(\mathbf{r}_1)$ | $\mathbf{r}_1 + \mathbf{r}_2 + \mathbf{r}_3 + \mathbf{r}_4$ |
| $T_2$: | $(\mathbf{r}_1)$ | $3\mathbf{r}_1 - \mathbf{r}_2 - \mathbf{r}_3 - \mathbf{r}_4$ |
| | $(2\mathbf{r}_2 - \mathbf{r}_3 - \mathbf{r}_4)$ | $2\mathbf{r}_2 - \mathbf{r}_3 - \mathbf{r}_4$ |
| | $(\mathbf{r}_3 - \mathbf{r}_4)$ | $\mathbf{r}_3 - \mathbf{r}_4$ |

All are orthogonal to each other, as required.

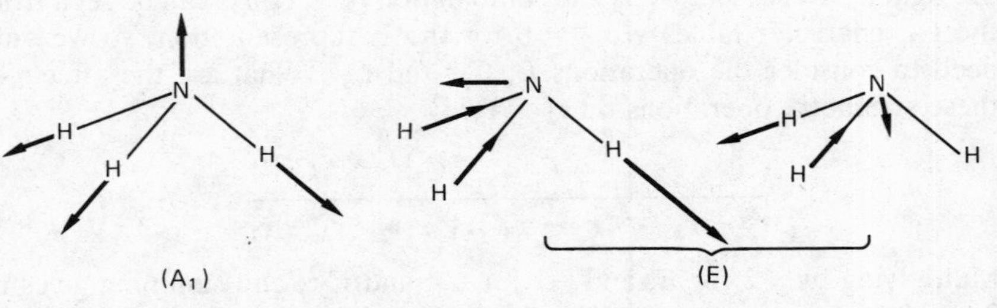


**Figure 7.7** $A_1$ *and* E *SALCs of the bond-stretching vectors of* $NH_3$

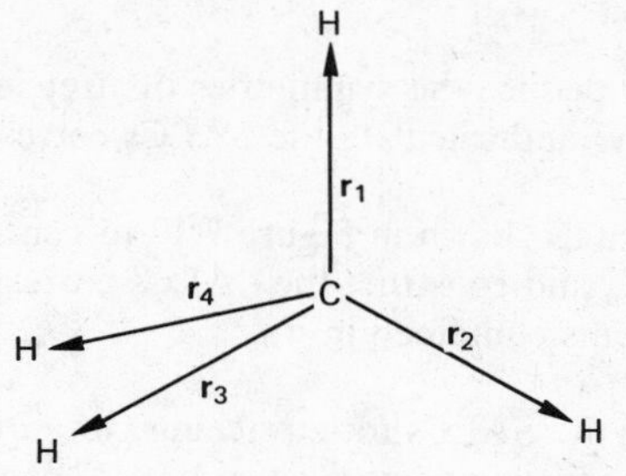


**Figure 7.8** *Bond-stretching vectors for* $CH_4$ ($\mathbf{T}_d$)

For an octahedral system, such as $SF_6$, the bond vectors are shown in Figure 7.9. Here, $\Gamma_{bond}$ reduces to $A_{1g} + E_g + T_{1u}$, and the (unnormalised) SALCs are (again with the generating vectors in brackets):

$$A_{1g}: \quad (\mathbf{r}_1) \qquad \mathbf{r}_1 + \mathbf{r}_2 + \mathbf{r}_3 + \mathbf{r}_4 + \mathbf{r}_5 + \mathbf{r}_6$$

$$E_g: \quad (\mathbf{r}_1) \qquad 2\mathbf{r}_1 - \mathbf{r}_2 - \mathbf{r}_3 - \mathbf{r}_4 - \mathbf{r}_5 + 2\mathbf{r}_6$$
$$(\mathbf{r}_2 - \mathbf{r}_3) \qquad \mathbf{r}_2 - \mathbf{r}_3 + \mathbf{r}_4 - \mathbf{r}_5$$

$$T_{1u}: \quad (\mathbf{r}_1) \qquad \mathbf{r}_1 - \mathbf{r}_6$$
$$(\mathbf{r}_2) \qquad \mathbf{r}_2 - \mathbf{r}_4$$
$$(\mathbf{r}_3) \qquad \mathbf{r}_3 - \mathbf{r}_5$$

All of the examples given in this chapter have used bond vectors to illustrate the formation of SALCs by projection operators. Exactly the same principles govern the use of other vectors (some of which, in addition to bond vectors, will be illustrated in Chapter 9) or functions (the use of sets of atomic orbitals will be discussed at length in Chapter 10).

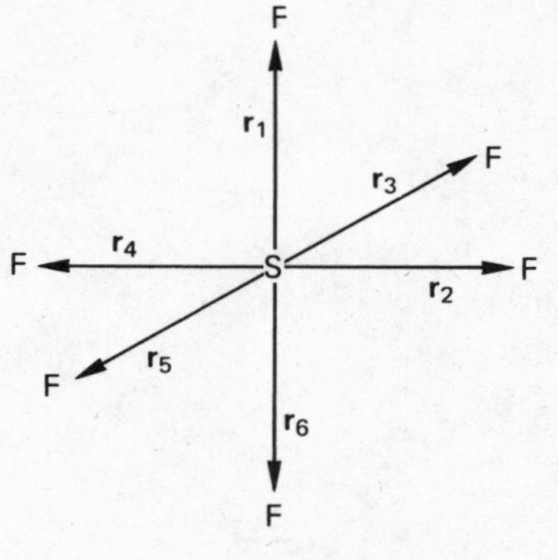


**Figure 7.9** *Bond-stretching vectors for* $SF_6$ ($\mathbf{O}_h$)

## EXERCISES

**1** Use bond vectors to deduce the symmetries of stretching vibrations for $NO_3^-$ ($\mathbf{D}_{3h}$ symmetry) and calculate the SALCs corresponding to them.

**2** Use the set of p-orbitals shown in Figure 7.10 to generate a reducible representation of $\mathbf{D}_{3h}$ and construct the SALCs corresponding to the irreducible components contained in it.

**3** Show explicitly how the SALCs for stretching vibrations of $CH_4$ and $SF_6$ are derived using the generating vectors given.

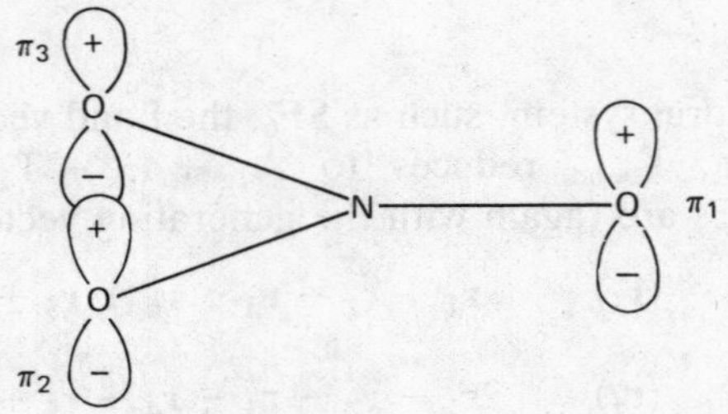


**Figure 7.10** *π-bonding* p*-orbitals for* $NO_3^-$ ($\mathbf{D}_{3h}$)

# 8

# Group theory and vibrational spectroscopy

We have shown how to obtain a representation of the point group of any molecule using a set of $3N$ vectors (three Cartesian coordinate vectors on each of the $N$ atoms) and how to reduce this (or any other reducible representation) into its irreducible components. We shall now see that, using these principles, we can obtain a good deal of useful information from the vibrational spectrum of any molecule.

It will be necessary at this stage to give a very brief account of the experimental methods for obtaining vibrational spectra and the sort of information that we may wish to extract from them. A fuller account of these matters will be found in any of the texts on molecular spectroscopy listed in the Bibliography.

An $N$-atomic molecule possesses $3N$ dynamic degrees of freedom, since each atom has three degrees of freedom, and so there are $3N$ different, independent ways in which the atoms in the molecule can move. For a non-linear molecule, there are three *translational* (translation of the whole molecule along any three mutually perpendicular axes) and three *rotational* (rotation about these three axes) degrees of freedom. This leaves $(3N - 6)$ independent *vibrational* degrees of freedom. For a linear molecule, there are only two rotational degrees of freedom, since rotation about the molecular axis is forbidden, leaving $(3N - 5)$ vibrational degrees of freedom. Each of these $(3N - 6)$ (or $(3N - 5)$) vibrations is independent of the others; that is, none of the vibrations can be expressed in terms of the others, and they are said to be the $(3N - 6)$ (or $(3N - 5)$) **vibrational modes** of that molecule. Each vibrational mode gives rise to a certain pattern of atomic displacements within the molecule, and as an example Figure 8.1 shows the three possible vibrational modes for the bent triatomic molecule $SO_2$ ($3N - 6 = 3$), where the arrows show the directions and are approximately proportional to the magnitudes of the atomic displacements. It will be seen that two of the vibrations, (a) and (b), primarily involve stretching of the S—O bonds, while one, (c), is chiefly

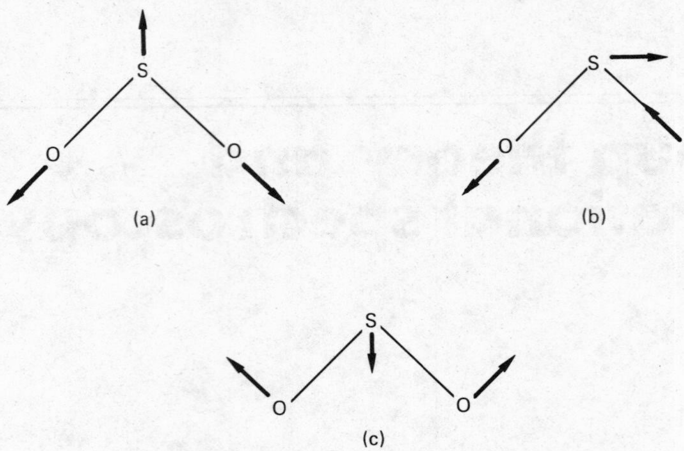


**Figure 8.1** *The vibrational modes of the* $SO_2$ *molecule*

an angle deformation. Such classification into stretching and bending vibrations of various types will be discussed later in this chapter.

In each of the vibrational modes, the atomic displacements occur at a characteristic *frequency*, which depends on the restoring forces acting against the molecular displacements (**force constants**). It is the aim of a vibrational analysis of a molecule to find the frequency corresponding to each of the vibrational modes.

## 8.1 Infrared absorption and Raman scattering spectroscopy

The frequency data come from two main sources: infrared absorption and Raman scattering spectroscopy. These are complementary, and in almost all cases it is necessary to use both, to obtain all the requisite information. The infrared technique is a 'direct' measurement of the vibrational frequencies, which lie in the range corresponding in energy to the infrared part of the electromagnetic spectrum. If a sample is irradiated with infrared radiation, absorption of that radiation occurs at frequencies corresponding to those of the vibrational modes of the molecule. The positions of these absorptions, therefore, give the vibrational frequencies of that molecule.

In Raman spectroscopy, the molecules are irradiated in the ultraviolet or (more commonly) visible region of the spectrum. The electromagnetic field associated with the radiation causes a perturbation of the molecule and induces vibrational transitions. Energy is, therefore, taken up from or given out to the incident radiation, which is scattered at a changed frequency. The *differences* in frequency between the incident light and the Raman-scattered light correspond to vibrational frequencies. In addition, the incident light is almost always plane-polarised (laser) light, and it is possible to determine whether the Raman-scattered light is still *polarised*, or whether it has become *depolarised*. Certain frequencies, and hence certain vibrational modes, will be found to give polarised, while others give depolarised, Raman-scattered light.

The experimental data consist of a series of infrared absorption frequencies and a series of Raman scattering frequencies (with the states of polarisation of the scattered light). We need to assign each frequency to a vibrational mode, and it is in this task that we must utilise the symmetry of the molecule.

## 8.2 Vibrational modes as bases for group representations

Each of the vibrational modes corresponds to a certain pattern of atomic displacements, and for each mode this can be represented by a vector. This vector can then be used to generate an irreducible representation of the molecular point group. Whether a vibration gives rise to infrared absorption and/or Raman scattering depends on the symmetry properties of the vibration vector; that is, the irreducible representation for which it is a basis. Consequently, we need to know the irreducible representations to which all of the vibration vectors give rise.

As we saw for the translation and rotation vectors, this is a simple process, if one knows what the vector looks like. The difficulty with the vibrational analysis is that, at the outset, one does *not* know the explicit form of the vibration vectors, except in the simplest cases. Therefore, an indirect method must be used.

There are $(3N - 6)$ vibration vectors, and together with the three translation and three rotation vectors we have a total of $3N$ vectors. These could be used, if we knew what they all looked like, to generate a $3N$-dimensional representation of the molecular point group. We do not know the forms of the vibration vectors, but this does not matter because we can use *any* set of $3N$ independent vectors as bases. It is a fundamental property of representations that any set of $n$ independent vectors will give the same representation; that is, the character of the matrix for a given symmetry operation will be the same for any set of $n$ independent basis vectors. Thus, any set of $3N$ vectors will give the same characters for all of the symmetry operations, as our set of $3N$ (translation + rotation + vibration) vectors would have done. A very convenient set comprises the $3N$ Cartesian coordinate axis vectors described in Chapter 6, and we can use the resulting characters ($= \Gamma_{3N}$) as though they had been derived from the (translation + rotation + vibration) vectors.

A straightforward method for finding the irreducible components of $\Gamma_{3N}$ (or any other reducible representation) was derived in Chapter 6, and these are the irreducible representations that we require. If we look again at the examples in Chapter 6, we have:

$SO_2$: $\Gamma_{3N} = 3A_1 + A_2 + 2B_1 + 3B_2$
$POCl_3$: $\Gamma_{3N} = 4A_1 + A_2 + 5E$
$PtCl_4^{2-}$: $\Gamma_{3N} = A_{1g} + A_{2g} + B_{1g} + B_{2g} + E_g + 2A_{2u} + B_{2u} + 3E_u$
$RuO_4$: $\Gamma_{3N} = A_1 + E + T_1 + 3T_2$

We need to know the irreducible representations given by the vibration vectors only, but $\Gamma_{3N}$ also includes the translation and rotation vectors. These can be easily removed, however, since we know the forms of the translation and rotation vectors, and we can find the irreducible representations generated by them (see Chapter 4). The relevant information is printed in the character table for every point group and so we can, in fact, remove these irreducible representations by inspection.

Consider our four examples, belonging to the point groups $\mathbf{C}_{2v}$, $\mathbf{C}_{3v}$, $\mathbf{D}_{4h}$ and $\mathbf{T}_d$. In each case, we find $\Gamma_{T+R}$ (the sum of the irreducible representations due to translation and rotation vectors) from the character table:

$\mathbf{C}_{2v}$: $\Gamma_{T+R} = A_1 + A_2 + 2B_1 + 2B_2$
$\mathbf{C}_{3v}$: $\Gamma_{T+R} = A_1 + A_2 + 2E$
$\mathbf{D}_{4h}$: $\Gamma_{T+R} = A_{2g} + E_g + A_{2u} + E_u$
$\mathbf{T}_d$: $\Gamma_{T+R} = T_1 + T_2$

Subtracting $\Gamma_{T+R}$ from $\Gamma_{3N}$ gives $\Gamma_{vib}$, the sum of the irreducible representations due to the vibration vectors alone:

$SO_2$: $\Gamma_{vib} = 2A_1 + B_2$
$POCl_3$: $\Gamma_{vib} = 3A_1 + 3E$
$PtCl_4^{2-}$: $\Gamma_{vib} = A_{1g} + B_{1g} + B_{2g} + A_{2u} + B_{2u} + 2E_u$
$RuO_4$: $\Gamma_{vib} = A_1 + E + 2T_2$

Knowing the symmetries of all the vibrational modes of any molecule, it is possible to predict which of them will be active in the infrared and Raman spectra. To do this, we need to discuss the symmetry selection rules for the two processes.

## 8.3 Direct-product representations

In order to explain the symmetry selection rules, we must introduce a new concept, that of a **direct product**. If we multiply together two or more vectors or functions, what is the symmetry of the product?

We know that each molecular vibration mode is a vector, a basis for an irreducible representation of the point group. We may need to know the symmetry properties of a molecule vibrating in two or more modes simultaneously (this problem is also discussed in Chapter 9). In Chapter 10, we will see that molecular orbitals are bases for irreducible representations. What are the symmetry properties of a system containing two or more electrons in such orbitals?

These questions are answered by forming direct-product representations. Consider a square–planar molecule such as $PtCl_4^{2-}$ (we saw earlier that there are bond-stretching vibrations of symmetries $A_{1g}$, $B_{1g}$ and $E_u$). Suppose that the molecule is vibrating with both the $B_{1g}$ and $E_u$ modes, then the resultant symmetry is obtained by taking the direct product of $B_{1g}$ and $E_u$, symbolised by $B_{1g} \times E_u$. The character for any symmetry operation in the direct-product representation is simply given by multiplying together the characters for that operation in the irreducible representations:

| $\mathbf{D}_{4h}$ | $E$ | $2C_4$ | $C_2$ | $2C_2'$ | $2C_2''$ | $i$ | $2S_4$ | $\sigma_h$ | $2\sigma_v$ | $2\sigma_d$ |
|---|---|---|---|---|---|---|---|---|---|---|
| $B_{1g}$ | 1 | −1 | 1 | 1 | −1 | 1 | −1 | 1 | 1 | −1 |
| $E_u$ | 2 | 0 | −2 | 0 | 0 | −2 | 0 | 2 | 0 | 0 |
| $B_{1g} \times E_u$ | 2 | 0 | −2 | 0 | 0 | −2 | 0 | 2 | 0 | 0 |

This shows that $B_{1g} \times E_u = E_u$; that is, the direct product is still an irreducible representation, and is in fact still $E_u$.

This was a very simple example, but there are many occasions where the direct product is reducible. This happens whenever two or more doubly- or triply-degenerate irreducible representations are involved.

Consider the direct product $E \times T_2$ for a tetrahedral system:

| $\mathbf{T}_d$ | $E$ | $8C_3$ | $3C_2$ | $6\sigma_d$ | $6S_4$ |
|---|---|---|---|---|---|
| E | 2 | −1 | 2 | 0 | 0 |
| $T_2$ | 3 | 0 | −1 | 1 | −1 |
| $E \times T_2$ | 6 | 0 | −2 | 0 | 0 |

This is a reducible representation and application of the reduction formula gives:

$$E \times T_2 = T_1 + T_2$$

We have just seen that there are vibrations of a tetrahedral molecule of E and $T_2$ symmetry. If such a molecule is vibrating with such modes simultaneously, the resultant vibration will have both $T_1$ and $T_2$ symmetry.

By working systematically through all of the possible direct products of pairs of irreducible representations for all of the point groups, many regularities are seen, and these are summarised in Appendix A. Direct products of more than two representations are simply obtained from the binary direct products, and examples of this will be given in the next section.

## 8.4 Symmetry selection rules for infrared and Raman spectra

We will discuss the infrared selection rule in more detail as it is easier to understand than that for the Raman effect, although the basic principles are very similar in the two cases.

### 8.4.1 Infrared spectra

Consider a transition from the vibrational ground state of a molecule (initial state, vibrational wave function $\psi_i$) to a vibrationally excited state, with the molecule possessing *one* quantum of energy in *one* vibrational mode (final state, vibrational wave function $\psi_f$). This is known as a **fundamental transition**.

A vibrational transition in the infrared occurs because of an interaction between the incident radiation and the molecular dipole moment, $\mu$. The probability of any such dipole-induced transition from an initial state (wave function $\psi_i$) to a final state (wave function $\psi_f$) is proportional to the **transition moment**:

$$\int \psi_i^* \mu \psi_f d\tau$$

where $\mu$ is the dipole moment of the molecule (a vector), $\psi_i^*$ is the complex conjugate of $\psi_i$ and $d\tau$ implies that the integration is carried out over all of the variables in the wave functions. As the vibrational ground state wave function is always real, $\psi_i^* = \psi_i$, and so the transition moment can be written:

$$\int \psi_i \mu \psi_f d\tau$$

If this integral is zero for a particular transition, then the probability of that transition occurring is zero – it is said to be *forbidden* in the infrared – and no absorption due to it will be seen. Furthermore, the integral will be zero unless the direct product of $\psi_i\mu\psi_f$ contains the totally symmetric irreducible representation, for which the character is +1 for all symmetry operations of the relevant point group.

The vector $\mu$ can be split up into three components, $\mu_x$, $\mu_y$ and $\mu_z$, along the three Cartesian coordinate axes, and only *one* of the three integrals:

$$\int \psi_i \mu_k \psi_f d\tau \qquad (k = x, y \text{ or } z)$$

needs to be non-zero.

What are the symmetries of the three components of the integral? The vibrational ground state wave function $\psi_i$ (with all vibrational quantum numbers zero) has the same mathematical form as that for an s-orbital. It is thus spherically symmetrical. Since a sphere is totally symmetric in any point group, the vibrational ground state wave function is always totally symmetric. The symmetry properties of the component of the dipole moment along the $k$ axis, $\mu_k$, are the same as those of a translation vector along the same axis, $\mathbf{T_k}$. The symmetry properties of the wave function of the vibrationally excited state $\psi_f$ are the same as those of the vector that describes the vibrational mode involved. Therefore, we need to form the direct products of the totally symmetric representation ($\psi_i$), the irreducible representations of each of the translation vectors ($\mathbf{T_x}$, $\mathbf{T_y}$ and $\mathbf{T_z}$) and the irreducible representation of the vibration being considered ($\psi_f$).

Consider the vibrations of the bent triatomic, $\mathbf{C}_{2v}$, molecule – that is, $A_1$ or $B_2$ symmetries. Will they occur in the infrared spectrum of such a molecule? Remember that $\psi_i$ has symmetry $A_1$ in a $\mathbf{C}_{2v}$ environment (that is, totally symmetric). The character table for $\mathbf{C}_{2v}$ shows that $\mathbf{T_x}$ has $B_1$ symmetry, $\mathbf{T_y}$, $B_2$ and $\mathbf{T_z}$, $A_1$. Forming the direct products, we have:

$$\Gamma(\psi_i) \times \begin{pmatrix} \Gamma(\mathbf{T_x}) \\ \Gamma(\mathbf{T_y}) \\ \Gamma(\mathbf{T_z}) \end{pmatrix} \times \Gamma(\psi_f)$$

Hence, for $A_1$ vibrations:

$$A_1 \times \begin{pmatrix} B_1 \\ B_2 \\ A_1 \end{pmatrix} \times A_1$$

which is:

$$\begin{aligned} A_1 \times B_1 \times A_1 &= B_2 \\ A_1 \times B_2 \times A_1 &= B_1 \\ A_1 \times A_1 \times A_1 &= A_2 \end{aligned}$$

(from the rules in Appendix A). The products include the totally symmetric $A_1$ irreducible representation, and hence the $A_1$ modes are infrared active.

Similarly, for the $B_2$ mode:

$$A_1 \times \begin{pmatrix} B_1 \\ B_2 \\ A_1 \end{pmatrix} \times B_2$$

which is:

$$A_1 \times B_1 \times B_2 = A_2$$
$$A_1 \times B_2 \times B_2 = A_1$$
$$A_1 \times A_1 \times B_2 = B_2$$

Thus, $A_1$ is again present and the $B_2$ mode is also infrared active.

As a further example, consider the tetrahedral case, where there are vibrations of $A_1$, E and $T_2$ symmetry. Let us deduce the infrared activity for each of them. Remember $\psi_i$ has $A_1$ symmetry. Inspecting the character table for $\mathbf{T}_d$ shows that $\mathbf{T_x}$, $\mathbf{T_y}$ and $\mathbf{T_z}$ together have $T_2$ symmetry. Forming the direct product, therefore, gives:

$A_1$ vibration: $A_1 \times T_2 \times A_1 = T_2$
E vibration: $A_1 \times T_2 \times E = T_2 \times E = T_1 + T_2$
$T_2$ vibrations: $A_1 \times T_2 \times T_2 = T_2 \times T_2 = A_1 + E + T_1 + T_2$

Thus, the $T_2$ vibrations are infrared active ($A_1$ present), but the $A_1$ and E vibrations are not, and will not appear in the infrared spectrum.

Similar calculations can be made for any other case. A very important result is that if a vibrational mode has the same symmetry as one or more of the translation vectors $\mathbf{T_x}$, $\mathbf{T_y}$ or $\mathbf{T_z}$ for that point group, then the totally-symmetric irreducible representation is present and a transition from the ground state to that mode will be infrared active.

### *8.4.2* Raman spectra

The Raman selection rule can be derived similarly, since the probability of a vibrational transition occurring in Raman scattering is proportional to:

$$\int \psi_i \alpha \psi_f d\tau$$

where $\alpha$ is the **polarisability** of the molecule. The Raman effect depends on a molecular dipole *induced* in the molecule by the electromagnetic field of the incident radiation. The induced dipole is proportional to the polarisability of the molecule, which is a measure of the ease with which the molecular electron distribution can be distorted. $\alpha$ is a **tensor**, a $3 \times 3$ array of components; that is, $\alpha_{x^2}$, $\alpha_{xy}$, $\alpha_{xz}$, $\alpha_{yx}$, $\alpha_{y^2}$, $\alpha_{yz}$, $\alpha_{zx}$, $\alpha_{zy}$ and $\alpha_{z^2}$. For vibrational transitions, $\alpha_{jk} = \alpha_{kj}$ (where $j$, $k = x$, $y$ or $z$), and so there will be six distinct components. Consequently, we need one non-zero integral from the six of the form:

$$\int \psi_i \alpha_{jk} \psi_f d\tau \qquad (j,\ k = x,\ y \text{ or } z)$$

It is again possible to determine the activity by forming the appropriate direct products, making use of the fact (which will not be proved here) that the symmetry properties of $\alpha_{jk}$ are the same as for the function $jk$. Thus, $\alpha_{x^2}$ has the same symmetry properties as $x^2$, and $\alpha_{xy}$ as $xy$. The symmetries of $x^2, y^2, z^2, xy, yz$ and $zx$ (or combinations of them) are listed in the character tables in Appendix A.

Let us choose as examples the same vibrations as for the infrared case – those of $SO_2$ and $RuO_4$. In $\mathbf{C}_{2v}$ symmetry, $x^2$, $y^2$ and $z^2$ all have $A_1$ symmetry; $xy$, $A_2$; $zx$, $B_1$; and $yz$, $B_2$. Thus, the required direct products for an $A_1$ vibration are:

$$A_1 \times \begin{pmatrix} A_1 \\ A_2 \\ B_1 \\ B_2 \end{pmatrix} \times A_1 = A_1 \text{ or } A_2 \text{ or } B_1 \text{ or } B_2$$

That is, it is Raman allowed.

For $B_2$ vibrations, we have:

$$A_1 \times \begin{pmatrix} A_1 \\ A_2 \\ B_1 \\ B_2 \end{pmatrix} \times B_2 = B_2 \text{ or } B_1 \text{ or } A_2 \text{ or } A_1$$

Thus, these are also Raman allowed.

In the tetrahedral case, the components of the polarisability have symmetries $A_1$ $(x^2 + y^2 + z^2)$, E $(2z^2 - x^2 - y^2, x^2 - y^2)$ and $T_2$ $(xy, yz, zx)$, and the vibrations $A_1$, E and $T_2$. Thus, the direct products are:

$$A_1 \times \begin{pmatrix} A_1 \\ E \\ T_2 \end{pmatrix} \times A_1 = A_1 \text{ or E or } T_2 \qquad (A_1 \text{ vibration})$$

$$A_1 \times \begin{pmatrix} A_1 \\ E \\ T_2 \end{pmatrix} \times E = E \text{ or } (A_1 + A_2 + E) \text{ or } (T_1 + T_2) \qquad (\text{E vibration})$$

$$A_1 \times \begin{pmatrix} A_1 \\ E \\ T_2 \end{pmatrix} \times T_2 = T_2 \text{ or } (T_1 + T_2) \text{ or } (A_1 + E + T_1 + T_2) \qquad (T_2 \text{ vibrations})$$

Thus, all of the vibrations of a tetrahedral molecule are Raman active.

Multiplying out all of the possible direct products for Raman activity shows that the product will be non-zero only if at least one of $\alpha_{jk}$ $(jk)$ has the same symmetry as the mode described by the wave function $\psi_f$. Thus, if a normal mode has the same symmetry as one or more of these binary combinations of $x$, $y$ and $z$ (listed in the character tables), then a transition from the ground state to that mode will be Raman active.

Since the selection rules for infrared and Raman spectra have different physical bases, there is no necessary relationship between them. Thus, an infrared active mode might or might not be Raman active, and vice versa. Some modes may be active in both, some in one only and some in neither. The more symmetrical the molecule, the fewer the number of modes that are active in both spectra, and for such systems a study of infrared and Raman spectra is needed if the maximum amount of vibrational data is to be obtained.

For any molecule with a centre of symmetry, a **mutual exclusion rule** exists. For such a molecule, *no* vibration can be active in both infrared and Raman spectra. The reason for this is that $\mathbf{T_x}$, $\mathbf{T_y}$ and $\mathbf{T_z}$ are always antisymmetric with respect to inversion (u), whereas $x^2$, etc., are always symmetric (g). Therefore, modes of u-symmetry cannot be Raman active, while those of g-symmetry cannot produce infrared absorption.

### *8.4.3* Use of the selection rules

We can now return to our four examples, to summarise which of their vibrations are infrared and/or Raman active.

$SO_2$ ($\mathbf{C}_{2v}$):

$2A_1$: $\mathbf{T_x}$; $x^2$, $y^2$ and $z^2$ – active in both

$B_2$: $\mathbf{T_y}$; $yz$ – active in both

There should, therefore, be three infrared and three (coincident) Raman bands.

$POCl_3$ ($\mathbf{C}_{3v}$):

$3A_1$: $\mathbf{T_z}$; $x^2 + y^2$, $z^2$ – active in both

$3E$: $(\mathbf{T_x}, \mathbf{T_y})$; $(yz, zx)$, $(x^2 - y^2, xy)$ – active in both

Six bands in the infrared and six in the Raman – all coincident.

$PtCl_4^{2-}$ ($\mathbf{D}_{4h}$):

$A_{1g}$: $x^2 + y^2$, $z^2$ – Raman only
$B_{1g}$: $x^2 - y^2$ – Raman only

$B_{2g}$: $xy$ – Raman only
$A_{2u}$: $\mathbf{T_z}$ – infrared only
$B_{2u}$: – totally inactive
$2E_u$: $(\mathbf{T_x}, \mathbf{T_y})$ – infrared only

Three Raman bands and three (non-coincident) infrared bands. Note that $PtCl_4^{2-}$ possesses a centre of symmetry, and hence the mutual exclusion rule applies.

$RuO_4$ ($\mathbf{T}_d$):

$A_1$: $x^2 + y^2 + z^2$ – Raman only
E: $(2z^2 - x^2 - y^2, x^2 - y^2)$ – Raman only
$T_2$: $(\mathbf{T_x}, \mathbf{T_y}, \mathbf{T_z})$; $(xy, yz, zx)$ – active in both

Therefore, $RuO_4$ should show four Raman bands and two infrared bands, coinciding with two of the former.

It will be recalled that it is our aim to assign one specific frequency to each vibrational mode. The analysis so far has not taken us far towards achieving that, especially for less symmetrical molecules, where all of the vibrations tend to be active in both infrared and Raman spectra. There is one piece of experimental evidence, however, which can be used to help solve this problem without further theoretical analysis.

Raman spectra are normally excited using plane-polarised (laser) radiation. It is possible to determine whether a given Raman band comprises polarised or depolarised scattered radiation. A more detailed treatment of the theory of the Raman effect shows, moreover, that only transitions involving *totally symmetric* vibrational modes give rise to polarised Raman bands (see the book by Woodward listed in the Bibliography). All others are depolarised. Therefore, all bands in the Raman spectrum that are polarised arise from vibrations that have a character of +1 for every symmetry operation – that is, are totally symmetric. This is a considerable help in the assignment.

Of the three Raman bands expected for $SO_2$, two belong to the totally symmetric irreducible representation $A_1$ and should be polarised, while the third belongs to the $B_2$ (non-totally symmetric) representation and should give a depolarised Raman band. For $POCl_3$, the three $A_1$ bands will be polarised and the three E bands depolarised. For $PtCl_4^{2-}$, the band due to the $A_{1g}$ vibration will be polarised, while those due to $B_{1g}$ and $B_{2g}$ will be depolarised. Finally, for $RuO_4$, the two Raman bands with coincident infrared absorptions ($T_2$ symmetry) will be depolarised, and of the other two, one ($A_1$) will be polarised and the other (E) depolarised.

By considering both the infrared and Raman spectra (with polarisation data for the latter), we can make certain decisions as to which frequencies correspond to particular vibrational modes, but a complete assignment is rarely possible on the basis of the analysis presented so far.

## 8.5 Classification of vibrational modes

The different vibrational modes of a molecule can be divided into various types, such as bond stretching, angle deformation vibrations, and so on. It is then possible to determine the number and symmetry species for each of the different types. The arguments of group theory cannot tell us anything about the expected frequency of a particular vibration, but *ab initio* molecular orbital calculations on simple molecules and the accumulated experience of molecular spectroscopists can often suggest a reasonably accurate prediction of the frequency of a given type of vibration.

The vectors suitable for describing bond-stretching vibrations have already been mentioned in Chapter 6. The relevant vectors for $SO_2$ are illustrated in Figure 8.2; they are coincident in length and direction with the S—O bonds. The characters for $\Gamma_{str}$ generated by these vectors are calculated using the following:

(a) Vectors shifted to a new position by a symmetry operation $R$ contribute zero to $\chi(R)$.
(b) Unshifted vectors contribute +1 to $\chi(R)$.

Thus, for the S—O stretching vectors, we have:

| $C_{2v}$ | $E$ | $C_2$ | $\sigma(xz)$ | $\sigma(yz)$ |
|---|---|---|---|---|
| $\Gamma_{str}$ | 2 | 0 | 0 | 2 |

$C_2$ and $\sigma(xz)$ interchange the two vectors, while E and $\sigma(yz)$ leave both unshifted. This is a reducible representation and by the usual formula:

$$\Gamma_{str} = A_1 + B_2$$

(For a simple case such as this, the reduction may often be done by inspection.) Thus, there should be two S—O stretching frequencies, both active in the infrared and the Raman, with one of the Raman bands being polarised ($A_1$).

The remaining vibration for $SO_2$ may be easily recognised as involving deformation of the O—S—O angle. The vector used as a basis for $\Gamma_{bend}$ is just the angle being deformed (Figure 8.3). This is a rather unusual 'vector', since it must be regarded as a 'double-ended' arrow. We can now

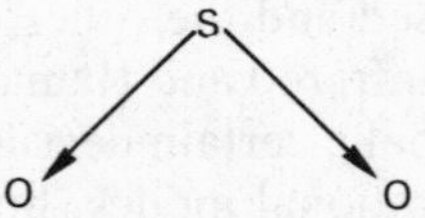


**Figure 8.2** *Bond-stretching vectors for the* $SO_2$ *molecule*

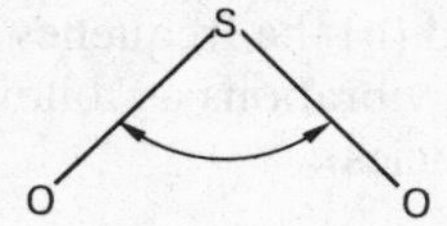


**Figure 8.3** *Angle deformation vector for the* $SO_2$ *molecule*

examine the effects of the $\mathbf{C}_{2v}$ symmetry operation on this:

$E \rightarrow +1$
$C_2 \rightarrow +1$ (one-half of the angle is taken into the other; the final angle is unchanged)
$\sigma(xz) \rightarrow +1$ (as for $C_2$)
$\sigma(yz) \rightarrow +1$

The characters are those of the $A_1$ irreducible representation, hence the angle-bending vibration is of that symmetry, giving a polarised Raman band and infrared absorption.

We can now compare these predictions with the observed infrared and Raman spectra, which are listed in Table 8.1.

**Table 8.1** Vibrational spectrum of $SO_2$

| Infrared (vapour) | Raman (liquid) |
|---|---|
| 518 | 524 (polarised) |
| 1151 | 1145 (polarised) |
| 1362 | 1336 (depolarised) |

All of the vibrational frequencies are expressed in terms of wavenumbers, $cm^{-1}$.
These are proportional to the actual frequencies in Hz, since $\nu$ ($cm^{-1}$) = $f$ (Hz)/$c$, where $f$ is the frequency and $c$ is the velocity of light *in vacuo* (cm/$s^{-1}$).

We should first note that there are differences in the frequencies as measured by the two techniques. This is entirely due to the fact that the measurements were made in different phases. The frequency of any vibration is phase dependent and, ideally, measurements of infrared and Raman spectra should be made on the same phase.

The $A_1$ modes are easy to pick out because they are polarised in the Raman spectrum. But which is which? Group theory cannot help here, but in practice stretching vibrations are at *higher* frequencies than bending vibrations involving similar atoms. Therefore, we can assign the 1145 $cm^{-1}$ band as the $A_1$ (symmetric) stretch, with the 524 $cm^{-1}$ band as the O—S—O deformation. The remaining vibration must be the $B_2$ (anti-symmetric) stretch. This is confirmed by the facts that: (a) it gives a depolarised Raman band and (b) the frequency is close to that of the other stretch. We can list the $SO_2$ vibrations as follows (taking the mean of the infrared and Raman frequencies):

$\nu_1$ ($A_1$): symmetric S—O stretch – 1148 $cm^{-1}$
$\nu_2$ ($A_1$): O—S—O deformation – 521 $cm^{-1}$
$\nu_3$ ($B_2$): antisymmetric S—O stretch – 1349 $cm^{-1}$

The vibrations are conventionally numbered in decreasing order of frequency within each symmetry species, working through the latter in the order given in the character table.

## 8.6 Further examples of vibrational analysis

Let us now work through two further examples of vibrational analyses, which illustrate some further points about bond-stretching and angle-bending vectors.

### 8.6.1 $POCl_3$

The vectors for the P═O and P—Cl bond-stretching vibrations are shown in Figure 8.4. The representations for which these are bases are:

| $C_{3v}$ | $E$ | $2C_3$ | $3\sigma_v$ |
|---|---|---|---|
| $\Gamma_{P—O\ str}$ | 1 | 1 | 1 |
| $\Gamma_{P—Cl\ str}$ | 3 | 0 | 1 |

$\Gamma_{P—O\ str}$ is clearly an irreducible representation (in fact the $A_1$ representation). $\Gamma_{P—Cl\ str}$ is reducible, and it can be easily seen that it reduces to $A_1 + E$. Thus, three stretching vibrations are predicted, two of which should give polarised Raman bands.

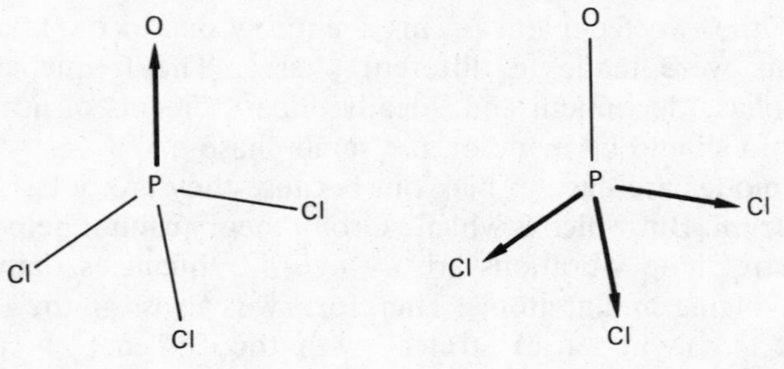


**Figure 8.4** P═O *and* P—Cl *bond-stretching vectors for the* $POCl_3$ *molecule*

Since $\Gamma_{vib}$ for $POCl_3$ comprises $3A_1 + 3E$, we are left with $A_1 + 2E$, which must correspond to the deformations. This can be checked using the bond angle vectors (Figure 8.5). There are six of these, giving:

| $\mathbf{C}_{3v}$ | $E$ | $2C_3$ | $3\sigma_v$ |
|---|---|---|---|
| $\Gamma_{bend}$ | 6 | 0 | 2 |

The three-fold rotation shifts all of the angles, while the $\sigma_v$ planes leave one completely unchanged and reflect half of a second into the other half of the same angle, hence two unshifted angles.

This reduces to $2A_1 + 2E$, which does not agree with our expected result, since we have found one $A_1$ too many. We can, however, see one totally symmetric deformation that is physically impossible; that is, the simultaneous increase or decrease of all six angles. Another way of looking at the problem is that all six angles are not *independent*; if any five are defined, the sixth can be expressed in terms of them. The usual way of expressing this is to say that there is one **redundant coordinate** present. The surplus $A_1$ irreducible representation can safely be ignored, since it does not correspond to a physically possible vibration. Therefore, we should expect three deformation frequencies, one of which should give a polarised Raman band.

The observed infrared and Raman spectra of $POCl_3$ are listed in Table 8.2 (all figures in $cm^{-1}$).

**Table 8.2** Vibrational spectrum of $POCl_3$

| Infrared (liquid) | Raman (liquid) |
|---|---|
| 1292 | 1290 (polarised) |
| 580 | 581 (depolarised) |
| 487 | 486 (polarised) |
| 340 | 337 (depolarised) |
| 267 | 267 (polarised) |
| (not accessible) | 193 (depolarised) |

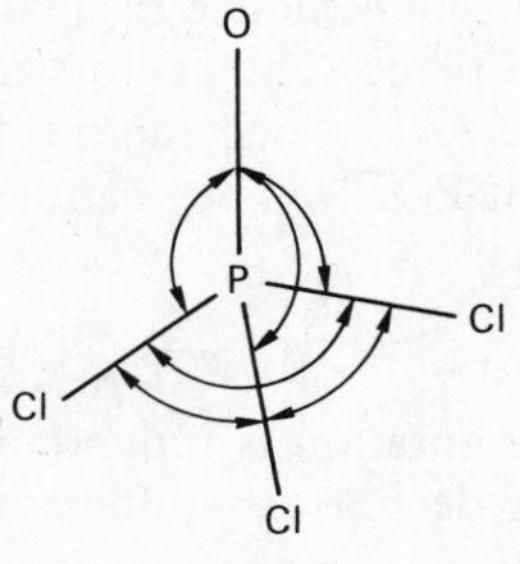


**Figure 8.5** *Angle deformation vectors for the* $POCl_3$ *molecule*

From our discussion of $SO_2$, it is reasonable to suppose that the three stretches correspond to the three highest frequencies. The E P—Cl stretch must be that at 581 $cm^{-1}$ (depolarised), leaving the two polarised bands at 1291 $cm^{-1}$ and 486 $cm^{-1}$. (The differences between infrared and Raman figures can be regarded as being due wholly to experimental error.) The former is assigned to the P═O stretch, the latter to the P—Cl symmetric stretch (both $A_1$). There are three reasons for making this assignment:

**1** We might expect the two P—Cl stretches to be quite close in frequency.

**2** Frequency generally decreases with increased atomic mass.

**3** Double bonds have a higher stretching frequency than similar, single bonds.

Of the three deformations, the 267 $cm^{-1}$ band must be the symmetric mode ($A_1$), with the other two as the E modes. It is not possible to distinguish between these with the available data. Therefore, we can list the vibrational frequencies of $POCl_3$ as follows:

$\nu_1$ ($A_1$): P═O stretch – 1290 $cm^{-1}$
$\nu_2$ ($A_1$): symmetric P—Cl stretch – 486 $cm^{-1}$
$\nu_3$ ($A_1$): symmetric deformation – 267 $cm^{-1}$
$\nu_4$ (E): degenerate P—Cl stretch – 581 $cm^{-1}$
$\nu_5$ (E): deformations – 337 $cm^{-1}$
$\nu_6$ (E): 193 $cm^{-1}$

### *8.6.2* $PtCl_4^{2-}$

The bond-stretching vectors for this $\mathbf{D}_{4h}$ ion are shown in Figure 8.6. They can be shown to reduce to:

$$\Gamma_{Pt-Cl\ str} = A_{1g} + B_{1g} + E_u$$

The deformations, for convenience in analysis, are divided into two types: in plane and out of plane. The vectors for the former are the four Cl—Pt—Cl angles (Figure 8.7), which can be treated in the same way as the deformation vectors of $POCl_3$. They can be reduced to the following irreducible representations:

$$\Gamma_{i.p.def} = A_{1g} + B_{2g} + E_u$$

The $A_{1g}$ irreducible representation is redundant, however, since all four angles cannot increase or decrease simultaneously in an in-plane movement. Therefore:

$$\Gamma_{i.p.def} = B_{2g} + E_u$$

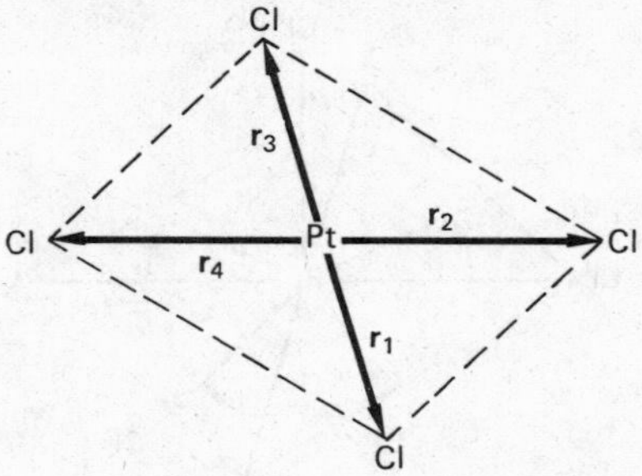


**Figure 8.6** *Bond-stretching vectors for the* $PtCl_4^{2-}$ *ion*

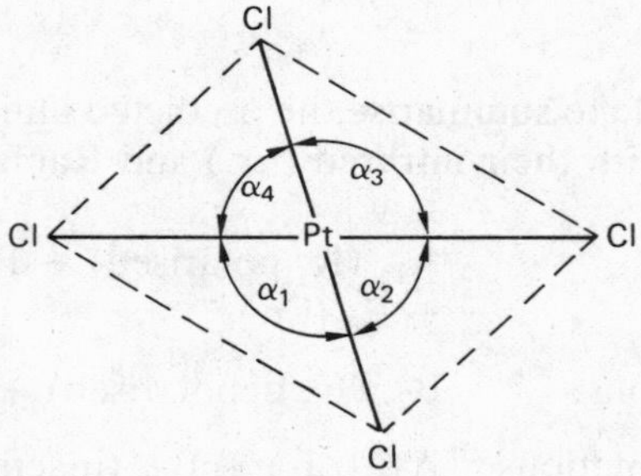


**Figure 8.7** *In-plane deformation vectors for the* $PtCl_4^{2-}$ *ion*

There remain two irreducible representations still unaccounted for ($A_{2u}$ + $B_{2u}$), which must correspond to the out-of-plane deformations. In order to determine the symmetry of these directly, we must use a new type of vector (Figure 8.8). We must assume that all four Pt—Cl bonds are bent out of the equilibrium planar configuration by the same angle. The set of four angles so defined is the basis for the reducible representation corresponding to the out-of-plane deformations. The characters of this representation are as follows. (If the distortions are left unshifted and in the same direction, then each one contributes +1 to the character; but if the distortion is in the opposite direction, then each one contributes −1.)

| $\mathbf{D}_{4h}$ | $E$ | $2C_4$ | $C_2$ | $2C_2'$ | $2C_2''$ | $i$ | $2S_4$ | $\sigma_h$ | $2\sigma_v$ | $2\sigma_d$ |
|---|---|---|---|---|---|---|---|---|---|---|
| $\Gamma_{\text{o.o.p.def}}$ | 4 | 0 | 0 | −2 | 0 | 0 | 0 | −4 | 2 | 0 |

This is clearly a reducible representation, and it contains $E_g$ + $A_{2u}$ + $B_{2u}$. $\Gamma_{vib}$ for $PtCl_4^{2-}$, however, contains no $E_g$ representation, and so the first of these must correspond to a redundancy. In fact, the $E_g$ representation relates to a molecular rotation about the *x* and *y* axes. The easiest method for spotting such redundancies is by the difference from $\Gamma_{vib}$.

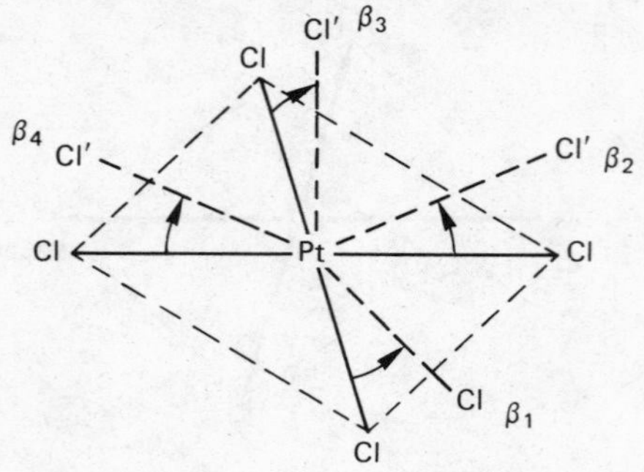


**Figure 8.8** *Out-of-plane deformation vectors for the* $PtCl_4^{2-}$ *ion*

It is now possible to summarise the predicted numbers of vibrations for $PtCl_4^{2-}$, together with their infrared (i.r.) and Raman (R) activities:

| | |
|---|---|
| Pt—Cl stretches: | $A_{1g}$ (R, polarised) + $B_{1g}$ (R, depolarised) + $E_u$ (i.r.) |
| In-plane deformations: | $B_{2g}$ (R, depolarised) + $E_u$ (i.r.) |
| Out-of-plane deformations: | $A_{2u}$ (i.r.) + $B_{2u}$ (inactive) |

The observed spectra are given in Table 8.3 (all figures in $cm^{-1}$).

No infrared/Raman coincidences are found, in agreement with the mutual exclusion rule. (As both spectra refer to the same phase, the frequencies should be the same, within experimental error, in both spectra.) The values 314 $cm^{-1}$ (Raman) and 320 $cm^{-1}$ (infrared) are just outside the combined range of experimental error for the two techniques, and are not, therefore, coincident. Of the Raman-active vibrations, the 332 $cm^{-1}$ band must be the symmetric ($A_{1g}$) Pt—Cl stretch, while that at 314 $cm^{-1}$ is the antisymmetric ($B_{1g}$) stretch. The band at 170 $cm^{-1}$ is the

**Table 8.3** Vibrational spectrum of $PtCl_4^{2-}$ in aqueous solution

| Infrared | Raman |
|---|---|
| – | 332 (polarised) |
| 320 | – |
| – | 314 (depolarised) |
| 183 | – |
| – | 170 (depolarised) |
| 93 | – |

$B_{2g}$ in-plane deformation. In the infrared spectrum, the highest frequency band, at 320 $cm^{-1}$, must be the $E_u$ Pt—Cl stretch, leaving the 183 $cm^{-1}$ absorption as the $E_u$ in-plane deformation (close to the $B_{2g}$ in-plane deformation) and that at 93 $cm^{-1}$ as the $A_{2u}$ out-of-plane deformation.

A list of the $PtCl_4^{2-}$ vibrations can now be made:

$\nu_1$ ($A_{1g}$): symmetric Pt—Cl stretch – 332 $cm^{-1}$
$\nu_2$ ($B_{1g}$): antisymmetric Pt—Cl stretch – 314 $cm^{-1}$
$\nu_3$ ($B_{2g}$): in-plane deformation – 170 $cm^{-1}$
$\nu_4$ ($A_{2u}$): out-of-plane deformation – 93 $cm^{-1}$
$\nu_5$ ($B_{2u}$): out-of-plane deformation – inactive
$\nu_6$ ($E_u$): Pt—Cl stretch – 320 $cm^{-1}$
$\nu_7$ ($E_u$): in-plane deformation – 183 $cm^{-1}$

In principle, the vibrational spectrum of any molecule can be analysed to give a specific frequency corresponding to every vibrational mode (or at least all of those active in the infrared or Raman spectra) using the techniques developed in this chapter. Several complicating factors may interfere, however. Some of these will be dealt with in the next chapter, but some may be mentioned briefly here.

Large molecules with low symmetry have selection rules that give little differentiation between modes, and in such cases specific assignments may be impossible. In addition, a molecule may possess more than one likely structure. In such a case, it is necessary to calculate the expected spectrum for every possible structure and compare these with the experimental spectrum. In favourable cases, it will be possible to decide unambiguously the symmetry of a molecule from its vibrational spectrum; that is, only one model fits the experimental data. Often, however, ambiguities can remain, since the spectroscopic differences between different models may be slight.

A further difficulty is that all of the vibrations that are formally allowed in the infrared or Raman spectra may not appear with sufficient intensity to be observed, and this can lead to uncertainties in the final analysis.

A final point is that the description of individual vibrations as 'X—Y stretch' or 'Y—X—Y deformation' is an approximation. Vibrations of the same symmetry (especially when their unperturbed frequencies are similar) *couple* together, and the resulting motions are mixtures of the original vibrations. A simple example is found for the linear molecule DCN, for which the two stretching modes, nominally C—D and C≡N stretches, have the same symmetry and very similar frequencies. As a result, the band thought of as the C—D stretch is only 66% C—D stretching, with a 34% contribution from C≡N stretching (H. Siebert, *Anwendungen der Schwingungsspektroskopie in der anorganischen Chemie*, Springer (Berlin) 1966, p. 11).

## EXERCISES

**1** For each of the molecules in Exercise 1 of Chapter 6, determine $\Gamma_{3N}$, find the symmetries of the vibrational modes, and their activities in the infrared and Raman spectra.

**2** The observed vibrational spectrum of the tetrahedral ion $ClO_4^-$ is as follows (all figures in $cm^{-1}$):

| Raman (aqueous solution) | Infrared (solid)* |
|---|---|
| 1102 (depolarised) | 1111 |
| 935 (polarised) | – |
| 628 (depolarised) | 625 |
| 462 (depolarised) | – |

*It is often difficult to obtain good infrared spectra of aqueous solutions.

Assign all of these bands to the vibrational modes of $ClO_4^-$.

**3** $BF_3$ possesses $\mathbf{D}_{3h}$ symmetry. Determine the numbers, symmetry species, and infrared and Raman activities for the different types of vibration for this molecule. Assign frequencies to each of the modes using the following data for gaseous $BF_3$ (all figures in $cm^{-1}$):

| Raman | Infrared |
|---|---|
| 1453 (depolarised) | 1454 |
| 888 (polarised) | – |
| – | 692 |
| 481 (depolarised) | 479 |

**4** In non-polar solvents, phosphorus pentachloride exists as a covalent monomer, $PCl_5$, with $\mathbf{D}_{3h}$ symmetry. As in Exercise 3, determine the numbers, symmetries and spectroscopic activities for the different types of vibration. Assign the following frequencies to vibrational modes of the molecule (all figures in $cm^{-1}$):

| Raman | Infrared |
|---|---|
| 579 (depolarised) | 581 |
| – | 444 |
| 393 (polarised) | – |
| 385 (polarised) | – |
| – | 299 |
| 279 (depolarised) | 277 |
| 261 (depolarised) | – |
| 98 (depolarised) | 100 |

# 9

# Further aspects of vibrational spectroscopy

## 9.1 Exact forms of the vibration vectors

Chapter 7 introduced the technique of projection operators to generate symmetry-adapted linear combinations (SALCs) of vectors or functions, and several examples of bond-stretching vibrations were used as illustrations.

All of the bond-stretching vibrations for the molecules discussed in Chapter 8 have either been used as examples in Chapter 7 or can be dealt with in exactly the same way. It will be necessary, however, to examine the vectors for other types of vibration.

Figures 8.7 and 8.8 show suitable vectors for typical in-plane and out-of-plane deformation modes, respectively, for $PtCl_4^{2-}$. As was shown in Chapter 8, these generate the representations:

$$\Gamma_{\text{i.p.def}} = (A_{1g}) + B_{2g} + E_u$$
$$\Gamma_{\text{o.o.p.def}} = (E_g) + A_{2u} + B_{2u}$$

where the representations in brackets are redundant.

For the in-plane deformations, using $\alpha_1$ as a generating vector gives the following SALCs for $A_{1g}$ and $B_{2g}$:

$$A_{1g}: \quad \alpha_1 + \alpha_2 + \alpha_3 + \alpha_4$$
$$B_{2g}: \quad \alpha_1 - \alpha_2 + \alpha_3 - \alpha_4$$

The former is clearly impossible, thus confirming that this corresponds to a redundancy.

For the $E_u$ representations, however, it is necessary to use $(\alpha_1 + \alpha_4)$ and $(\alpha_1 + \alpha_2)$ as generating vectors. The reason for not using simply $\alpha_1$ and $\alpha_2$ is that we used $\mathbf{r_1}$ and $\mathbf{r_2}$ for the bond stretches, and it is a requirement that all generating vectors or functions for degenerate SALCs must have the same symmetry properties. Now $\alpha_1$ does not have the same symmetry properties as $\mathbf{r_1}$, but $(\alpha_1 + \alpha_4)$ does. We, therefore, have the following projection operator calculation:

| $E$ | $C_2$ | $i$ | $\sigma_h$ |
|---|---|---|---|
| $(\alpha_1 + \alpha_4)$ | $(\alpha_3 + \alpha_2)$ | $(\alpha_3 + \alpha_2)$ | $(\alpha_1 + \alpha_4)$ |
| $(\alpha_1 + \alpha_2)$ | $(\alpha_3 + \alpha_4)$ | $(\alpha_3 + \alpha_4)$ | $(\alpha_1 + \alpha_2)$ |

(All other symmetry operations of $\mathbf{D}_{4h}$ have zero characters in the $E_u$ representation.) Multiplying by the characters for $E_u$ and summing gives the following SALCs:

$$\alpha_1 - \alpha_2 - \alpha_3 + \alpha_4$$
$$\alpha_1 + \alpha_2 - \alpha_3 - \alpha_4$$

for the $E_u$ in-plane deformation. Figure 9.1 shows the forms of all the in-plane deformations.

For the out-of-plane modes, $\beta_1$ can be used for the $A_{2u}$, $B_{2u}$ and one of the $E_g$ combinations, and $\beta_2$ for the second $E_g$ combination, giving:

$$\begin{aligned} A_{2u}&: \quad \beta_1 + \beta_2 + \beta_3 + \beta_4 \\ B_{2u}&: \quad \beta_1 - \beta_2 + \beta_3 - \beta_4 \\ E_g&: \quad \beta_1 - \beta_3 \\ &\quad\;\; \beta_2 - \beta_4 \end{aligned}$$

These are illustrated in Figure 9.2, which also shows that the $E_g$ mode in fact corresponds to rotations about the $x$ and $y$ axes, and not to vibrations.

Projection operators can be used in a similar manner to construct the exact forms of any other molecular vibrations.

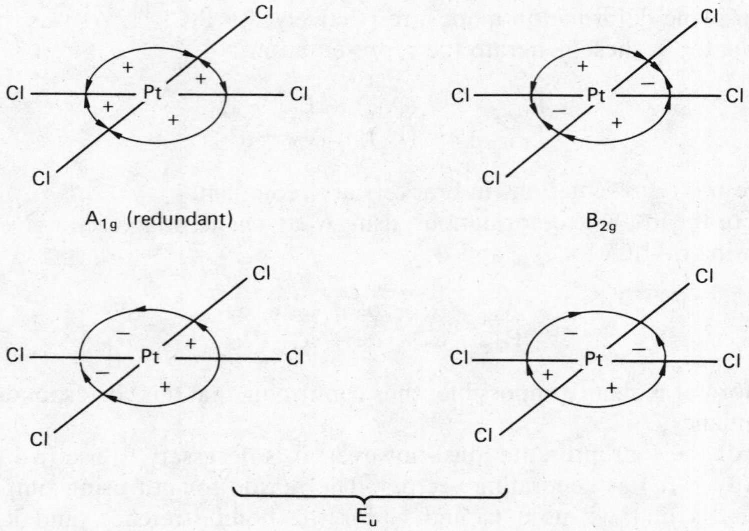


**Figure 9.1** *SALCs for in-plane deformation modes of* $PtCl_4^{2-}$

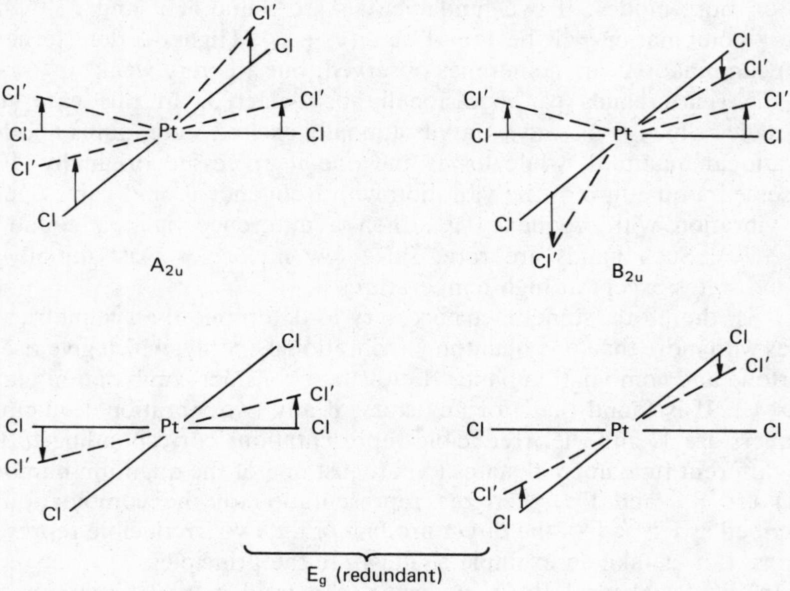


**Figure 9.2** *SALCs for out-of-plane deformation modes of* $PtCl_4^{2-}$

## *9.2* Overtone and combination bands

We have been concerned so far only with transitions between the vibrational ground state and an excited state where the molecule has acquired one quantum of energy in one vibrational mode. As we saw earlier, such a transition is known as a fundamental transition, and the resulting (infrared or Raman) band is a fundamental band. If all of the vibrations are simple harmonic, then all other transitions are forbidden. However, vibrations are generally **anharmonic**; further types of vibrational transition then become allowed and corresponding bands are often observed (although they are weaker than the fundamental bands). The two commonest types of band seen are overtone bands and combination bands.

**Overtone bands** arise from vibrational transitions in which the molecule gains two or more quanta in the *same* vibrational mode. If a fundamental band is found at $\nu_i$, then the first overtone band is found at $\approx 2\nu_i$, the second overtone band at $\approx 3\nu_i$, and so on. The difference between the overtone frequency and an integral multiple of the fundamental is a measure of the anharmonicity of the vibration. The overtones are always at lower frequency than $2\nu_1$, $3\nu_1$, etc.

**Combination bands** arise from transitions to an excited state where the molecule has acquired two or more vibrational quanta, distributed among two or more modes. If two fundamentals are found at $\nu_i$ and $\nu_j$, then a binary combination will be found at $\approx(\nu_i + \nu_j)$. Higher-order (ternary, etc.) combinations are sometimes observed, but are very weak.

**Difference bands** can occasionally be detected. In this case, the molecule, which is already in a vibrationally excited state, gains another vibrational quantum, while losing the one it possessed originally. If it possessed a quantum of the vibration with frequency $\nu_n$ and gains one of the vibration with frequency $\nu_m$, then a difference band is found at $(\nu_m - \nu_n)$. Such bands are rare, since few molecules exist initially in excited states except at high temperatures.

It is, therefore, sometimes necessary to determine the symmetries of states with more than one quantum of vibrational energy, which give rise to overtone and combination bands. Let us first consider combination bands $(\nu_i \neq \nu_j)$. It is found that, for any state, if any two vibrational quantum numbers are 1, and the irreducible representations corresponding to the two different fundamental states (where just one of the quantum numbers is 1) are $\Gamma^{(i)}$ and $\Gamma^{(j)}$, then the representation of the combination is described as $\Gamma^{(i)} \times \Gamma^{(j)}$, the direct product of the two irreducible representations. Let us take an example to illustrate the principles.

In the tetrahedral $RuO_4$ molecule, the fundamental vibrations are $A_1 + E + 2T_2$ (see Chapter 7). Consider a state with one quantum in the E mode ($\nu_2$) and one in one of the $T_2$ modes ($\nu_3$ or $\nu_4$). The E mode, a deformation, occurs at 338 cm$^{-1}$, while $\nu_3$, the $T_2$ Ru—O stretch, is at 915 cm$^{-1}$. The $(\nu_2 + \nu_3)$ combination is expected at about $(338 + 915) = 1253$ cm$^{-1}$. The direct product $E \times T_2$ is required (see p. 95):

$$E \times T_2 = T_1 + T_2$$

That is, the combination belongs to the symmetry classes $T_1$ and $T_2$.

The symmetries of overtone bands are calculated in exactly the same way when one-dimensional irreducible representations (non-degenerate) are concerned. With degenerate (two- or higher-dimensional) representations, however, the procedure is different, since the direct product representation gives an incorrect answer. (Readers wishing to study this problem further should refer to Chapter 22 of *Introduction to the Theory of Molecular Vibrations and Vibrational Spectroscopy* by L. A. Woodward (see Bibliography).) The result for overtones of doubly-degenerate vibrations (E symmetry) is that the character $\chi_n(R)$ for any operation $R$, when the quantum number is $n$ ($n = 1$ for fundamental, $n = 2$ for the first overtone, and so on), is given by:

$$\chi_n(R) = \frac{1}{2}\left[\chi(R)\,\chi_{n-1}(R) + \chi(R^n)\right]$$

where $\chi(R^n)$ is the character for the operation $R$ carried out $n$ times. The resulting representation can then be reduced in the usual way.

For any $\mathbf{C}_{3v}$ molecule, for example, the first overtone of an E mode will have symmetries $A_1 + E$ and the second overtone $A_1 + A_2 + E$. Note that the totally symmetric representation is present for all first overtones.

The presence in the infrared and Raman spectra of (in some cases) substantial numbers of overtone and combination bands can introduce complications in the vibrational analysis, since the overtone of an intense band may be more pronounced than a weak fundamental. Occasionally, however, they can be useful, as totally inactive fundamentals may be active as overtones or combination bands in the infrared or Raman spectra, and this can give approximate frequencies for such vibrations.

## 9.3 Accidental degeneracy and Fermi resonance

As we have seen, group theory alone cannot give any information on the values of frequencies and, especially in complicated molecules, it can happen that two vibrations might have the same frequency (within experimental error). In such a case, they are said to be **accidentally degenerate**, and there will be fewer observed bands than might have been expected.

When the two accidentally degenerate vibrations are of different symmetries, no interaction can occur between them, and the two are merely superimposed in the spectrum. If they are of the same symmetry (bases for the same irreducible representation of the point group), interaction occurs between them, which is known as **Fermi resonance**. The result of Fermi resonance occurring between two vibrations of almost the same frequency is to decrease the frequency of the lower-frequency one and increase the frequency of the higher, and if one of the bands would have been much weaker than the other, to equalise their intensities – the weaker 'borrows' intensity from the stronger. Fermi resonance can occur between two fundamentals or, quite commonly, between one fundamental and one combination or overtone.

A good example of Fermi resonance occurs in the Raman spectrum of $CCl_4$ (Figure 9.3). For this $\mathbf{T}_d$ molecule, four Raman fundamentals are predicted (C—Cl stretches $A_1 + T_2$; deformations $E + T_2$), but *five* bands are found. The 459 $cm^{-1}$ band is clearly the $A_1$ stretch ($\nu_1$) as it is strongly polarised. The two lowest frequency features (315 $cm^{-1}$ and 217 $cm^{-1}$) must be the E ($\nu_2$) and $T_2$ ($\nu_4$) deformations, leaving the $T_2$ stretch ($\nu_3$) to be assigned to *two* bands (762 $cm^{-1}$ and 791 $cm^{-1}$). This can be explained as follows: the $T_2$ stretch would have a frequency of 770–780 $cm^{-1}$, while the combination ($\nu_1 + \nu_4$) would have a frequency of $(459 + 315) = 774$ $cm^{-1}$. The symmetry of this combination is given by the direct product $A_1(\nu_1) \times T_2(\nu_4)$ – that is, $T_2$. This is the same as for $\nu_3$ and, therefore, Fermi resonance takes place, decreasing one frequency and increasing the

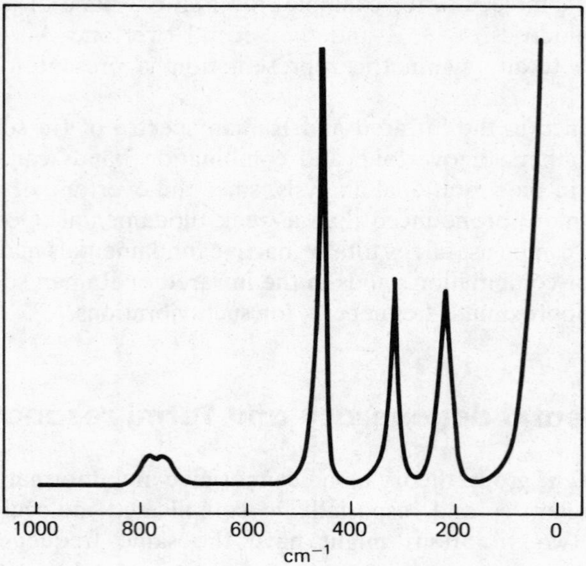


**Figure 9.3** *Raman spectrum of* $CCl_4$

other, while at the same time decreasing the expected intensity of the fundamental and increasing that of the combination. The result of Fermi resonance in such a case is to introduce an uncertainty as to the exact frequency of the fundamental vibration.

## 9.4 Decreasing symmetry and correlation tables

It may frequently happen that we are interested in a series of related molecules whose symmetries are gradually decreased. Consider, for example, methane, $CH_4$, and its mono- and di-deuteriated derivatives, $CH_3D$ and $CH_2D_2$. The symmetries of these three molecules are $\mathbf{T}_d$, $\mathbf{C}_{3v}$ and $\mathbf{C}_{2v}$, respectively. How would such isotopic substitutions affect the vibrational spectra of these molecules? Clearly, it would be possible to carry out a full analysis of each one independently, but this would be rather time consuming, and there is an easier way.

Both $\mathbf{C}_{3v}$ and $\mathbf{C}_{2v}$ are subgroups of $\mathbf{T}_d$; that is, all of their symmetry operations are present (together with others) in $\mathbf{T}_d$. We find that it is only necessary to carry out the detailed analysis for the highest symmetry case, and then the others can be derived from this using simple rules.

In the case of the vibrations of $CH_4$, we know that:

$$\Gamma_{vib} = A_1 + E + T_2$$

The characters for these irreducible representations are:

| $\mathbf{T}_d$ | $E$ | $8C_3$ | $3C_2$ | $6S_4$ | $6\sigma_d$ |
|---|---|---|---|---|---|
| $A_1$ | +1 | +1 | +1 | +1 | +1 |
| E | +2 | −1 | +2 | 0 | 0 |
| $T_2$ | +3 | 0 | −1 | −1 | +1 |

If we now decrease the symmetry from $\mathbf{T}_d$ to $\mathbf{C}_{3v}$, the $C_2$ and $S_4$ axes are lost, together with three of the four $C_3$ axes and three of the six planes. The characters for the remaining operations, however, will not be changed, and so for the $\mathbf{C}_{3v}$ case we have:

| $\mathbf{C}_{3v}$ | $E$ | $2C_3$ | $3\sigma_v$ |
|---|---|---|---|
| "$A_1$" | +1 | +1 | +1 |
| "E" | +2 | −1 | 0 |
| "$T_2$" | +3 | 0 | +1 |

Looking at the $\mathbf{C}_{3v}$ character table, we see that the ($\mathbf{T}_d$) $A_1$ and E representations are still irreducible, and indeed are ($\mathbf{C}_{3v}$) $A_1$ and E, respectively. The ($\mathbf{T}_d$) $T_2$ representation is now reducible, however, and use of the reduction formula shows that it corresponds to ($\mathbf{C}_{3v}$) $A_1$ + E. Hence, we obtain the following correlation between irreducible representations in $\mathbf{T}_d$ and $\mathbf{C}_{3v}$ symmetry:

$$\mathbf{T}_d \rightarrow \mathbf{C}_{3v}$$

$$A_1 \rightarrow A_1$$
$$E \rightarrow E$$
$$T_2 \rightarrow A_1 + E$$

Thus, the $A_1$ and E vibrational modes of $CH_4$ retain these symmetry labels on reducing the symmetry to $\mathbf{C}_{3v}$, but each of the $T_2$ modes splits into two, of $A_1$ and E symmetry. It is then simple to deduce the spectroscopic activities of the vibrations in the new (lower) symmetry.

For the change in symmetry $\mathbf{T}_d \rightarrow \mathbf{C}_{2v}$, the process is exactly the same. We have now lost all of the $\mathbf{T}_d$ symmetry operations except $E$, $C_2$ and two symmetry planes. The representations are now, therefore:

| $\mathbf{C}_{2v}$ | $E$ | $C_2$ | $\sigma(xz)$ | $\sigma(yz)$ | |
|---|---|---|---|---|---|
| "$A_1$" | +1 | +1 | +1 | +1 | i.e. $A_1$ |
| "E" | +2 | +2 | 0 | 0 | i.e. $A_1 + A_2$ |
| "$T_2$" | +3 | −1 | +1 | +1 | i.e. $A_1 + B_1 + B_2$ |

Now we see the ($\mathbf{T}_d$) $A_1$ mode remains as such, but the E mode is split into $A_1$ and $A_2$ components, and the $T_2$ modes into three components each ($A_1$, $B_1$ and $B_2$).

Such relationships between irreducible representations for any point group and those of its subgroups are quite general, and can be summarised by a set of **correlation tables**. Some of the most important of these are given in Appendix A.

The principles apply to all areas where group theory is used – we have introduced the topic in the context of molecular vibrations, but it also applies to molecular orbitals, electronic states, and so on. Thus, the effects on such properties of isotopic or other substitution, or of molecular distortions, can be deduced with very little effort.

## 9.5 Vibrational spectra of linear molecules

Since linear molecules (point groups $\mathbf{C}_{\infty v}$ or $\mathbf{D}_{\infty h}$) possess an infinite number of symmetry operations, it is not possible to use the standard reduction formula to determine the number and symmetry properties of the vibrational modes (since $g = \infty$). It is, therefore, necessary to carry out the reduction process by inspection.

As an example, consider the O═N═O$^+$ ion. This belongs to the point group $\mathbf{D}_{\infty h}$, as it has a centre of symmetry. It is only necessary to consider the operations $E$, $2C_\infty(\phi)$, $2S_\infty(\phi)$ (clockwise and anti-clockwise rotations by any arbitrary small angle $\phi$), $\infty\sigma_v$ and $\infty C_2$. The normal method for obtaining $\Gamma_{3N}$ gives:

| $\mathbf{D}_{\infty h}$ | $E$ | $2C_\infty(\phi)$ | . . . | $\infty\sigma_v$ | $i$ | $2S_\infty(\phi)$ | . . . | $\infty C_2$ |
|---|---|---|---|---|---|---|---|---|
| Unshifted atoms | 3 | 3 | . . . | 3 | 1 | 1 | | 1 |
| $\Gamma_{3N}$ | 9 | $3(1 + 2\cos\phi)$ | . . . | 3 | $-3$ | $(-1 + 2\cos\phi)$ | . . . | $-1$ |

The only terms that require an explanation are those for $2C_\infty(\phi)$ and $2S_\infty(\phi)$. Figure 9.4 shows the Cartesian vectors for $NO_2{}^+$. Rotation about the $z$ axis by $\phi°$ leaves the **z** vectors of unshifted atoms unaltered, and converts **x** and **y** vectors into **x′** and **y′** exactly as shown in Figure 4.4 (p. 42). The component of **x′** along the $x$ direction, and of **y′** along the $y$ direction, is $\cos\phi$, giving characters of $2\cos\phi$ per unshifted atom. Thus, we have a total of $1 + 2\cos\phi$ per unshifted atom for rotations about the $z$ axis. The case of rotation–reflections about the $z$ axis is exactly analogous,

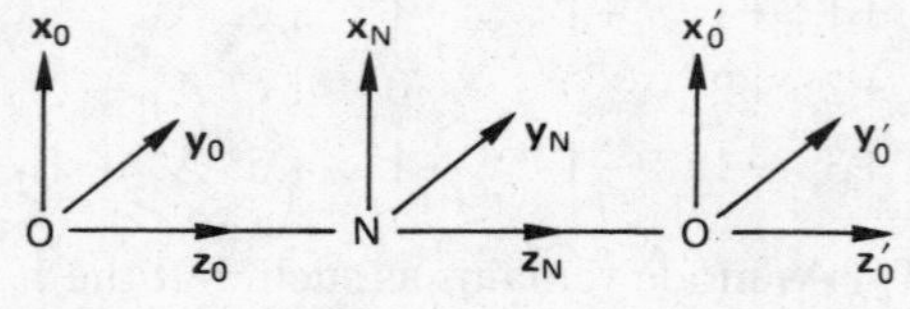


**Figure 9.4** *Cartesian vectors for* O═N═O$^+$($\mathbf{D}_{\infty h}$)

except that reflection (in the $xy$ plane) leads to $\mathbf{z}' = -\mathbf{z}$; this contributes $-1$ to the character, giving $-1 + 2\cos\phi$ per unshifted atom.

It is now convenient to remove $\Gamma_{T+R}$ from $\Gamma_{3N}$ to give $\Gamma_{vib}$. The character table for $\mathbf{D}_{\infty h}$ shows that:

$$\Gamma_{T+R} = \Sigma_u^+ + \Pi_g + \Pi_u$$

(Note that the only allowed rotations for a linear molecule are $R_x$ and $R_y$.) Thus, we have:

| $\mathbf{D}_{\infty h}$ | $E$ | $2C_\infty(\phi)$ | ... | $\infty\sigma_v$ | $i$ | $2S_\infty(\phi)$ | ... | $\infty C_2$ |
|---|---|---|---|---|---|---|---|---|
| $\Gamma_{3N}$ | 9 | $3 + 6\cos\phi$ | ... | 3 | $-3$ | $-1 + 2\cos\phi$ | ... | $-1$ |
| $\Gamma_{T+R}$ | 5 | $1 + 4\cos\phi$ | ... | 1 | $-1$ | $-1$ | ... | $-1$ |
| $\Gamma_{vib}$ | 4 | $2 + 2\cos\phi$ | ... | 2 | $-2$ | $2\cos\phi$ | ... | 0 |

From the character table, it is clear that:

$$\Gamma_{vib} = \Sigma_g^+ + \Sigma_u^+ + \Pi_u$$

That is, there are two non-degenerate vibrations, one of which is totally symmetric, and two doubly-degenerate vibrations.

Internal coordinates can be used to analyse these in terms of bond-stretching and angle-bending modes. Figure 9.5 shows the bond-stretching vectors. These generate the reducible representation:

| $\mathbf{D}_{\infty h}$ | $E$ | $2C_\infty(\phi)$ | ... | $\infty\sigma_v$ | $i$ | $2S_\infty(\phi)$ | ... | $\infty C_2$ |
|---|---|---|---|---|---|---|---|---|
| $\Gamma_{stretch}$ | 2 | 2 | ... | 2 | 0 | 0 | ... | 0 |

which reduces by inspection to $\Sigma_g^+ + \Sigma_u^+$. This leaves the bending vibrations, by difference, as the doubly-degenerate mode $\Pi_u$.

The character table also tells us that the $\Sigma_g^+$ mode will be Raman active (and polarised), while the $\Sigma_u^+$ and $\Pi_u$ modes will be infrared active. The mutual exclusion rule is, of course, obeyed for this centrosymmetric molecule. The assignment of the observed vibrational data is straightforward, with a Raman band at 1396 $cm^{-1}$ as the symmetric ($\Sigma_g^+$) stretch, and infrared bands at 2360 $cm^{-1}$ and 570 $cm^{-1}$ as the antisymmetric ($\Sigma_u^+$) stretch and ($\Pi_u$) bend, respectively.

## 9.6 Vibrational spectra of gases

In liquids, the free rotation of molecules is quenched, and so it is possible to study vibrational transitions free from the effects of rotations. In a

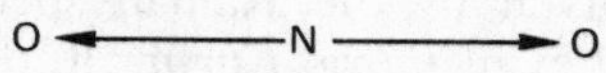


**Figure 9.5** *Bond-stretching vectors for* $O{=}N{=}O^+$

gaseous sample, however, molecules are free to rotate, as well as vibrate, and there can, therefore, be simultaneous changes in rotational and vibrational quantum numbers. This leads to the appearance of extensive **rotational fine structure** to vibrational bands.

This is not the place to discuss this in detail (see, for example, Chapter 6 of *Modern Spectroscopy* by J. M. Hollas, published by John Wiley & Sons), but it is worth noting that for simple symmetric molecules the analysis of rotational fine structure can give a great deal of detailed information about molecular geometry and dimensions. Even in more complex and/or less symmetric molecules, the resultant shapes of vibrational bands can help in vibrational assignments.

## 9.7 Vibrational spectra of solids

All of the discussions about molecular vibrations have so far been concerned with *isolated* molecules. This is a fair approximation when considering gases, and it seems to be sufficiently near to the truth for solutions and pure liquids to give good agreement between predicted and observed spectra. In solids, however, *intermolecular forces* are so great that, in many cases, a treatment designed for isolated molecules does not give even an approximation to the truth. Furthermore, the molecule may be situated in a position where its environment has a lower symmetry than that of the molecule itself. The point group of the site within the crystal lattice may, therefore, involve fewer symmetry operations than the point group of the free molecule, and it is this *site symmetry* that governs the vibrational spectrum.

Let us consider such a case. The site symmetry is usually lower (that is, there are fewer symmetry operations) than the symmetry of the free molecule, although occasionally it is the same, and in such a case there should be no difference between the solid-phase spectrum and that of the liquid phase (except for shifts in the band positions). Where the site symmetry is lower than that of the free molecule, two changes can occur:

**1** Bands that are infrared or Raman forbidden for the free molecule may become allowed.

**2** Bands arising from degenerate vibrations (that is, those belonging to E or T irreducible representations) may split in the solid, as shown by the appropriate correlation table (see Section 9.4).

A very good illustration of the effects of a lowering of effective symmetry in the solid phase is given by the Raman spectrum of solid osmium tetroxide, $OsO_4$ (I. W. Levin, *Inorg. Chem.*, **8**, p. 1018 (1969)). This is a tetrahedral molecule with four predicted Raman bands ($A_1 + E + 2T_2$), and four are indeed found in the liquid-phase spectrum, at 964 $cm^{-1}$, 953 $cm^{-1}$, 338 $cm^{-1}$ and 334 $cm^{-1}$. In the crystal, however, the site symmetry is $\mathbf{C}_2$, and the correlation between modes in $\mathbf{T}_d$ and $\mathbf{C}_2$ symmetries is:

$$A_1 \rightarrow A$$
$$E \rightarrow 2A$$
$$T_2 \rightarrow A + 2B$$

Thus, the band due to the $A_1$ mode should remain a singlet, while that due to the E mode will be a doublet and those due to $T_2$ will each give a triplet. The following results were observed:

| | |
|---|---|
| 964 → 961 | (therefore $A_1$ in the free molecule) |
| 953 → 967.5 + 951.5 + 940 | ($T_2$) |
| 338 → 342 + 338 | (E) |
| 334 → 327 + 319 + 316 | ($T_2$) |

giving a total of nine bands, and incidentally confirming earlier assignments.

Further complication of solid-phase spectra can arise from **factor group splitting** (sometimes referred to as **correlation splitting**). This is due to strong intermolecular forces where there are two or more molecules in the unit cell. The resulting calculations are more complex than in the case of single molecules, the chief result being that even modes that are non-degenerate when one molecule is considered can give two or more components in the solid-phase spectrum. Thus, the compound $\eta^6$-benzene chromium tricarbonyl ($(C_6H_6)Cr(CO)_3$: Figure 9.6) crystallises with two molecules per unit cell and the $A_1$ CO stretching mode (for the free molecule of $\mathbf{C}_{3v}$ symmetry), which is found (H. J. Buttery *et al.*, *J. Chem. Soc., A*, p. 2077 (1969)) in the infrared spectrum of a solution in $CCl_4$ at 1978 $cm^{-1}$, gives two bands in the solid at 1966 $cm^{-1}$ (Raman) and 1945 $cm^{-1}$ (infrared; the crystal structure is centrosymmetric and so the mutual exclusion rule applies).

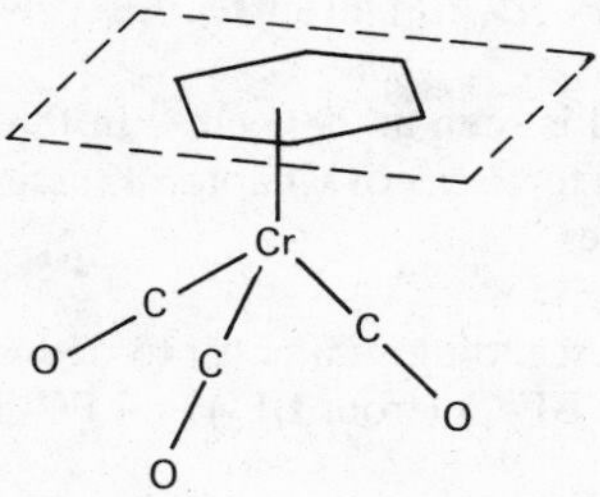


**Figure 9.6** *Molecular structure of $\eta^6$-benzene chromium tricarbonyl*

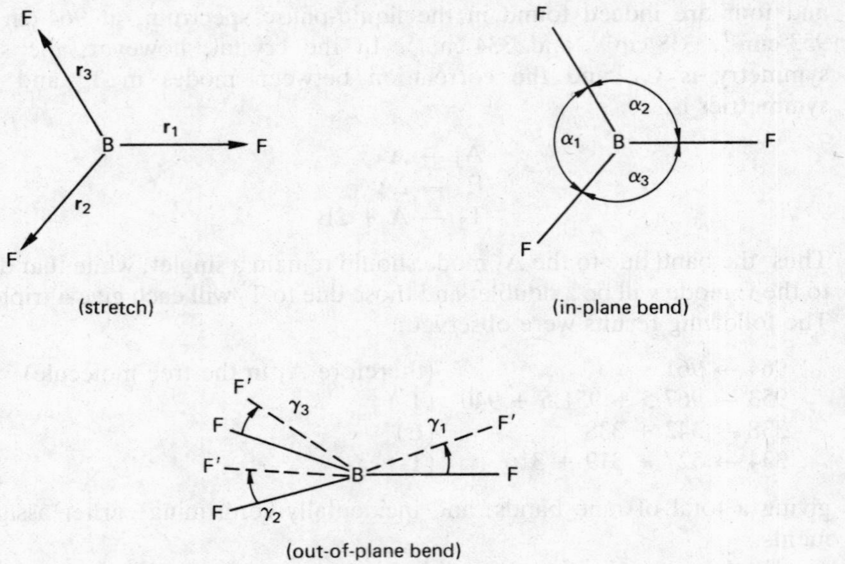


**Figure 9.7** *Bond-stretching and angle-bending vectors for* $BF_3$

For a detailed account of the vibrational spectra of crystalline solids, see J. C. Decius and R. M. Hexter, *Molecular Vibrations in Crystals*, McGraw-Hill (1978).

One further practical problem for Raman spectra of polycrystalline solids is that measurement of the polarisation state of the Raman-scattered light is not possible, since reflections of the light at the solid surfaces lead to all of the scattered light always being depolarised.

## EXERCISES

**1** Construct SALCs corresponding to bond stretches, and in- and out-of-plane bending modes for $BF_3$ ($\mathbf{D}_{3h}$: Figure 9.7).

**2** A weak infrared band is seen at 2903 $cm^{-1}$ in the infrared spectrum of $BF_3$. Using the results of Exercise 3 of Chapter 8, assign this feature and deduce its symmetry properties.

**3** Use the method of descending symmetry to deduce the symmetries of the vibrational modes for $BF_2Cl$ (from $BF_3$) and $PCl_4F$ (axial or equatorial F atoms; from $PCl_5$).

# 10

# Symmetry and bonding

It is possible to obtain valuable insights into chemical bonding from a simplified and qualitative study of molecular orbitals. Making use of symmetry enables such a study to be carried out for any molecular geometry.

## 10.1 σ-bonding in $AX_n$ molecules

Whenever there is a single central atom, surrounded by a set of $n$ ligands, the construction of a qualitative molecular orbital energy level diagram follows a similar pattern, if only σ-bonding is significant.

The irreducible representations to which the atomic orbitals of the central atom A give rise are listed in the character table for the relevant point group. In order to determine which of these will be able to interact with the ligand σ-orbitals, it is then necessary to use a suitable set of such orbitals as a basis set to generate a reducible representation of the point group. Reduction of this, using the standard reduction formula, then tells us the symmetries of the possible linear combinations of the ligand orbitals, as shown in Chapter 6.

Whenever there is a match in symmetry between a central atom atomic orbital and a possible linear combination of ligand orbitals, interaction can occur, with the formation of bonding and antibonding molecular orbitals. Orbitals (either on A or $X_n$) where such a match does not occur must necessarily remain non-bonding.

Using projection operators, it is also possible to construct the explicit forms of the symmetry-adapted linear combinations of the ligand orbitals, as described in Chapter 7.

To construct an accurate quantitative molecular orbital energy level diagram it is necessary to know the exact energies of all the participating atomic orbitals and the extent, for example, of the mixing of atomic orbitals on the central atom. Except for the simplest molecules, this is very difficult, and so we will concentrate on a qualitative picture in each case.

Let us begin with some simple $AX_n$ systems where the A atom has only s- and p-orbitals available for bonding.

### *10.1.1* $AX_2$ molecules

Here there are two possible geometries: bent ($\mathbf{C}_{2v}$ symmetry; for example, $H_2O$) or linear ($\mathbf{D}_{\infty h}$ symmetry; for example, monomeric $BeH_2$). Taking the bent molecule first, because of the greater simplicity of the $\mathbf{C}_{2v}$ point group, the character table tells us that the 2s and $2p_z$ (using the coordinate axes shown in Figure 10.1) atomic orbitals of oxygen are each bases for the $a_1$ irreducible representation, the $2p_x$ for the $b_1$ and the $2p_y$ for the $b_2$ irreducible representations. (Note that lower-case Mulliken symbols are used by convention for all (single-electron) orbitals.)

To determine the symmetries of the possible combinations of hydrogen 1s atomic orbitals, we then use $\phi_1$ and $\phi_2$ (see Figure 10.1) to generate a reducible representation of $\mathbf{C}_{2v}$:

| $\mathbf{C}_{2v}$ | $E$ | $C_2$ | $\sigma(xz)$ | $\sigma(yz)$ |
|---|---|---|---|---|
| $\Gamma(\sigma)$ | 2 | 0 | 0 | 2 |

By inspection, or use of the reduction formula, this reduces to:

$$\Gamma(\sigma) = a_1 + b_2$$

That is, it is possible to construct one linear combination of $a_1$ and one of $b_2$ symmetry. Using $\phi_1$ as a generating function, the projection operator

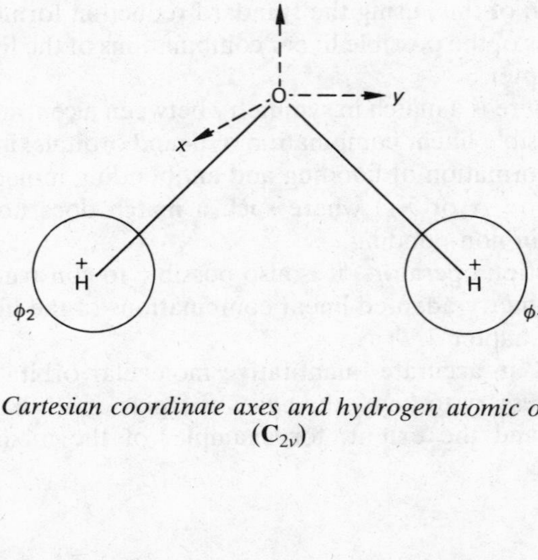


**Figure 10.1** *Cartesian coordinate axes and hydrogen atomic orbitals for* $H_2O$ ($\mathbf{C}_{2v}$)

method gives us the forms of these, as follows:

| $\mathbf{C}_{2v}$ | $E$ | $C_2$ | $\sigma(xz)$ | $\sigma(yz)$ |
|---|---|---|---|---|
| $\phi_1$ | $\phi_1$ | $\phi_2$ | $\phi_2$ | $\phi_1$ |
| $a_1$ | +1 | +1 | +1 | +1 |
| $b_2$ | +1 | −1 | −1 | +1 |

This shows that the $a_1$ combination, when normalised, is $\psi(a_1) = (1/\sqrt{2})(\phi_1 + \phi_2)$ and the $b_2$ combination is $\psi(b_2) = (1/\sqrt{2})(\phi_1 - \phi_2)$.

Let us assume (an approximation!) that the oxygen 2s and 2p orbitals are independent, and that the 2s orbitals are too tightly bound (low in energy) to take part in molecular orbital formation. We then see that $\psi(a_1)$ and $2p_z$ form bonding and antibonding molecular orbitals, as do $\psi$ $(b_2)$ and $2p_y$, leaving $2p_x$ non-bonding ($b_1$ symmetry), as shown in Figure 10.2.

We then have an approximate molecular orbital energy level diagram as shown in Figure 10.3. The available electrons fill all of the bonding and non-bonding molecular orbitals to give a stable electronic configuration.

For a linear $AX_2$ molecule, the process is exactly analogous, using the character table for the $\mathbf{D}_{\infty h}$ point group. This shows that the central atom atomic orbitals have the following symmetries: 2s, $\sigma_g{}^+$; $(2p_x, 2p_y)$, $\pi_u$; and $2p_z$, $\sigma_u{}^+$ (where the $z$ axis is the molecular axis; Figure 10.4).

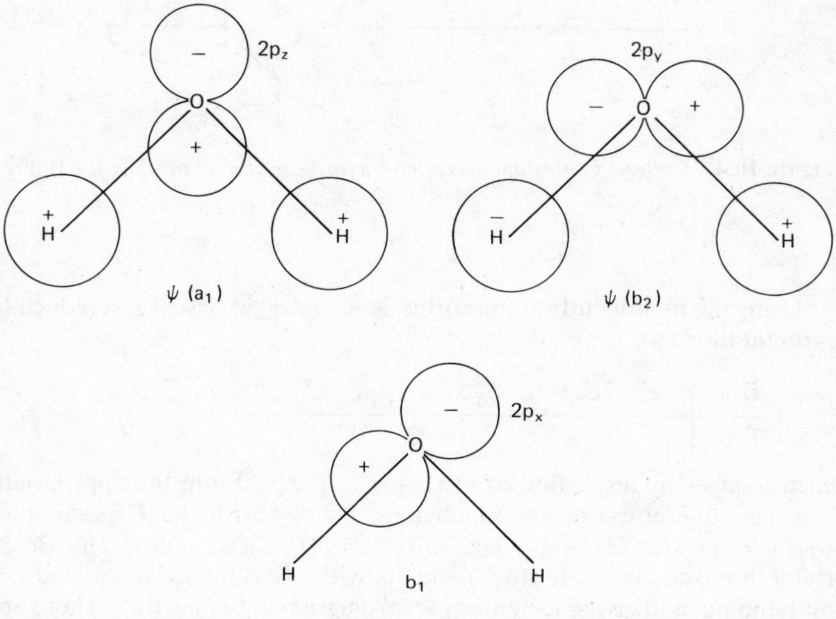


**Figure 10.2** *Interaction between atomic orbitals of oxygen and SALCs of hydrogen atomic orbitals in* $H_2O$

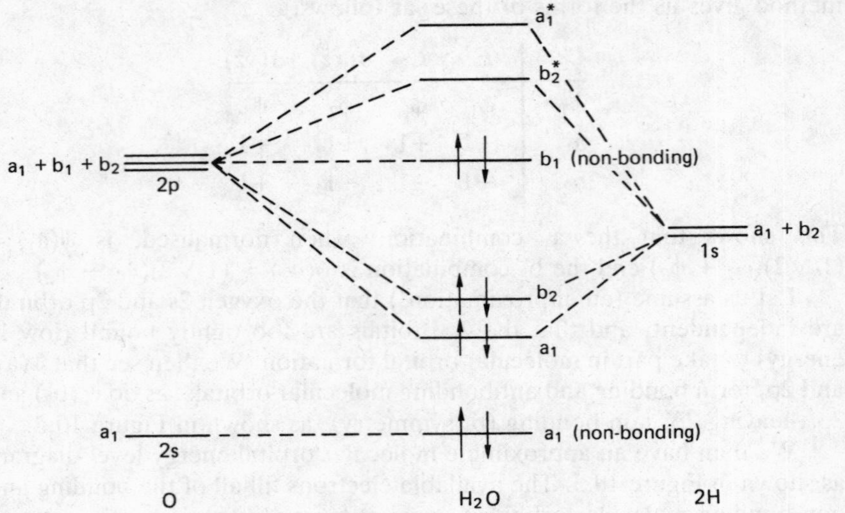


**Figure 10.3** *Qualitative molecular orbital energy level diagram for* $H_2O$

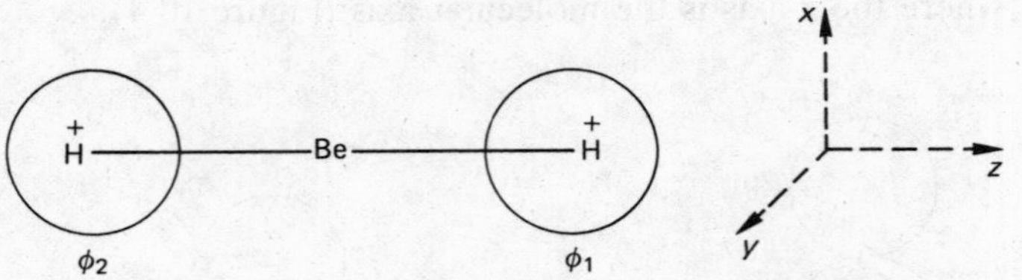


**Figure 10.4** *Cartesian coordinate axes and hydrogen atomic orbitals for* $BeH_2$

Using the hydrogen 1s atomic orbitals $\phi_1$ and $\phi_2$ as bases for a reducible representation, we have:

| $\mathbf{D}_{\infty h}$ | $E$ | $2C_\infty(\Phi)$ | ... | $\infty\sigma_v$ | $i$ | $2S_\infty(\Phi)$ | ... | $\infty C_2$ |
|---|---|---|---|---|---|---|---|---|
| $\Gamma(\sigma)$ | 2 | 2 | ... | 2 | 0 | 0 | ... | 0 |

which reduces by inspection to $\Gamma(\sigma) = \sigma_g^+ + \sigma_u^+$. From the appropriate projection operators, or by an obvious analogy with the $\mathbf{C}_{2v}$ example, $\psi(\sigma_g^+) = (1/\sqrt{2})(\phi_1 + \phi_2)$ and $\psi(\sigma_u^+) = (1/\sqrt{2})(\phi_1 - \phi_2)$. The Be 2s orbital thus interacts with $\psi(\sigma_g^+)$ and $2p_z$ with $\psi(\sigma_u^+)$, leaving $2p_x$ and $2p_y$ non-bonding, and giving the energy level diagram in Figure 10.5. There are four electrons to be accommodated, two from Be and two from 2H, thus filling the $\sigma_g^+$ and $\sigma_u^+$ bonding molecular orbitals (Figure 10.6).

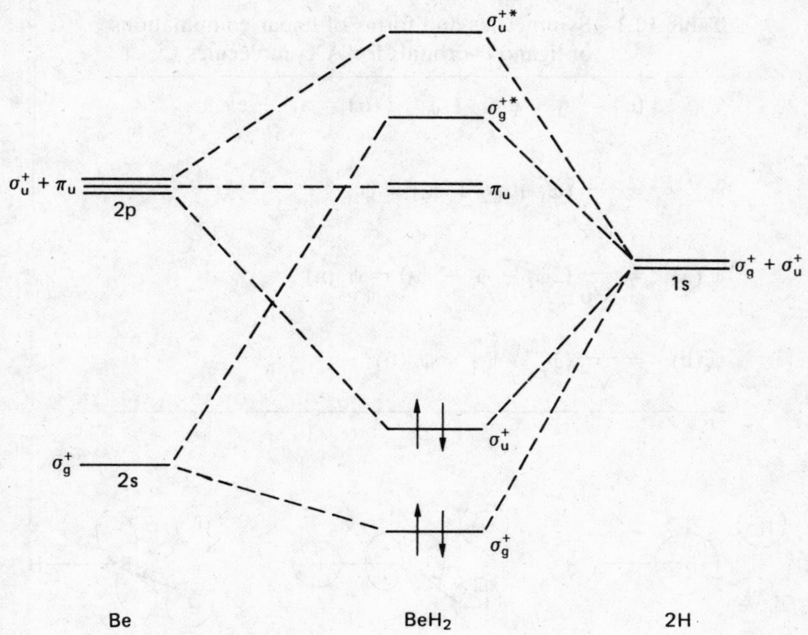


**Figure 10.5** *Qualitative molecular orbital energy level diagram for* $BeH_2$

## *10.1.2* $AX_3$ molecules

Here again, just using s- and p-orbitals on A, we have two possible geometries: pyramidal ($\mathbf{C}_{3v}$) and trigonal–planar ($\mathbf{D}_{3h}$). The principles are exactly as for $AX_2$ molecules. The symmetries of the s- and p-orbitals are read from the character tables; that is, s and $p_z$, $a_1$; ($p_x$, $p_y$), e ($\mathbf{C}_{3v}$); and s, $a_1'$; $p_z$, $a_2''$; ($p_x$, $p_y$), e′ ($\mathbf{D}_{3h}$). Note that in each case the $C_3$ axis is taken as the *z* axis.

Using the results from Chapters 6 and 7, the symmetries and forms of the SALCs of X σ-orbitals ($\phi_1$, $\phi_2$, $\phi_3$) are also calculated (Table 10.1). As

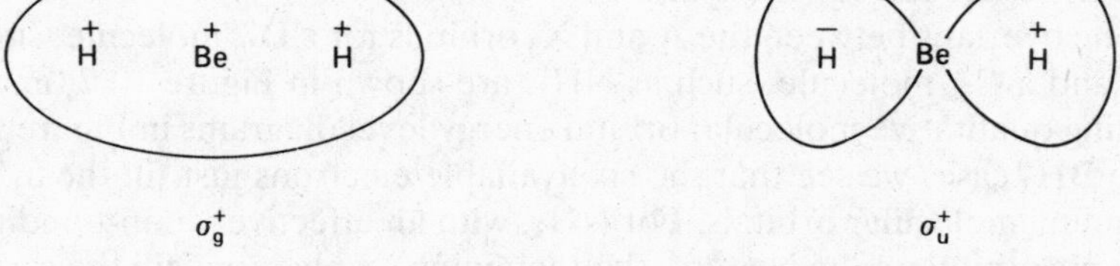


**Figure 10.6** $\sigma_g{}^+$ *and* $\sigma_u{}^+$ *bonding molecular orbitals for* $BeH_2$

**Table 10.1** Symmetries and forms of linear combinations of ligand σ-orbitals for $AX_3$ molecules

| | | |
|---|---|---|
| $\mathbf{C}_{3v}$: $\Gamma(\sigma) = a_1 + e$ | | $\mathbf{D}_{3h}$: $\Gamma(\sigma) = a_1' + e'$ |
| $\psi_{a_1}$ | $= \frac{1}{\sqrt{3}}(\phi_1 + \phi_2 + \phi_3) = \psi_{a_1'}$ | |
| $\psi_e(a)$ | $= \frac{1}{\sqrt{6}}(2\phi_1 - \phi_2 - \phi_3) = \psi_{e'}(a)$ | |
| $\psi_e(b)$ | $= \frac{1}{\sqrt{2}}(\phi_2 - \phi_3) = \psi_{e'}(b)$ | |

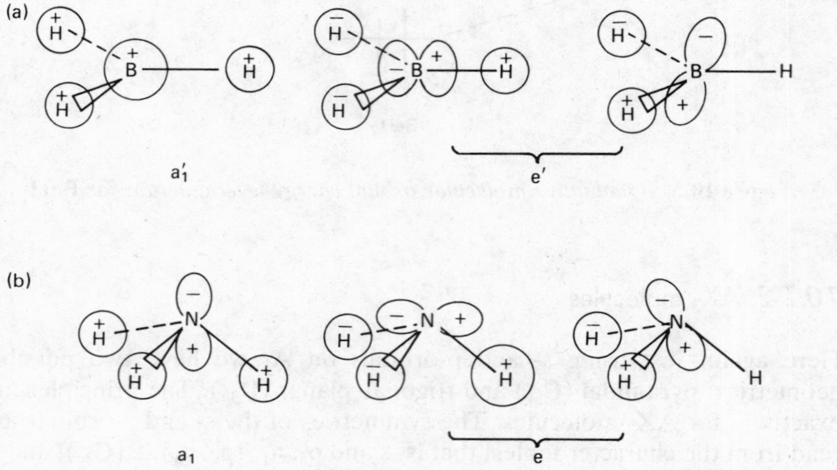


**Figure 10.7** *Molecular orbital formation in*: (a) $\mathbf{D}_{3h}$ *and* (b) $\mathbf{C}_{3v}$ $AX_3$ *molecules*

we now have to deal with doubly-degenerate combinations of orbitals, it is of course necessary to use $\phi_1$ and $(\phi_2 - \phi_3)$ as the generating functions for the SALCs needed for the e and e′ sets.

The overlaps between the A and $X_3$ orbitals for a $\mathbf{D}_{3h}$ molecule, such as $BH_3$, and a $\mathbf{C}_{3v}$ molecule, such as $NH_3$, are shown in Figure 10.7, and the resulting qualitative molecular orbital energy level diagrams in Figure 10.8. In the $BH_3$ case, we see that the six available electrons just fill the $a_1'$ and e′ bonding molecular orbitals. For $NH_3$, with an effectively non-bonding $a_1$ 2s atomic orbital on the N atom, the remaining six electrons fill the $a_1$ and e bonding molecular orbitals.

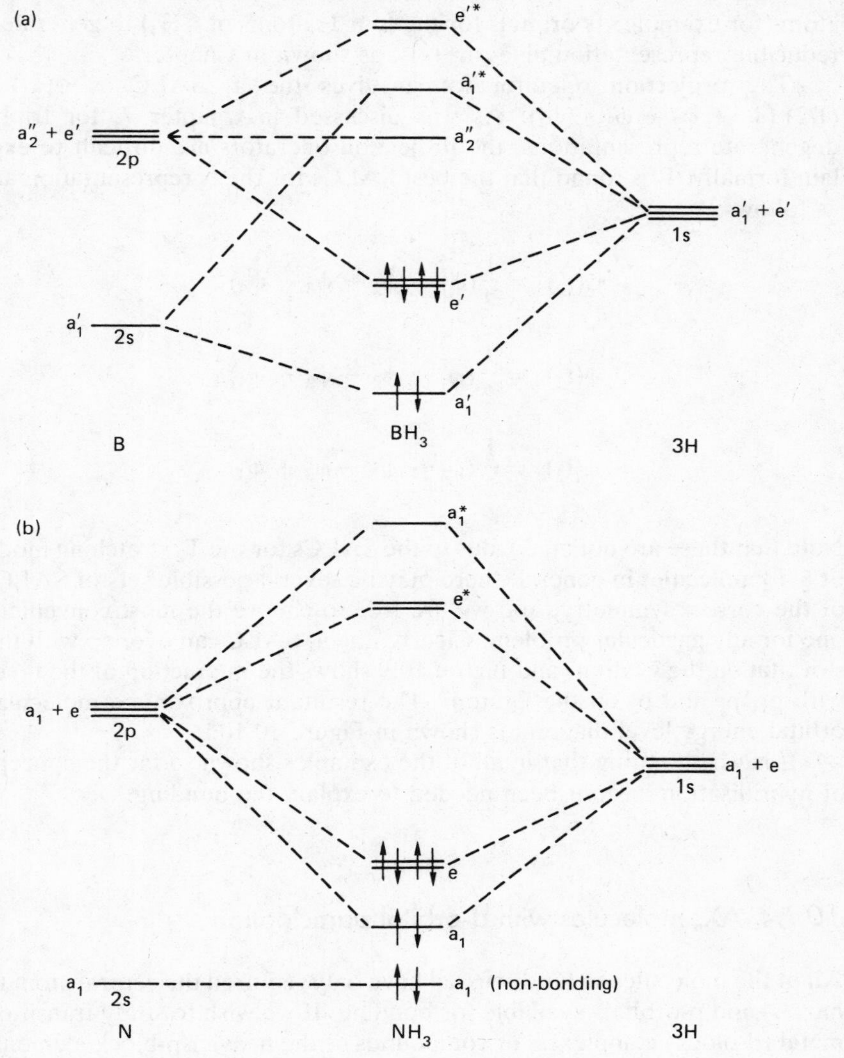


**Figure 10.8** *Qualitative molecular orbital energy level diagram for*: (a) $\mathbf{D}_{3h}$ *and* (b) $\mathbf{C}_{3v}$ $AX_3$ *molecules*

## *10.1.3* $AX_4$ molecules

The only remaining case where only s- and p-orbitals are involved is a regular tetrahedral ($\mathbf{T}_d$) $AX_4$ molecule, such as $CH_4$.

From the character table for $\mathbf{T}_d$, we see that an s-orbital on the central atom has $a_1$ symmetry, while the $p_x$, $p_y$ and $p_z$ orbitals together give rise to the triply-degenerate representation $t_2$. Using one σ-orbital on each X atom (for example, 1s orbitals for the four H atoms of $CH_4$) to generate a reducible representation gives $a_1 + t_2$, as shown in Chapter 6.

The projection operator for $a_1$ gives the $a_1$ SALC as $\psi(a_1) = (1/2)(\phi_1 + \phi_2 + \phi_3 + \phi_4)$. As was discussed in Chapter 7, for triply-degenerate representations, the projection operators are difficult to explain formally. It is found that the best SALCs for the $t_2$ representation are as follows:

$$\psi(t_2)_a = \frac{1}{2}(\phi_1 - \phi_2 + \phi_3 - \phi_4)$$

$$\psi(t_2)_b = \frac{1}{2}(\phi_1 + \phi_2 - \phi_3 - \phi_4)$$

$$\psi(t_2)_c = \frac{1}{2}(\phi_1 - \phi_2 - \phi_3 + \phi_4)$$

Note that these are not analogous to the SALCs for the $T_2$ stretching mode of a $\mathbf{T}_d$ molecule; in general, there may be several possible sets of SALCs of the correct symmetry, and we are free to choose the most convenient one for any particular problem. Clearly, the $a_1$ SALC can overlap with the s-orbital on the C atom, and Figure 10.9 shows the interaction of the $t_2$ set with $p_x$, $p_y$ and $p_z$ on the C atom. The resultant approximate molecular orbital energy level diagram is shown in Figure 10.10.

It is worth noting that in all of the examples shown so far the concept of hybridisation has not been needed to explain the bonding.

### *10.1.4* $AX_n$ molecules with d-orbital participation

All of the molecules so far discussed have only required the central atom to have s- and p-orbitals available for bonding. If we wish to study transition metal (d-block) complexes, or compounds of the heavier p-block elements with geometries other than those already described, then it is essential to include d-orbitals in the bonding scheme.

The commonest geometry for transition metal complexes is regular octahedral $ML_6$ ($\mathbf{O}_h$), which we will therefore look at in some detail, particularly for elements of the first transition series, for which 3d, 4s and 4p atomic orbitals are available for bonding. Consulting the $\mathbf{O}_h$ character table reveals that the symmetries of the orbitals are as follows: 4s, $a_{1g}$; ($3d_{x^2-y^2}$, $3d_{z^2}$), $e_g$; ($3d_{xy}$, $3d_{yz}$, $3d_{zx}$), $t_{2g}$; ($4p_x$, $4p_y$, $4p_z$), $t_{1u}$.

Using the set of $\sigma$-orbitals (Figure 10.11) to generate a reducible representation for $\mathbf{O}_h$, we have $\Gamma(\sigma) = a_{1g} + e_g + t_{1u}$. As for the $\mathbf{T}_d$ example, the projection operator method is rather complex in an octa-

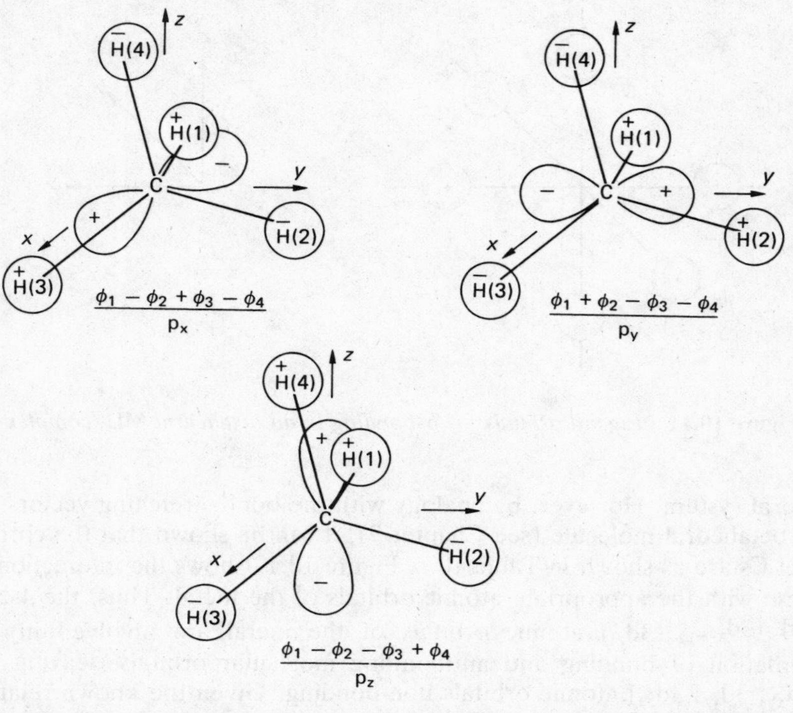


**Figure 10.9** *Overlap of carbon* p*-orbitals with SALCs of hydrogen orbitals of* $t_2$ *symmetry in* $CH_4$

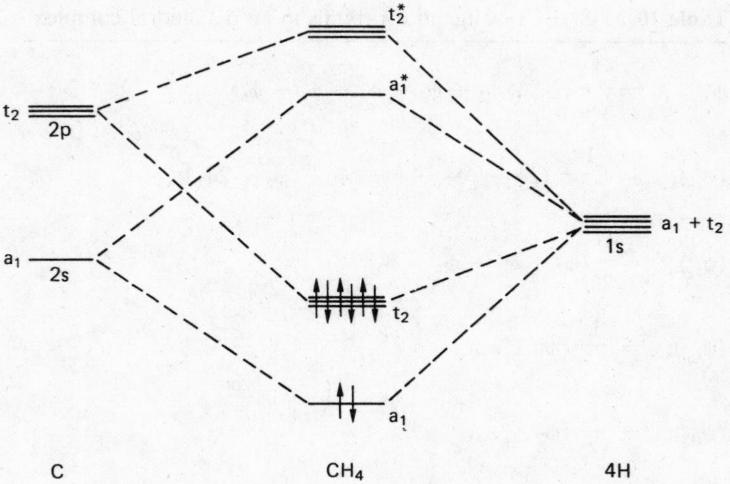


**Figure 10.10** *Qualitative molecular orbital energy level diagram for a* $\mathbf{T}_d$ $AX_4$ *molecule*

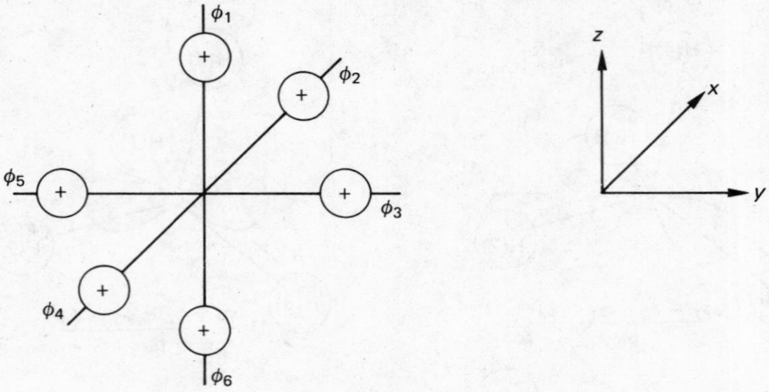


**Figure 10.11** *Ligand orbitals for σ-bonding in an octahedral* $ML_6$ *complex*

hedral system. However, by analogy with the bond-stretching vectors for an octahedral molecule (see Chapter 7), it can be shown that the correct SALCs are as shown in Table 10.2. Figure 10.12 shows the interaction of these with the appropriate atomic orbitals of the metal. Thus, the 4s, 4p and ($3d_{x^2-y^2}$, $3d_{z^2}$) atomic orbitals of the metal are involved in the formation of bonding and antibonding molecular orbitals, leaving the ($3d_{xy}$, $3d_{yz}$, $3d_{zx}$) atomic orbitals non-bonding. Given the known relative energies of the 3d, 4s and 4p atomic orbitals, and the knowledge that the

**Table 10.2** SALCs of ligand σ-orbitals in an octahedral complex

$$\psi_{a_{1g}} = \frac{1}{\sqrt{6}}(\phi_1 + \phi_2 + \phi_3 + \phi_4 + \phi_5 + \phi_6)$$

$$(\psi_{e_g})_a = \frac{1}{\sqrt{12}}(2\phi_1 - \phi_2 - \phi_3 - \phi_4 - \phi_5 + 2\phi_6)$$

$$(\psi_{e_g})_b = \frac{1}{2}(\phi_2 - \phi_3 + \phi_4 - \phi_5)$$

$$(\psi_{t_{1u}})_a = \frac{1}{\sqrt{2}}(\phi_1 - \phi_6)$$

$$(\psi_{t_{1u}})_b = \frac{1}{\sqrt{2}}(\phi_2 - \phi_4)$$

$$(\psi_{t_{1u}})_c = \frac{1}{\sqrt{2}}(\phi_3 - \phi_5)$$

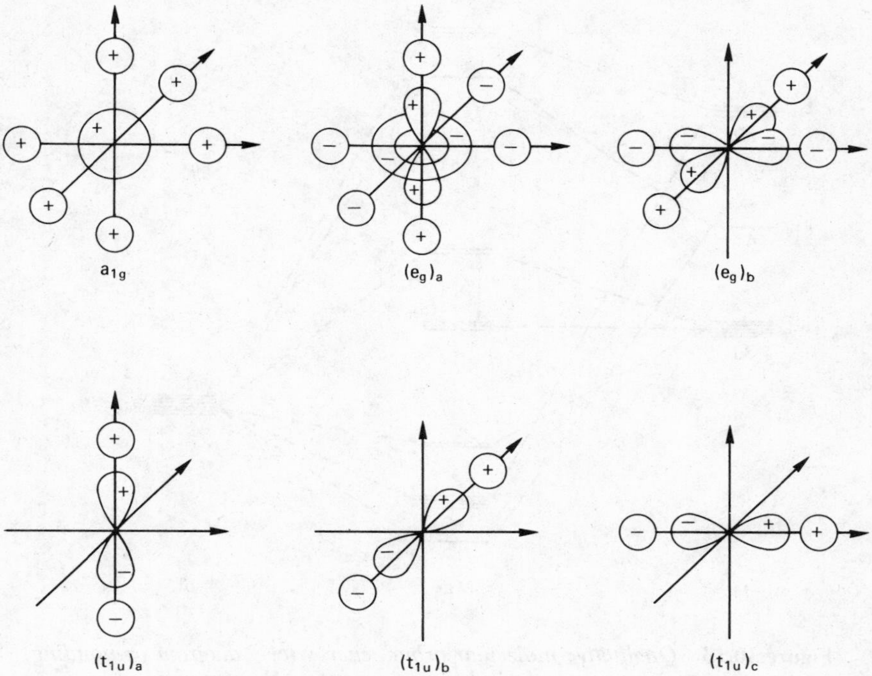


**Figure 10.12** *Construction of σ-bonding molecular orbitals for octahedral* $ML_6$

ligand orbitals are lower in energy than the metal orbitals, we can construct an approximate molecular orbital energy level diagram for a transition metal $ML_6$ complex with only σ-bonding (Figure 10.13). As the six ligands are all electron-pair donors, the number of electrons to be fed into the molecular orbitals is $(12 + n)$, where the metal ion has the electronic configuration $d^n$. All of the bonding $(a_{1g} + e_g + t_{1u})$ molecular orbitals are closer in energy to the ligand than to the metal atomic orbitals, so the ligand electrons go predominantly into these molecular orbitals, filling them, and the metal electrons are then placed successively in the non-bonding $t_{2g}$ and antibonding $e_g{}^*$ orbitals. Thus, the molecular orbital approach mirrors the simple ideas of crystal-field theory, with the metal electrons being distributed between a lower-energy $t_{2g}$ and a higher-energy $e_g$ set of orbitals, with an energy gap between them of $\Delta_{oct}$.

Before going on to transition metal complexes of other geometries, it is worth noting that there are also octahedral compounds of p-block elements for which the symmetry arguments are exactly the same. Because the ordering of the central atom atomic orbitals is different, however, the resultant molecular orbital energy level diagram is markedly different, as shown by Figure 10.14 for $SF_6$. The six valence electrons of sulphur, with

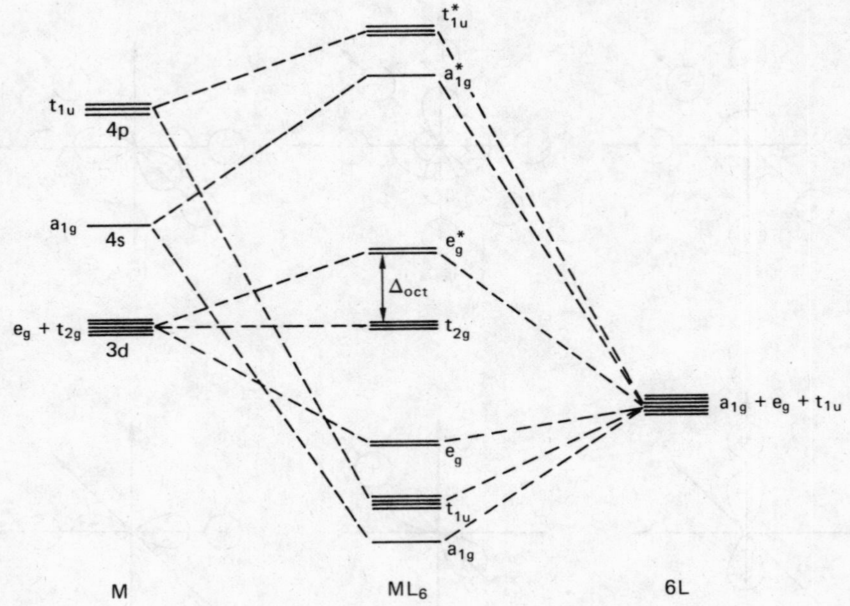


**Figure 10.13** *Qualitative molecular orbital energy level diagram (σ-bonding only) for an octahedral transition metal* $ML_6$ *complex*

six from the six fluorines, will of course fill the $a_{1g}$, $t_{1u}$ and $e_g$ bonding molecular orbitals. As there is a very large energy gap between the $e_g$ bonding and the $t_{2g}$ non-bonding orbitals, this rationalises the very great stability of $SF_6$.

Transition metal or heavier main group element compounds with other geometries can be handled in exactly the same way as for $ML_6$ systems. Four-coordinate transition metal complexes are quite common, with either tetrahedral ($\mathbf{T}_d$) or square–planar ($\mathbf{D}_{4h}$) geometry. Using the procedures outlined here for $\mathbf{O}_h$ complexes, qualitative molecular orbital energy level diagrams can be obtained, as shown in Figures 10.15 ($\mathbf{T}_d$) and 10.16($\mathbf{D}_{4h}$). In both cases, mixing between metal atomic orbitals of the same symmetry (for example, p- and d-orbitals of $t_2$ symmetry for $\mathbf{T}_d$) is neglected. For the tetrahedral case, the metal electrons will be largely distributed among the e (non-bonding) and $t_2{}^*$ (antibonding) orbitals, with an energy gap conventionally described as $\Delta_{tet}$ (corresponding to the crystal-field splitting for a tetrahedral complex).

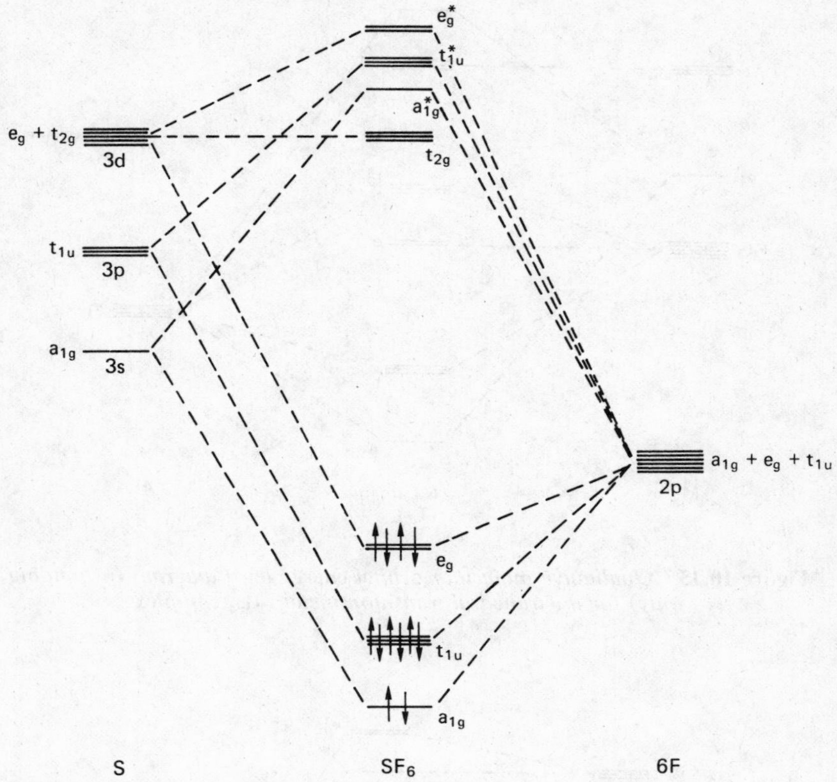


**Figure 10.14** *Qualitative molecular orbital energy level diagram for* $SF_6$

## *10.2* π-bonding in $AX_n$ molecules

There are, of course, many molecules where π-bonding is important, so we will look at some representative examples of p- and d-block molecules involving π-bonding.

### *10.2.1* Nitrite ion

The valence bond description of the bonding in this ion involves resonance forms with one N═O double bond (Figure 10.17). In the molecular orbital description of the bonding, the single (σ) bonds are constructed exactly as for $H_2O$. With one lone pair of electrons on the N atom, two lone pairs on

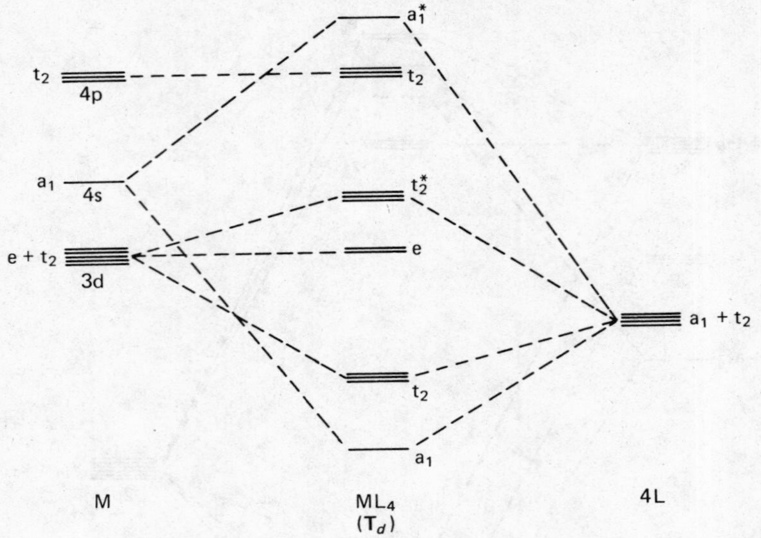


**Figure 10.15** *Qualitative molecular orbital energy level diagram (σ-bonding only) for a tetrahedral transition metal* $ML_4$ *complex*

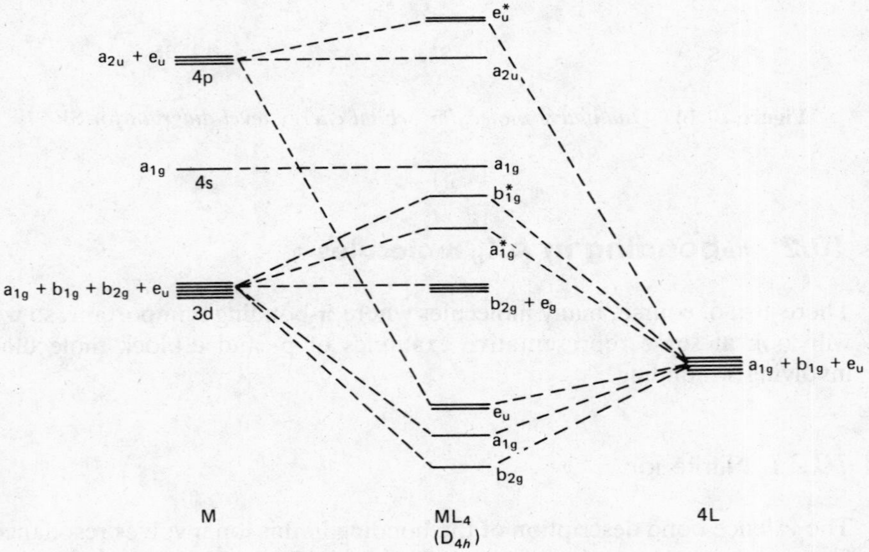


**Figure 10.16** *Qualitative molecular orbital energy level diagram (σ-bonding only) for a square–planar transition metal* $ML_4$ *complex*

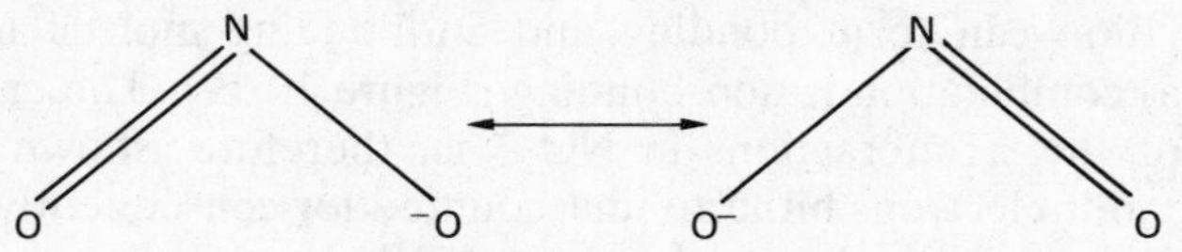


**Figure 10.17**

each O atom and two σ-bonds, 14 electrons have been accounted for. The ion has a total of 18 valence electrons, so the remaining four electrons must be accommodated in π molecular orbitals.

With the Cartesian axes as shown in Figure 10.1, the $p_x$ orbital on the central (N) atom ($b_1$ symmetry) was non-bonding when only σ-bonding was considered (see Figure 10.3). There are equivalent orbitals on each O atom, giving a total of three atomic orbitals available to form π molecular orbitals (Figure 10.18).

Using the oxygen orbitals $\pi_1$ and $\pi_2$ as bases, we generate the following representation of the $\mathbf{C}_{2v}$ point group:

| $\mathbf{C}_{2v}$ | $E$ | $C_2$ | $\sigma(xz)$ | $\sigma(yz)$ |
|---|---|---|---|---|
| $\Gamma(\pi)$ | 2 | 0 | 0 | −2 |

which reduces to $\Gamma(\pi) = a_2 + b_1$. If we use $\pi_1$ as a generating function, the projection operator method gives us:

| $\mathbf{C}_{2v}$ | $E$ | $C_2$ | $\sigma(xz)$ | $\sigma(yz)$ |
|---|---|---|---|---|
| $\pi_1$ | $\pi_1$ | $-\pi_2$ | $\pi_2$ | $-\pi_1$ |
| $a_2$ | +1 | +1 | −1 | −1 |
| $b_1$ | +1 | −1 | +1 | −1 |

Thus, the $a_2$ combination is $(1/\sqrt{2})\,(\pi_1 - \pi_2)$ and the $b_1$ combination is $(1/\sqrt{2})\,(\pi_1 + \pi_2)$. As the nitrogen $p_x$ orbital has $b_1$ symmetry, clearly the

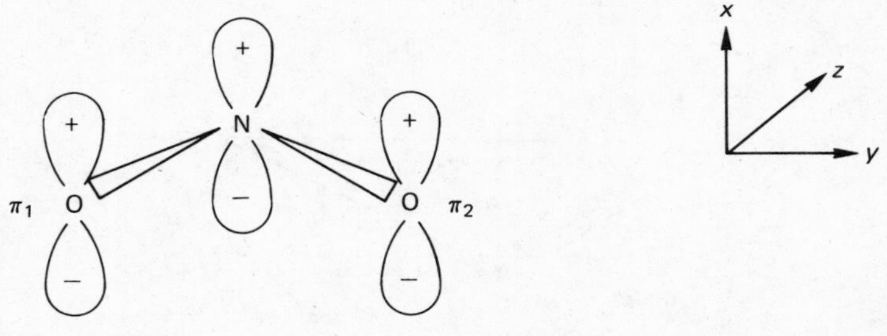


**Figure 10.18** *Atomic orbitals for π molecular orbital formation in* $NO_2^-$

$b_1$ combination can form bonding and antibonding molecular orbitals, while the $a_2$ combination is non-bonding (Figure 10.19). The energy level diagram for the $\pi$ interactions in $NO_2^-$ is, therefore, shown in Figure 10.20. The four electrons hitherto unaccounted for consequently fill the $b_1$ bonding and $a_2$ non-bonding molecular orbitals.

## *10.2.2* Carbonate ion

This is a planar trigonal ion, of $\mathbf{D}_{3h}$ symmetry, and so the σ-bonded framework will be as described earlier for $BH_3$, Given that there are two lone pairs of electrons on each O atom and six electrons filling the σ-bonding molecular orbitals, 18 valence electrons have been accounted for, out of a total of 24 for $CO_3^{2-}$. The remaining six electrons must go into the $\pi$ molecular orbitals, constructed from the carbon $p_z$ orbital ($a_2''$, non-bonding in the σ-bonding only case) and equivalent atomic orbitals on each oxygen (Figure 10.21).

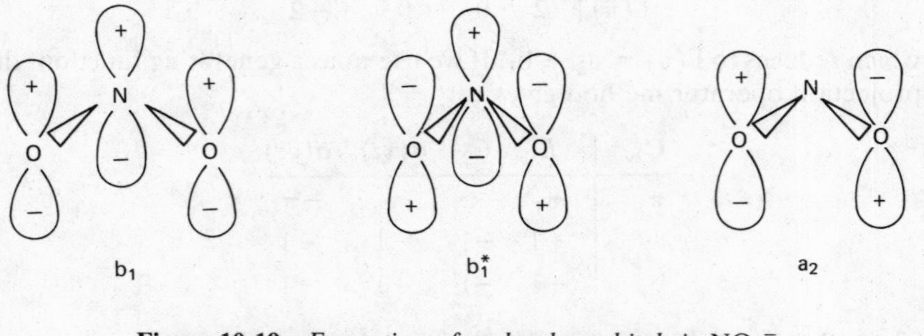


**Figure 10.19** *Formation of molecular orbitals in* $NO_2^-$

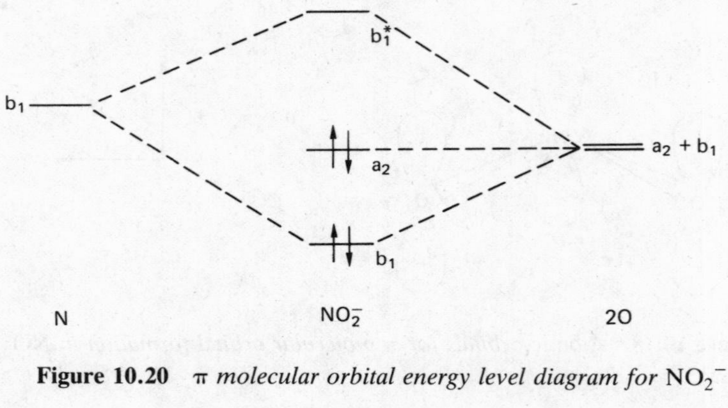


**Figure 10.20** *$\pi$ molecular orbital energy level diagram for* $NO_2^-$

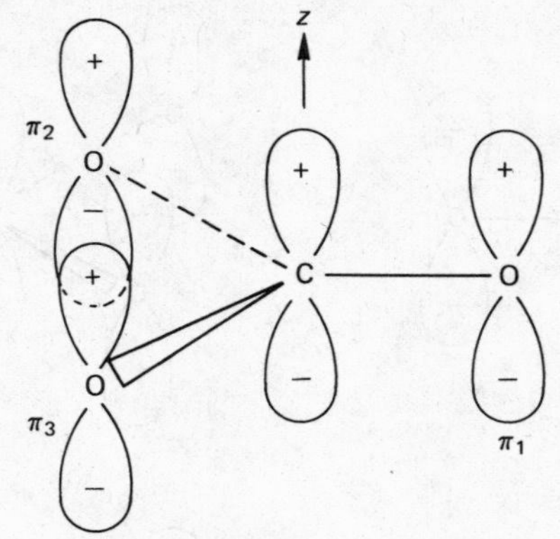


**Figure 10.21** *Atomic orbitals for π molecular orbital formation in $CO_3^{2-}$*

Using $\pi_1$, $\pi_2$ and $\pi_3$ as basis functions gives the representation of $\mathbf{D}_{3h}$:

| $\mathbf{D}_{3h}$ | $E$ | $2C_3$ | $3C_2$ | $\sigma_h$ | $2S_3$ | $3\sigma_v$ |
|---|---|---|---|---|---|---|
| $\Gamma(\pi)$ | 3 | 0 | −1 | −3 | 0 | 1 |

which reduces to $\Gamma(\pi) = a_2'' + e''$.

Projection operators (see Chapter 7) give the following SALCs for the π-orbitals:

$$a_2'': \quad \frac{1}{\sqrt{3}}(\pi_1 + \pi_2 + \pi_3)$$

$$(e'')_a: \quad \frac{1}{\sqrt{6}}(2\pi_1 - \pi_2 - \pi_3)$$

$$(e'')_b: \quad \frac{1}{\sqrt{2}}(\pi_2 - \pi_3)$$

The $a_2''$ combination can, therefore, interact with the carbon $p_z$ atomic orbital ($a_2''$), leaving the e″ combinations non-bonding (Figure 10.22). The resultant π molecular orbital energy level diagram is shown in Figure 10.23, and the six remaining electrons fill the $a_2''$ bonding and e″ non-bonding molecular orbitals. As the electrons in the e″ molecular orbitals do not contribute to the bonding, this electron distribution corresponds to one π-bond delocalised over the whole molecule.

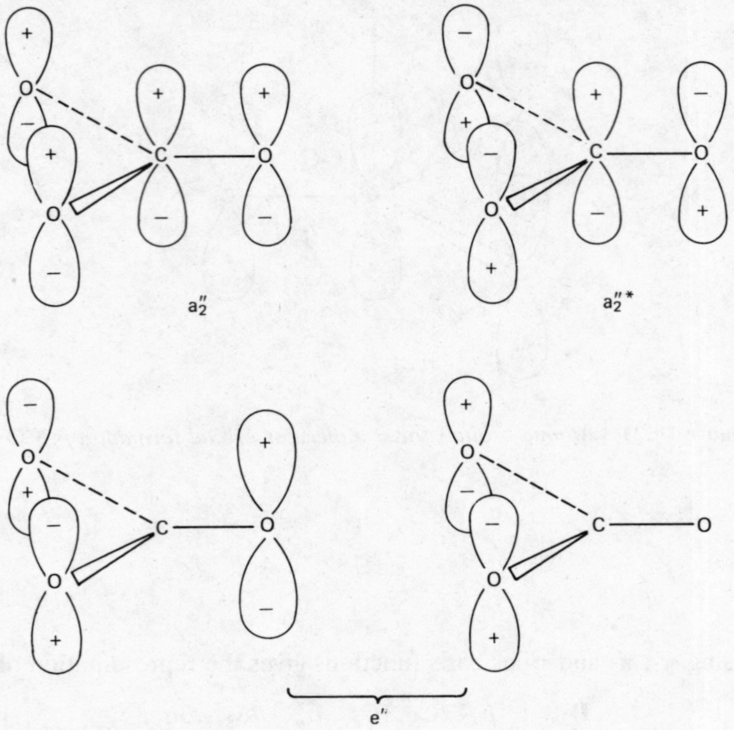


**Figure 10.22** *π molecular orbital formation in* $CO_3^{2-}$

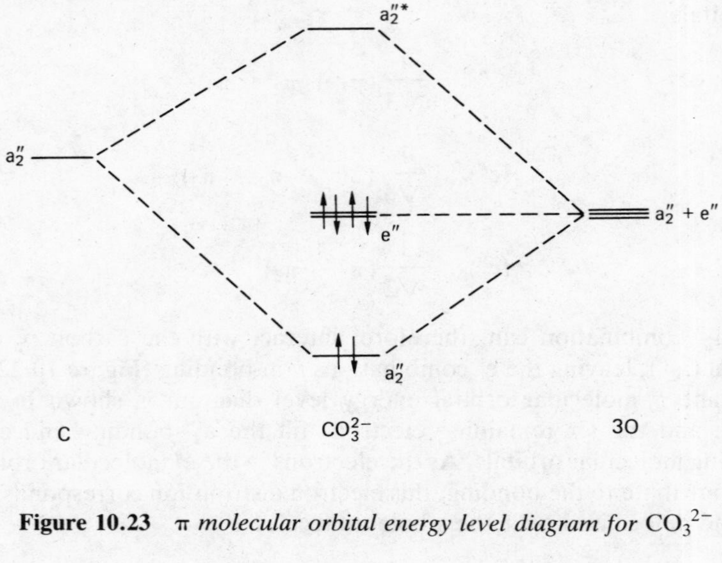


**Figure 10.23** *π molecular orbital energy level diagram for* $CO_3^{2-}$

### 10.2.3 Octahedral transition metal complexes

In order to consider the possibility of $\pi$-bonding in octahedral $ML_6$ complexes, we need to define a suitable set of ligand orbitals (Figure 10.24). Using these, two perpendicular p-orbitals on each ligand, we obtain the following representation of $\mathbf{O}_h$:

| $\mathbf{O}_h$ | $E$ | $8C_3$ | $6C_2$ | $6C_4$ | $3C_2\ (\equiv C_4^2)$ | $i$ | $6S_4$ | $8S_6$ | $3\sigma_h$ | $6\sigma_d$ |
|---|---|---|---|---|---|---|---|---|---|---|
| $\Gamma(\pi)$ | 12 | 0 | 0 | 0 | −4 | 0 | 0 | 0 | 0 | 0 |

This is reduced to $\Gamma(\pi) = t_{1g} + t_{2g} + t_{1u} + t_{2u}$. The only available metal orbitals in an $ML_6$ complex, after $\sigma$-orbitals have been constructed, are the $t_{2g}$ orbitals ($d_{xy}$, $d_{yz}$, $d_{zx}$). Hence, all the combinations of ligand $\pi$-orbitals are non-bonding, except the $t_{2g}$ set, for which a typical interaction is shown in Figure 10.25. There are equivalent interactions in the *xy* and *zx* planes, giving three bonding and three antibonding molecular orbitals.

The effect of $\pi$-bonding on the molecular orbital energy level diagram depends on the relative energies of the ligand $\sigma$- and $\pi$-orbitals. If the latter are lower in energy than the ligand $\sigma$-orbitals (they will already be filled and the ligand is a $\pi$-donor; for example, $Cl^-$), the gap between the $t_{2g}$ and $e_g$* molecular orbitals will be decreased compared to the $\sigma$-bonding only case. If the ligand $\pi$-orbitals are higher in energy than the $\sigma$-orbitals

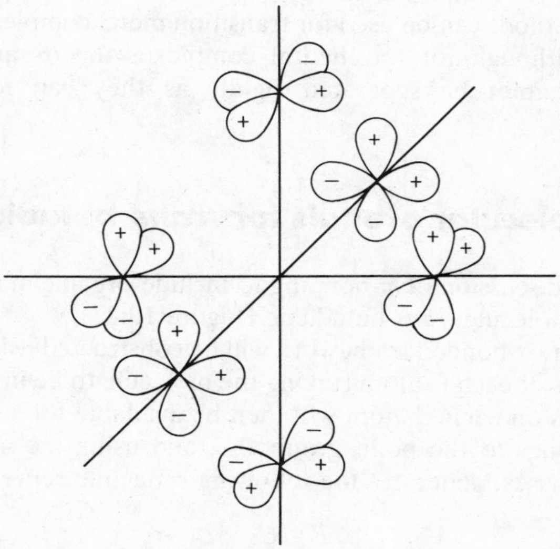


**Figure 10.24** *Ligand orbitals suitable for $\pi$-bonding in an octahedral* $ML_6$ *complex*

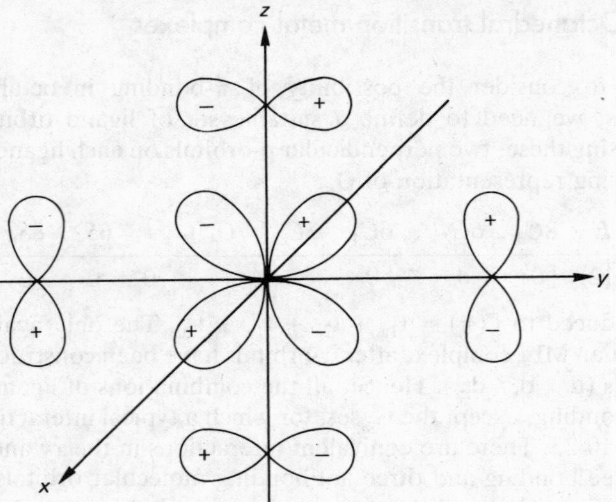


**Figure 10.25** *π interaction of one of the metal* $t_{2g}$ *orbitals* ($d_{yz}$) *with one component of the* $t_{2g}$ *ligand orbital set*

(originally vacant and the ligand is a π-acceptor; for example, the π* molecular orbital of CO), the energy gap will be increased (Figure 10.26).

Similar methods can be used for transition metal complexes with other geometries, although for tetrahedral complexes the σ- and π-bonding components cannot be separated rigidly as they can for octahedral complexes.

## *10.3* π molecular orbitals for *trans*-butadiene

To widen the discussion of π-bonding to include organic molecules, let us consider the molecule *trans*-butadiene (Figure 10.27).

The planar, σ-bonded framework will be constructed using s, $p_x$ and $p_y$ atomic orbitals of each C atom (taking the molecule to lie in the *xy* plane). The $p_z$ orbitals on each C atom will then be available for π-bonding. The molecule belongs to the point group $\mathbf{C}_{2h}$, and using the atomic orbitals ($\pi_1 - \pi_4$) as bases, generates the following reducible representation:

| $\mathbf{C}_{2h}$ | $E$ | $C_2$ | $i$ | $\sigma_h$ |
|---|---|---|---|---|
| $\Gamma(\pi)$ | 4 | 0 | 0 | −4 |

which reduces to $\Gamma(\pi) = 2a_u + 2b_g$.

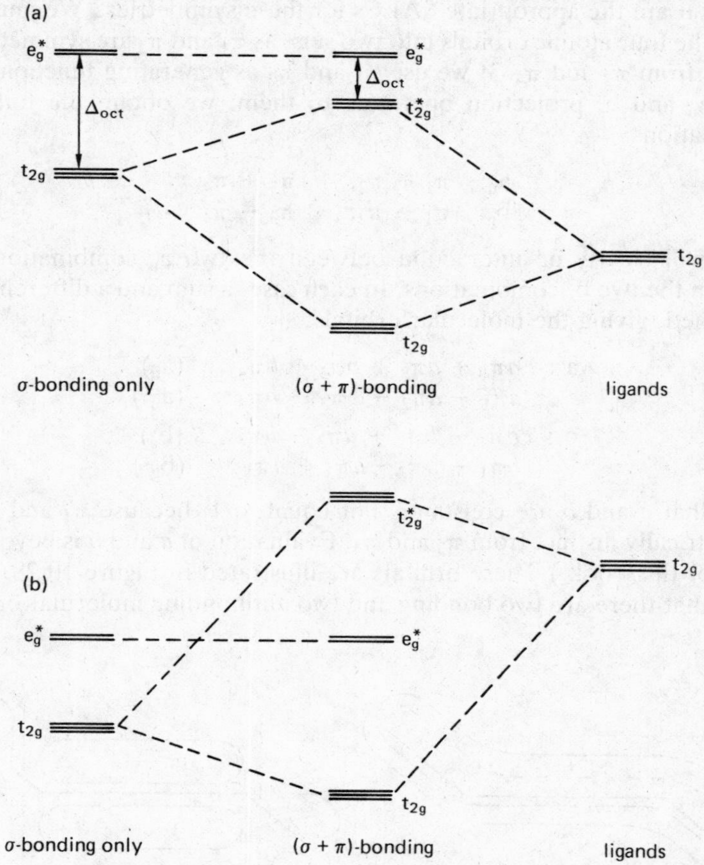


**Figure 10.26** *The effects of π-bonding on the energy levels in an octahedral* $ML_6$ *complex, when the ligand is*: (a) *a π-electron donor or* (b) *a π-electron acceptor*

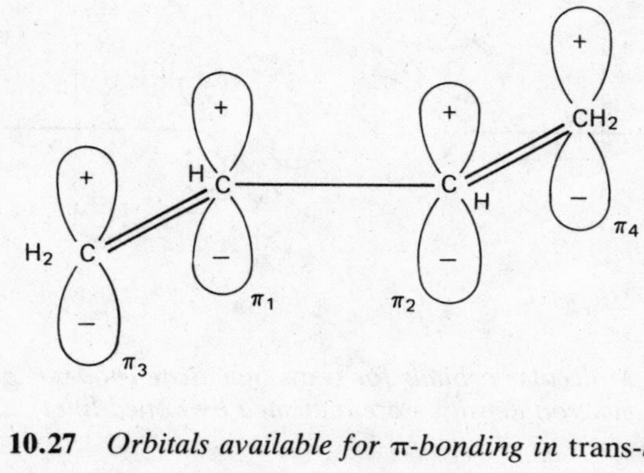


**Figure 10.27** *Orbitals available for π-bonding in* trans-*butadiene*

What are the appropriate SALCs for these symmetries? We must first divide the four atomic orbitals into two sets, as $\pi_1$ and $\pi_2$ are symmetrically distinct from $\pi_3$ and $\pi_4$. If we use $\pi_1$ and $\pi_3$ as generating functions, and apply $a_u$ and $b_g$ projection operators to them, we obtain the following combinations:

$$\begin{array}{lll} a_u: & \pi_1 + \pi_2; & \pi_3 + \pi_4 \\ b_g: & \pi_1 - \pi_2; & \pi_3 - \pi_4 \end{array}$$

There will clearly be interaction between the two $a_u$ combinations and between the two $b_g$ combinations. In each case, a sum and a difference can be formed, giving the molecular orbitals:

$$\begin{array}{lll} a_u: & a\pi_1 + a\pi_2 + b\pi_3 + b\pi_4 & (a_u) \\ & a\pi_1 + a\pi_2 - b\pi_3 - b\pi_4 & (a_u{}^*) \\ b_g: & b\pi_1 - b\pi_2 + a\pi_3 - a\pi_4 & (b_g) \\ & b\pi_1 - b\pi_2 - a\pi_3 + a\pi_4 & (b_g{}^*) \end{array}$$

(Note that $a$ and $b$ are constants, not equal to 1, because $\pi_1$ and $\pi_2$ are symmetrically distinct from $\pi_3$ and $\pi_4$. Evaluation of $a$ and $b$ is beyond the scope of this book.) These orbitals are illustrated in Figure 10.28, which shows that there are two bonding and two antibonding molecular orbitals.

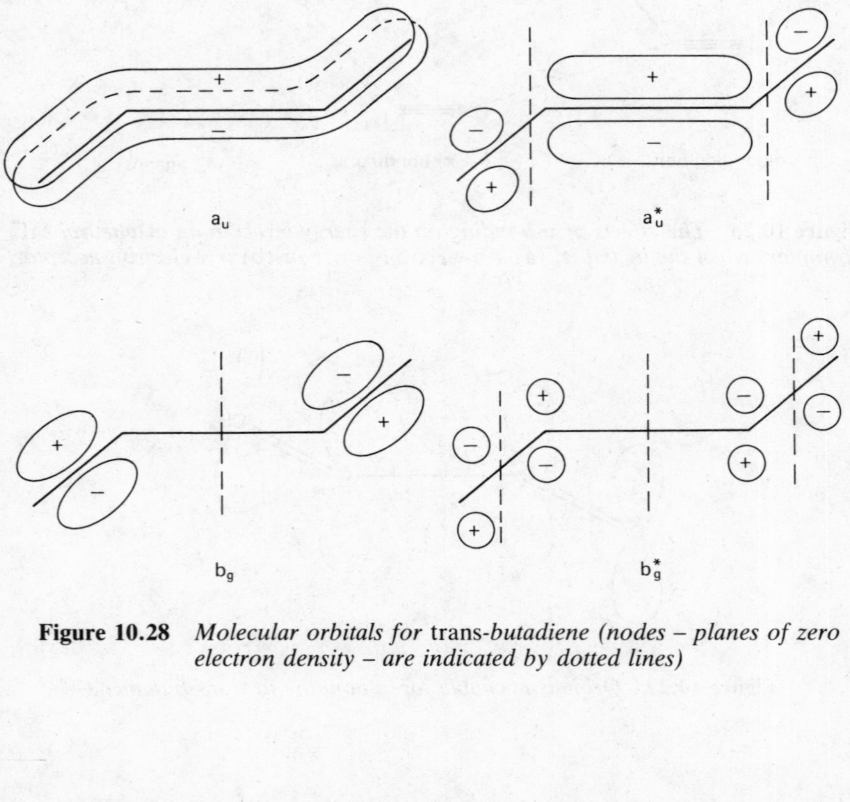


**Figure 10.28** *Molecular orbitals for* trans-*butadiene (nodes – planes of zero electron density – are indicated by dotted lines)*

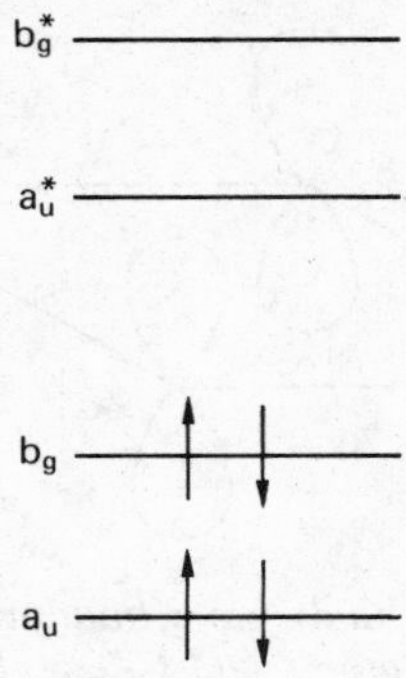


**Figure 10.29** *Qualitative molecular orbital energy level diagram for the π molecular orbitals of* trans-*butadiene*

A qualitative molecular orbital energy level diagram (Figure 10.29) can be drawn, showing that the energy of a molecular orbital increases with increasing numbers of nodes (0, 1, 2 and 3 for $a_u$, $b_g$, $a_u$* and $b_g$*, respectively). After constructing the σ-bonded framework, there remain four electrons, which will just fill the available bonding molecular orbitals ($a_u$, $b_g$). We see also that the π-electrons in this molecule are found in molecular orbitals that are *delocalised* over the whole $C_4$ skeleton.

## 10.4 π molecular orbitals for cyclobutadiene and (cyclobutadiene)iron tricarbonyl

As a simple example of the cyclic organic compounds of the general formula $C_nH_n$, let us consider the possibilities for π-bonding in the four-membered ring compound $C_4H_4$, cyclobutadiene. For this, we assume a square geometry, of $\mathbf{D}_{4h}$ symmetry.

After forming σ-bonds to the H atom and the two adjacent C atoms in the ring, each carbon will have one p-orbital free, perpendicular to the molecular plane (Figure 10.30). Using these to generate a representation of $\mathbf{D}_{4h}$, we obtain:

| $\mathbf{D}_{4h}$ | $E$ | $2C_4$ | $C_2$ | $2C_2'$ | $2C_2''$ | $i$ | $2S_4$ | $\sigma_h$ | $2\sigma_v$ | $2\sigma_d$ |
|---|---|---|---|---|---|---|---|---|---|---|
| $\Gamma(\pi)$ | 4 | 0 | 0 | −2 | 0 | 0 | 0 | −4 | 2 | 0 |

which reduces to $\Gamma(\pi) = a_{2u} + b_{2u} + e_g$. Using the projection operator

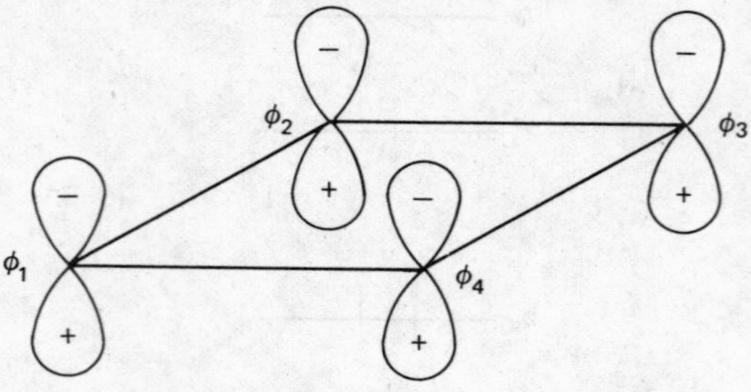


**Figure 10.30** *Carbon atomic orbitals for π-bonding in* $\mathbf{D}_{4h}$ *cyclobutadiene (note that* $C_2'$, $\sigma_v$ *contain C atoms and* $C_2''$, $\sigma_d$ *bisect C—C bonds)*

method, with $\phi_1$ as the generating function, we have:

| $\mathbf{D}_{4h}$ | $E$ | $C_4^1$ | $C_4^3$ | $C_2$ | $C_{2a}'$ | $C_{2b}'$ | $C_{2a}''$ | $C_{2b}''$ | $i$ | $S_4^1$ | $S_4^3$ | $\sigma_h$ | $\sigma_v$ | $\sigma_v'$ | $\sigma_d$ | $\sigma_d'$ |
|---|---|---|---|---|---|---|---|---|---|---|---|---|---|---|---|---|
| $\phi_1$ | $\phi_1$ | $\phi_2$ | $\phi_4$ | $\phi_3$ | $-\phi_3$ | $-\phi_1$ | $-\phi_2$ | $-\phi_4$ | $-\phi_3$ | $-\phi_2$ | $-\phi_4$ | $-\phi_1$ | $\phi_3$ | $\phi_1$ | $\phi_2$ | $\phi_4$ |
| $a_{2u}$ | 1 | 1 | 1 | 1 | −1 | −1 | −1 | −1 | −1 | −1 | −1 | −1 | 1 | 1 | 1 | 1 |
| $b_{2u}$ | 1 | −1 | −1 | 1 | −1 | −1 | 1 | 1 | −1 | 1 | 1 | −1 | 1 | 1 | −1 | −1 |
| $e_g$ | 2 | 0 | 0 | −2 | 0 | 0 | 0 | 0 | 2 | 0 | 0 | −2 | 0 | 0 | 0 | 0 |

and so the SALCs are:

$$a_{2u}: \quad \frac{1}{2}(\phi_1 + \phi_2 + \phi_3 + \phi_4)$$

$$b_{2u}: \quad \frac{1}{2}(\phi_1 - \phi_2 + \phi_3 - \phi_4)$$

$$(e_g)_a: \quad \frac{1}{\sqrt{2}}(\phi_1 - \phi_3)$$

Using $\phi_2$ as the generating function gives the remaining SALC:

$$(e_g)_b: \quad \frac{1}{\sqrt{2}}(\phi_2 - \phi_4)$$

These SALCs are shown in Figure 10.31. $a_{2u}$ is clearly bonding, $b_{2u}$

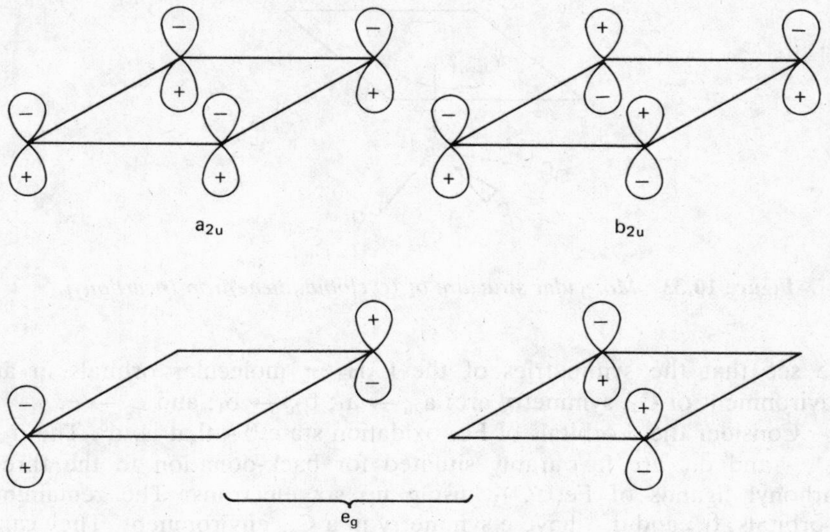


**Figure 10.31** *π molecular orbitals for cyclobutadiene*

antibonding and the $e_g$ pair non-bonding, giving the energy level diagram shown in Figure 10.32. There are four electrons to be placed in these molecular orbitals and therefore square–planar cyclobutadiene would be a diradical, and hence extremely unstable ('anti-aromatic'). It is, therefore, unknown in that form, although an extremely unstable $C_4H_4$ molecule (rectangular, with localised C═C bonds) has been detected at low temperatures. This should be contrasted with the case of benzene, $C_6H_6$, where a similar molecular orbital calculation shows that there is a full shell of bonding π molecular orbitals with consequent greater stability.

It is, however, possible to prepare stable compounds containing square–planar $C_4H_4$ – for example, (cyclobutadiene)iron tricarbonyl, $(C_4H_4)Fe(CO)_3$, which is shown in Figure 10.33. One can consider the two parts of the molecule separately: $(C_4H_4)Fe$, with $\mathbf{C}_{4v}$ symmetry, and $Fe(CO)_3$, with $\mathbf{C}_{3v}$ symmetry. Using the correlation table for $\mathbf{D}_{4h} \rightarrow \mathbf{C}_{4v}$,

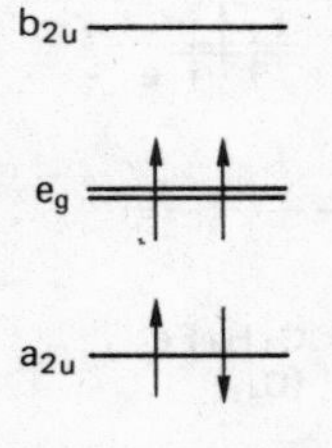


**Figure 10.32** *Qualitative π molecular orbital energy level diagram for* $C_4H_4$

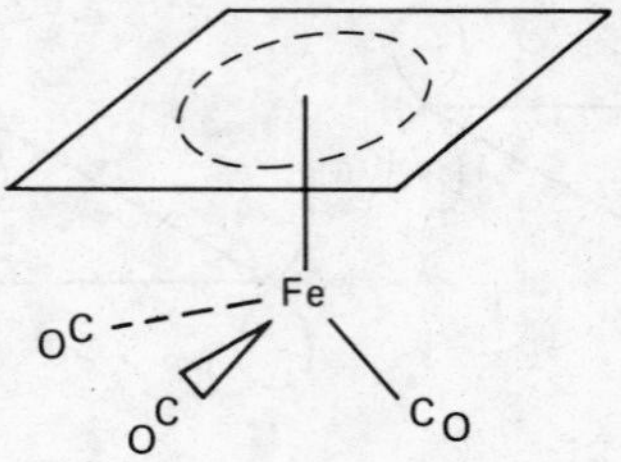


**Figure 10.33** *Molecular structure of (cyclobutadiene)iron tricarbonyl*

we see that the symmetries of the $C_4H_4$ $\pi$ molecular orbitals in an environment of $\mathbf{C}_{4v}$ symmetry are: $a_{2u} \rightarrow a_1$; $b_{2u} \rightarrow b_1$; and $e_g \rightarrow e$.

Consider the d-orbitals of Fe, oxidation state 0 – that is, $d^8$. The $d_{z^2}$, $d_{x^2-y^2}$ and $d_{xy}$ are favourably situated for back-donation to the three carbonyl ligands of $Fe(CO)_3$, using up six electrons. The remaining d-orbitals, $d_{xz}$ and $d_{yz}$, have e symmetry in a $\mathbf{C}_{4v}$ environment. They can, therefore, overlap with the e (formerly non-bonding) $\pi$ molecular orbitals of $C_4H_4$, giving the $\pi$ molecular orbital energy level diagram for $(C_4H_4)Fe$ as shown in Figure 10.34. The iron has two electrons in the $d_{xz}$ and $d_{yz}$ orbitals. With the four from the $C_4H_4$, this provides just enough electrons to fill all of the bonding $\pi$ molecular orbitals to give a stable, full shell, and explains the considerable stability of $(C_4H_4)Fe(CO)_3$.

Similar bonding schemes can be drawn up for the very large number of organo transition metal compounds involving interaction of metal electrons with the $\pi$ molecular orbitals of organic species.

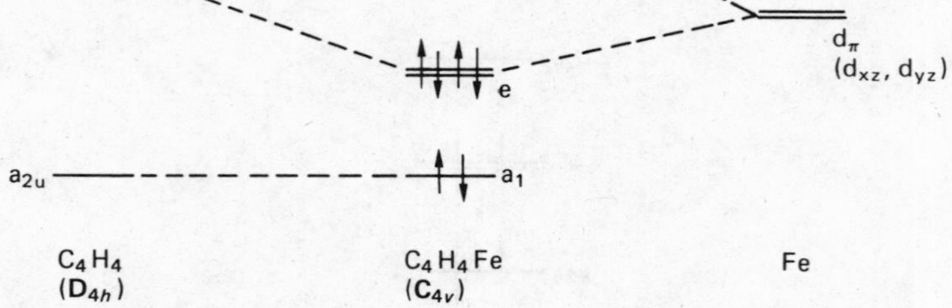

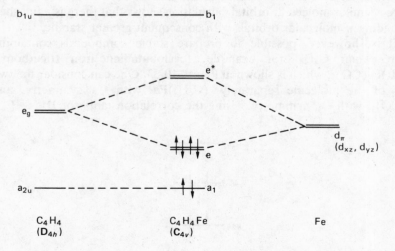

**Figure 10.34** *$\pi$ molecular orbital energy level diagram for* $(C_4H_4)Fe$

## EXERCISES

**1** (a) Determine the symmetries for the F σ-bonding atomic orbitals for $XeF_4$ ($\mathbf{D}_{4h}$). (Use F 2p orbitals with the lobes directed along the Xe—F bond directions.)

(b) Show which Xe atomic orbitals can participate in σ-bonding in $XeF_4$.

(c) Use projection operators to generate suitable SALCs of F σ-orbitals in $XeF_4$.

(d) Construct a qualitative σ-bonding molecular orbital energy level diagram for $XeF_4$.

**2** For $XeF_4$, show that suitable combinations of Xe and F atomic orbitals exist for π-bonding to occur, both parallel and perpendicular to the molecular plane. Use projection operators to construct appropriate SALCs for F atoms in each case.

**3** The 'bridge' bonding in $B_2H_6$ must be described in terms of delocalised molecular orbitals. Assuming that each B atom has two $sp^3$ hybrid orbitals available, and each bridging H atom a 1s orbital, show how molecular orbitals can be constructed for the $BH_2B$ unit. Use projection operators to generate appropriate SALCs of B and H atomic orbitals and construct a qualitative molecular orbital energy level diagram for the $BH_2B$ unit.

**4** Using $p_x$ orbitals on the C atoms of the allyl radical $CH_2CHCH_2\cdot$ (Figure 10.35), construct π molecular orbitals and a qualitative π energy level diagram for this species.

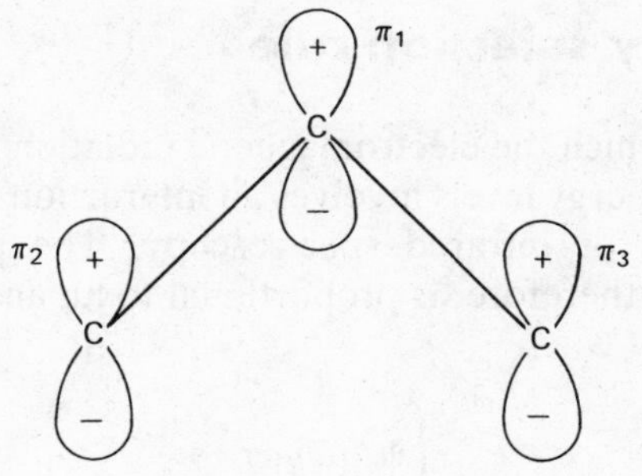


**Figure 10.35** *π-type atomic orbitals for the allyl radical,* $CH_2CHCH_2\cdot$

**5** Using the same method as that employed for $C_4H_4$, construct qualitative π molecular orbital energy level diagrams for tris(methylene)methane, $C(CH_2)_3$, ($\mathbf{D}_{3h}$ symmetry) and benzene ($\mathbf{D}_{6h}$ symmetry).

# 11 Electronic spectroscopy

Having deduced the forms and symmetry properties of molecular orbitals, we will now be able to work out the overall symmetries of a molecule with (in general) several electrons in such orbitals. There will, of course, be several possible electronic configurations for each molecule, and transitions between these are studied by electronic spectroscopy.

We will not consider all aspects of electronic spectroscopy, concentrating almost exclusively on symmetry aspects. Here group theory can help us in predicting and analysing the spectra, which occur in the visible and ultraviolet regions of the spectrum. Readers are referred to standard texts on spectroscopy for details of experimental methods and the results of analysing electronic spectra.

## 11.1 Symmetry selection rule

The mechanism by which the electromagnetic radiation induces transitions between electronic energy levels involves an interaction with the molecular dipole moment, as for infrared spectroscopy. The probability of the transition occurring, therefore, is proportional to an analogous integral to the infrared case:

$$\int \psi_i{}^* \mu \psi_f d\tau$$

for a transition from an initial state (wave function $\psi_i$) to a final state (wave function $\psi_f$). The dipole moment has components $\mu_x$, $\mu_y$ and $\mu_z$, whose symmetry properties are the same as those of $\mathbf{T_x}$, $\mathbf{T_y}$ and $\mathbf{T_z}$. We require the direct product $\psi_i \mu \psi_f$ to contain the totally symmetric representation for the electronic transition $i \rightarrow f$ to be allowed. The wave functions are, of course, electronic wave functions, and we will now consider their symmetry properties.

## 11.2 Symmetries of electronic states from non-degenerate molecular orbitals

All non-degenerate molecular orbitals are labelled a or b, and, by the Pauli principle, each one can only accommodate one or two electrons. For any singly-occupied molecular orbital the resultant symmetry is simply that of the molecular orbital itself; that is, in a $\mathbf{C}_{2v}$ molecule, the symmetry of an $(a_1)^1$ system will be $A_1$, $(b_1)^1$, $B_1$, and so on. (Note that for a single-electron orbital, a lower-case Mulliken symbol is used, and for any resultant electronic state, a capital letter.)

For a doubly-occupied orbital, we must form the appropriate direct product. Following the rules given in Appendix A, we have (for $\mathbf{C}_{2v}$) $(a_1)^2 = (a_2)^2 = (b_1)^2 = (b_2)^2 = A_1$. This shows that all full molecular orbitals belong to the totally symmetric representation, and this is always the case, for any point group.

If there is any electronic configuration with two or more singly-occupied molecular orbitals, the symmetry of the resulting configuration is again determined using the appropriate direct product. Thus, $(a_2)^1(b_1)^1$ would have the symmetry $B_2$.

### 11.2.1 $H_2O$ molecule

As an example, consider the $H_2O$ molecule, for which the molecular orbital energy level diagram was constructed in the last chapter. Figure 11.1 shows that the ground state electronic configuration is $(a_1)^2(b_2)^2(b_1)^2(b_2)^0(a_1)^0$. This contains only full (doubly-occupied) molecular orbitals, and hence the overall symmetry is $A_1$. The two lowest energy electronic transitions will be $b_1 \rightarrow b_2^*$ and $b_1 \rightarrow a_1^*$ (that is, $n \rightarrow \sigma^*$ transitions).

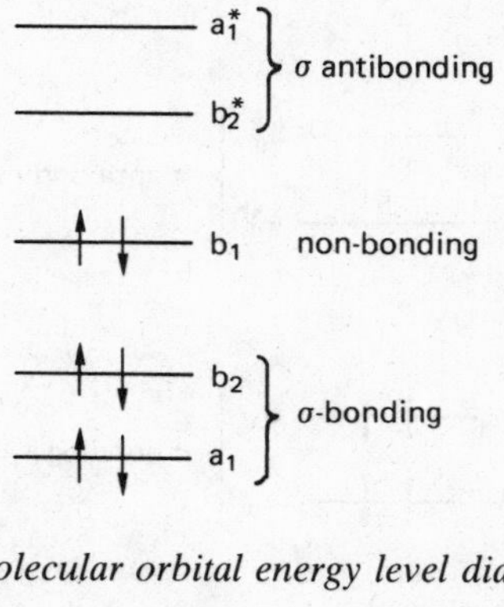


**Figure 11.1** *Molecular orbital energy level diagram for* $H_2O$

What will be the symmetries of the excited states – $(a_1)^2(b_2)^2(b_1)^1(b_2)^1$ or $(a_1)^2(b_2)^2(b_1)^1(a_1)^1$? The full molecular orbitals still have symmetry $A_1$, while the singly-occupied molecular orbitals have the symmetry of that molecular orbital; that is, the overall symmetries are $A_1 \times A_1 \times B_1 \times B_2 = A_2$ and $A_1 \times A_1 \times B_1 \times A_1 = B_1$, respectively (using the direct-product rules). The two possible transitions are, therefore, $A_1 \rightarrow A_2$ (an electron from $b_1$ to $b_2$) and $A_1 \rightarrow B_1$ (an electron from $b_1$ to $a_1$). Are these symmetry-allowed? In $\mathbf{C}_{2v}$, the symmetries of the dipole moment components are $A_1$, $B_1$ and $B_2$, and so the required direct products are:

$$(b_1 \rightarrow b_2):\quad A_1 \times \begin{pmatrix} A_1 \\ B_1 \\ B_2 \end{pmatrix} \times A_2$$

That is, $A_2$ or $B_2$ or $B_1$. The totally symmetric representation is absent, and so this transition is forbidden.

$$(b_1 \rightarrow a_1):\quad A_1 \times \begin{pmatrix} A_1 \\ B_1 \\ B_2 \end{pmatrix} \times B_1$$

That is, $B_1$ or $A_1$ or $A_2$, and so this transition is allowed. We would, therefore, expect to see only one $n \rightarrow \sigma^*$ band for $H_2O$, and this is indeed the case, in the ultraviolet part of the spectrum, near 172 nm.

## 11.2.2 *Trans*-butadiene

In the last chapter, the $\pi$ molecular orbitals for *trans*-butadiene ($\mathbf{C}_{2h}$) were constructed. Four electrons are to be fed into the $a_u$ and $b_g$ bonding $\pi$ molecular orbitals, leaving the $a_u$* and $b_g$* vacant. A schematic energy level diagram is shown in Figure 11.2.

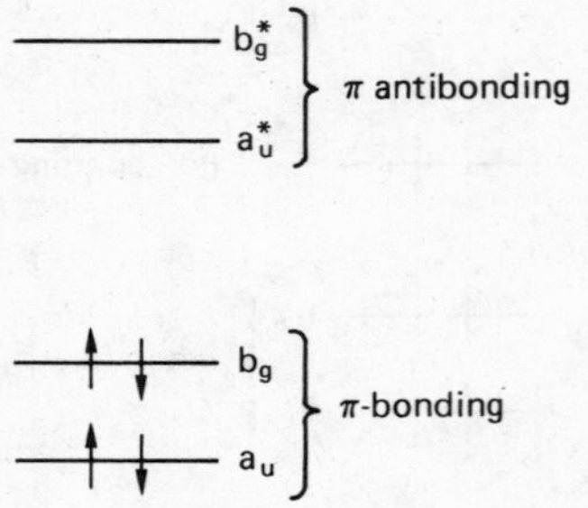


**Figure 11.2** *$\pi$ molecular orbital energy level diagram for* trans-*butadiene*

There will be four possible $\pi \rightarrow \pi^*$ transitions: $b_g \rightarrow a_u^*$, $b_g \rightarrow b_g^*$, $a_u \rightarrow a_u^*$ and $a_u \rightarrow b_g^*$. Which of these are allowed? The ground state is $(a_u)^2(b_g)^2$; the four possible excited states are $(a_u)^2(b_g)^1(a_u^*)^1$, $(a_u)^2(b_g)^1(b_g^*)^1$, $(a_u)^1(b_g)^2(a_u^*)^1$ and $(a_u)^1(b_g)^2(b_g^*)^1$. The overall symmetries of these states are $A_g$ (ground state), $B_u$ ($b_g \times a_u$), $A_g$ ($b_g \times b_g$), $A_g$ ($a_u \times a_u$) and $B_u$ ($a_u \times b_g$).

Forming the direct products, having established from the character table for $\mathbf{C}_{2h}$ that the dipole moment components have symmetries $B_u$ ($\mu_x$ and $\mu_y$) or $A_u$ ($\mu_z$), we see that the $A_g \rightarrow A_g$ transitions are forbidden, while the $A_g \rightarrow B_u$ transitions are allowed. Thus:

$$A_g \times \begin{pmatrix} A_u \\ B_u \end{pmatrix} \times A_g$$

give $A_u$ and $B_u$ only, while:

$$A_g \times \begin{pmatrix} A_u \\ B_u \end{pmatrix} \times B_u$$

give $B_g$ or $A_g$. Thus, we would only expect to see two $\pi \rightarrow \pi^*$ bands in the electronic spectrum of *trans*-butadiene; that is, the $b_g \rightarrow a_u^*$ and $a_u \rightarrow b_g^*$ transitions.

This example introduces a general rule for electronic transitions of centrosymmetric molecules. Transitions between u and g states can be symmetry allowed, but transitions between g and g (or between u and u) states are necessarily symmetry forbidden.

### *11.2.3* Effects of electron spin

We have so far ignored the fact that electrons have the property of *spin*, which must be taken into account when considering electronic spectra.

For $(a)^1$ or $(b)^1$ arrangements, there are two possible alignments for the electron spin ($+\frac{1}{2}$ or $-\frac{1}{2}$) and any such state is a **spin doublet**. This is symbolised by a superscript 2; that is, $^2A$ or $^2B$ states. For $(a)^2$ or $(b)^2$ states, the Pauli principle insists that the two electrons must have opposite spins, and so there is only one possible spin arrangement, with a total spin quantum number of zero. This is, therefore, a **spin singlet**, and as all $(a)^2$ and $(b)^2$ states have A orbital symmetry, they are given the symbol $^1A$. For an overall spin quantum number $S$, there are $(2S + 1)$ possible spin alignments; that is, a **multiplicity** of $(2S + 1)$.

There is a **spin selection rule**, which states that the only allowed electronic transitions are those that involve *no* change in the spin quantum number (or the spin multiplicity). For *trans*-butadiene, therefore, where the ground state is a spin singlet (all orbitals filled), but where the $\pi^*$

excited states could be either singlets (electron spins paired) or triplets (electron spins parallel), the allowed transitions ($A_g \rightarrow B_u$) will be to excited states that are singlets – namely, ${}^1A_g \rightarrow {}^1B_u$.

## 11.3 Symmetries of electronic states from degenerate molecular orbitals: Benzene

The overall orbital symmetry of a state involving degenerate molecular orbitals is generally determined by taking the appropriate direct products. There are, however, problems in deducing which spin multiplicities are possible. We will only be able to state the results without proof.

By using the techniques of the last chapter, it is possible to deduce the symmetries of the molecular orbitals for the π-electron system of benzene ($\mathbf{D}_{6h}$) – that is, $a_{2u}$ and $e_{1g}$ bonding, and $e_{2u}$ and $b_{2g}$ anti-bonding – with the qualitative molecular orbital energy level diagram shown in Figure 11.3. There are six π-electrons, thus completely filling the π-bonding molecular orbitals. The electronic spectrum of benzene will involve transitions from the $e_{1g}$ level to the $\pi^*$ $e_{2u}$ and $b_{2g}$ levels. In order to work out the overall symmetries of the electronic states of benzene, we must consider the symmetries of states derived from $(e)^n$ electronic configurations, and specifically for $(e_{1g})^n$ configurations.

$(e_{1g})^1$: Orbital symmetry $E_{1g}$, spin multiplicity 2; that is, ${}^2E_{1g}$.

$(e_{1g})^2$: Orbital symmetry is $E_{1g} \times E_{1g}$; that is, $A_{1g} + A_{2g} + E_{2g}$. What are the allowed spin multiplicities? With two electrons, we could have an $S$ (overall spin quantum number) of 0 or 1; that is, multiplicities of 1 or 3. The Pauli principle, however, does not allow all possible combinations of spin multiplicity and orbital symmetry when we have more than one electron in a degenerate set of orbitals. Application of the Pauli principle shows that the only allowed states are ${}^1A_{1g}$, ${}^1E_{2g}$ and ${}^3A_{2g}$

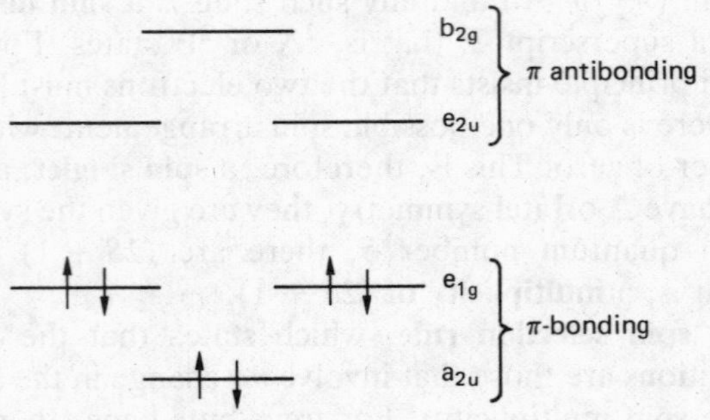


**Figure 11.3** *Energy levels for the benzene π-electron system*

$(e_{1g})^3$: The direct product $E_{1g} \times E_{1g} \times E_{1g}$ does not, in this case, give the correct answer for the orbital symmetry. Quantum mechanical restrictions simplify the problem. Whenever an orbital is more than half-full, we find a very useful relationship. If an orbital has a total capacity of *n* electrons (for example, 4 for $e_{1g}$), then the symmetry properties of an electronic configuration containing $(n - m)$ electrons are exactly the same as one containing *m* electrons. In this case, therefore, $(e_{1g})^3$ ($(n - 1)$ electrons) has exactly the same properties as $(e_{1g})^1$ (or $^2E_{1g}$). This behaviour is often explained as being due to the fact that for $(n - m)$ electrons there are *m* 'holes' in a full shell, and these holes have the same symmetry properties as *m* electrons in an empty shell.

$(e_{1g})^4$: This is a full shell. As for the non-degenerate molecular orbitals, there is only one possible arrangement for a full shell (that is, totally symmetric and with zero spin $S = 0$) for a $\mathbf{D}_{6h}$ molecule. This is $^1A_{1g}$.

Let us now consider the lowest energy transition for benzene: $e_{1g} \rightarrow e_{2u}$. The ground state level $(a_{2u})^2(e_{1g})^4$ has two full electronic shells, and so has an overall symmetry $^1A_{1g}$. What possible symmetries are there for the excited state $(a_{2u})^2(e_{1g})^3(e_{2u})^1$? We can ignore the remaining full shell $(a_{2u})^2$ (totally symmetric). The $(e_{1g})^3$ component has symmetry $^2E_{1g}$, as just explained, and by analogy with $(e_{1g})^1$, $(e_{2u})^1$ has symmetry $^2E_{2u}$.

The orbital symmetries for the excited states are given by the direct product $E_{1g} \times E_{2u}$, which are $B_{1u} + B_{2u} + E_{1u}$. What spin multiplicities are possible? Both the $(e_{1g})^3$ and $(e_{2u})^1$ components have $S = \frac{1}{2}$ (one unpaired electron), and so we have possible values of 0 or 1 for the total spin quantum number. Because the two unpaired electrons are in different orbitals, the Pauli principle imposes no restrictions, so both multiplicities are possible, and the $(a_{2u})^2(e_{1g})^3(e_{2u})^1$ arrangement gives the states $^1B_{1u}$, $^1B_{2u}$, $^1E_{1u}$, $^3B_{1u}$, $^3B_{2u}$ and $^3E_{1u}$. The resultant energy level diagram is shown in Figure 11.4.

In order to predict this part of the benzene electronic spectrum, we must now apply both spin and symmetry selection rules. The former states that there shall be no change in spin multiplicity in an allowed transition. Thus, the transitions $^1A_{1g} \rightarrow {}^3B_{1u}$ or $^3E_{1u}$ or $^3B_{2u}$ are all forbidden. The remaining three possible transitions are spin allowed. Application of the symmetry selection rule requires formation of the direct products:

$$\underset{\text{ground state}}{A_{1g}} \times \underset{\text{dipole moment}}{\begin{pmatrix} A_{2u} \\ E_{1u} \end{pmatrix}} \times \underset{\text{excited state}}{\begin{pmatrix} B_{1u} \\ B_{2u} \\ E_{1u} \end{pmatrix}}$$

Multiplication of these shows that the only allowed transition is $A_{1g} \rightarrow E_{1u}$, with $A_{1g} \rightarrow B_{1u}$ or $B_{2u}$ both being symmetry forbidden.

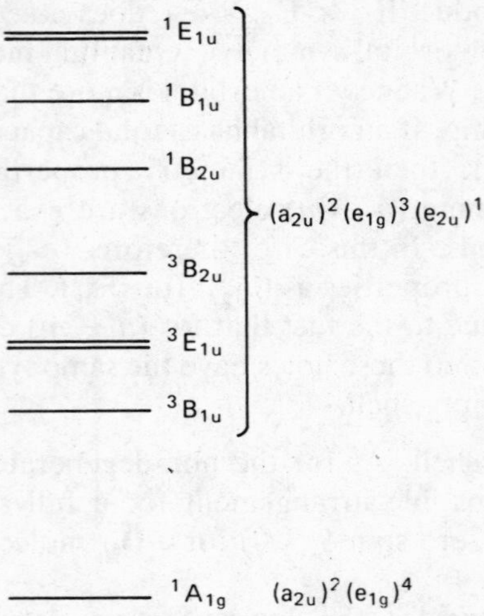


**Figure 11.4** *Energy levels of the ground and first-excited electronic states of benzene*

The only fully allowed transition for the lowest energy part of the benzene electronic spectrum is $^1A_{1g} \rightarrow {}^1E_{1u}$, and so we would only expect to see one strong absorption band. This is confirmed experimentally, although other, much weaker, bands are seen, due to formally forbidden transitions. It is generally the case that selection rules are not obeyed absolutely, but the mechanisms for their breakdown are outside the scope of this book to discuss.

## *11.4* Electronic spectra of transition metal complexes

Discussion will be restricted to complexes of regular octahedral and tetrahedral geometry. Systems of lower symmetry can be dealt with by the method of descending symmetry, which was described in Chapter 9.

The electronic spectra of greatest interest for transition metal complexes are those that involve electronic transitions among molecular orbitals that are mostly derived from the metal d-orbitals – d-d spectra. We will, therefore, restrict our discussion to the electronic states derived from the e and $t_2$* (**T**$_d$) or $t_{2g}$ and $e_g$* (**O**$_h$) molecular orbitals discussed in the previous chapter.

By analogy with the discussion for the $(e_{1g})^n$ arrangements for benzene, possible energy levels for all the possible electron configurations are as follows:

| | | |
|---|---|---|
| $\mathbf{T}_d$: | $(e)^1$, $(e)^3$ | $^2E$ |
| | $(e)^2$ | $^3A_2$, $^1A_1$, $^1E$ |
| | $(e)^4$ | $^1A_1$ |
| | $(t_2)^1$, $(t_2)^5$ | $^2T_2$ |
| | $(t_2)^2$, $(t_2)^4$ | $^3T_1$, $^1A_1$, $^1E$, $^1T_2$ |
| | $(t_2)^3$ | $^4A_2$, $^2E$, $^2T_1$, $^2T_2$ |
| | $(t_2)^6$ | $^1A_1$ |
| $\mathbf{O}_h$: | $(e_g)^1$, $(e_g)^3$ | $^2E_g$ |
| | $(e_g)^2$ | $^3A_{2g}$, $^1A_{1g}$, $^1E_g$ |
| | $(e_g)^4$ | $^1A_{1g}$ |
| | $(t_{2g})^1$, $(t_{2g})^5$ | $^2T_{2g}$ |
| | $(t_{2g})^2$, $(t_{2g})^4$ | $^3T_{1g}$, $^1A_{1g}$, $^1E_g$, $^1T_{2g}$ |
| | $(t_{2g})^3$ | $^4A_{2g}$, $^2E_g$, $^2T_{1g}$, $^2T_{2g}$ |
| | $(t_{2g})^6$ | $^1A_{1g}$ |

### *11.4.1* Electronic ground states for $\mathbf{T}_d$ and $\mathbf{O}_h$ complexes

From the information just given, it is possible to work out the electronic ground states for $MX_4$ ($\mathbf{T}_d$) and $MX_6$ ($\mathbf{O}_h$) transition metal complexes. We make use of Hund's rule, which requires that the ground state shall be the one of highest spin multiplicity – that is, of highest overall spin quantum number.

For octahedral complexes, it will also be necessary to take account of the fact, discussed at length in textbooks on transition metal chemistry, that for $d^4 - d^7$ complexes (inclusive), there are two possible ground state electronic configurations, of low or high spin: one with the greatest number of electrons in the lower-energy $t_{2g}$ orbitals (found when $\Delta_{oct}$ is large) and the other with the greatest number of unpaired electrons (for small values of $\Delta_{oct}$). For tetrahedral complexes, there is always a small energy gap between the e and $t_2$ orbitals ($\Delta_{tet}$), so that 'low-spin' tetrahedral complexes are not known, and only the high-spin forms need to be considered.

Let us look in detail at some of the possibilities for octahedral complexes: $d^1$ ($(t_{2g})^1$) will clearly have as its ground state $^2T_{2g}$; $d^2$ ($(t_{2g})^2$), $^3T_{1g}$; and $d^3$ ($(t_{2g})^3$), $^4A_{2g}$. Low-spin $d^4$ ($(t_{2g})^4$) will be $^3T_{1g}$, but what about high-spin $d^4$ ($(t_{2g})^3(e_g)^1$)? The highest multiplicity state must be derived from the highest multiplicity states of both $(t_{2g})^3$ and $(e_g)^1$ – that is, $^4A_{2g}$ and $^2E_g$, respectively. These have respective $S$ values of $\frac{3}{2}$ and $\frac{1}{2}$, giving an overall maximum value of $S = 2$ (or a state of multiplicity 5). The orbital symmetry will be given by the direct product $A_{2g} \times E_g$ ($E_g$), and so the ground state for high-spin $d^4$ is $^5E_g$.

The same principles give the following ground states for the $d^n$ electronic configurations for $MX_4$ ($\mathbf{T}_d$) and $MX_6$ ($\mathbf{O}_h$) complexes:

| | | | |
|---|---|---|---|
| $MX_4$ ($\mathbf{T}_d$): | $d^1$ | $(e)^1$ | $^2E$ |
| | $d^2$ | $(e)^2$ | $^3A_2$ |
| | $d^3$ | $(e)^2(t_2)^1$ | $^4T_1$ |
| | $d^4$ | $(e)^2(t_2)^2$ | $^5T_2$ |
| | $d^5$ | $(e)^2(t_2)^3$ | $^6A_1$ |
| | $d^6$ | $(e)^3(t_2)^3$ | $^5E$ |
| | $d^7$ | $(e)^4(t_2)^3$ | $^4A_2$ |
| | $d^8$ | $(e)^4(t_2)^4$ | $^3T_1$ |
| | $d^9$ | $(e)^4(t_2)^5$ | $^2T_2$ |

| | | | | | |
|---|---|---|---|---|---|
| $MX_6$ ($\mathbf{O}_h$): | $d_1$ | $(t_{2g})^1$ | $^2T_{2g}$ | | |
| | $d_2$ | $(t_{2g})^2$ | $^3T_{1g}$ | | |
| | $d_3$ | $(t_{2g})^3$ | $^4A_{2g}$ | | |
| | $d_4$ | $(t_{2g})^4$ | $^3T_{1g}$ or | $(t_{2g})^3(e_g)^1$ | $^5E_g$ |
| | $d_5$ | $(t_{2g})^5$ | $^2T_{2g}$ or | $(t_{2g})^3(e_g)^2$ | $^6A_{1g}$ |
| | $d_6$ | $(t_{2g})^6$ | $^1A_{1g}$ or | $(t_{2g})^4(e_g)^2$ | $^5T_{2g}$ |
| | $d_7$ | $(t_{2g})^6(e_g)^1$ | $^2E_g$ or | $(t_{2g})^5(e_g)^2$ | $^4T_{1g}$ |
| | $d_8$ | $(t_{2g})^6(e_g)^2$ | $^3A_{2g}$ | | |
| | $d_9$ | $(t_{2g})^6(e_g)^3$ | $^2E_g$ | | |

## *11.4.2* d-d Spectra of $\mathbf{T}_d$ and $\mathbf{O}_h$ complexes

Knowing the ground state symmetries, we now need to know the symmetries of the possible electronic excited states. Clearly, there will be many of these, and it would be very helpful if we could simplify the problem. Such a simplification comes about by considering the general spin selection rule for electronic transitions; that is, that there shall be no change of spin multiplicity as a result of the transition. Thus, we only need to be interested in transitions to excited states that have the same multiplicity as the ground state.

It will not be necessary to work systematically through all of the $d^n$ systems. We will look only at $d^1$ and $d^2$ systems for $\mathbf{T}_d$ and $\mathbf{O}_h$ complexes, and high-spin $d^5$ $\mathbf{O}_h$ complexes.

### $d^1$ complexes

These are very straightforward, there being only one possible transition for either $\mathbf{T}_d$ or $\mathbf{O}_h$ complexes: $(e)^1 \rightarrow (t_2)^1$ or $(t_{2g})^1 \rightarrow (e_g)^1$, respectively.

These correspond to the transitions:

$$\mathbf{T}_d: \quad {}^2E \longrightarrow {}^2T_2$$
$$\mathbf{O}_h: \quad {}^2T_{2g} \longrightarrow {}^2E_g$$

Both are spin allowed, but are they symmetry allowed? Forming the direct products, remembering that $\mu_x$, $\mu_y$ and $\mu_z$ dipole moment components have symmetries $T_2$ ($\mathbf{T}_d$) or $T_{1u}$ ($\mathbf{O}_h$):

$$\mathbf{T}_d: \quad E \times T_2 \times T_2$$
$$\mathbf{O}_h: \quad T_{2g} \times T_{1u} \times E_g$$

gives the components:

$$\mathbf{T}_d: \quad A_2 + E + T_1 + T_2 \text{ and } A_1 + E + T_1 + T_2$$
$$\mathbf{O}_h: \quad E_u, A_{1u} + A_{2u} + E_u \text{ and } T_{1u} + T_{2u}$$

The former contains the totally symmetric representation ($A_1$) and is thus allowed. For an octahedral $d^1$ complex, however, the totally symmetric representation ($A_{1g}$) is absent, and so there is no symmetry-allowed d-d transition.

It is generally the case that tetrahedral complexes can have symmetry-allowed d-d transitions, which give very intense absorptions. Octahedral complexes, however, have a centre of symmetry and electronic configurations due to mainly metal d-electron configurations always have g-symmetry. Thus, all d-d transitions are $g \rightarrow g$, and by the general symmetry selection rule, all such transitions are forbidden. Bands due to d-d transitions are seen for octahedral complexes, but they are always weak and appear only because the symmetry selection rule breaks down.

For $d^1$ complexes, therefore, we expect to see one strong d-d band for $\mathbf{T}_d$ complexes and one weak one for $\mathbf{O}_h$ complexes. This expectation is borne out in practice.

**$d^2$ complexes**

Possible transitions are: ($\mathbf{T}_d$) $(e)^2 \rightarrow (e)^1(t_2)^1$ or $(t_2)^2$; ($\mathbf{O}_h$) $(t_{2g})^2 \rightarrow (t_{2g})^1(e_g)^1$ or $(e_g)^2$. We need states derived from these excited electronic configurations which are spin triplets, to give spin-allowed transitions. For $(e)^1(t_2)^1$, we can have ${}^1T_1$, ${}^1T_2$, ${}^3T_1$ and ${}^3T_2$ states; for $(t_2)^2$, ${}^3T_1$, ${}^1A_1$, ${}^1E$ and ${}^1T_2$; for $(t_{2g})^1(e_g)^1$, we have ${}^1T_{1g}$, ${}^1T_{2g}$, ${}^3T_{1g}$ and ${}^3T_{2g}$; for $(e_g)^2$, ${}^3A_{2g}$, ${}^1A_{1g}$ and ${}^1E_g$. The spin-allowed transitions are, therefore:

$$\mathbf{T}_d: \quad {}^3A_2 \longrightarrow {}^3T_1,\ {}^3T_2 \text{ or } {}^3T_1$$
$$\mathbf{O}_h: \quad {}^3T_{1g} \longrightarrow {}^3T_{1g},\ {}^3T_{2g} \text{ or } {}^3A_{2g}$$

The ${}^3A_2 \rightarrow {}^3T_2$ transition for $\mathbf{T}_d$ is symmetry allowed; all of the others are forbidden. We should thus expect to see three d-d bands in the spectrum of either $\mathbf{T}_d$ $MX_4$ or $\mathbf{O}_h$ $MX_6$ $d^2$ complexes. For the former, one will be much stronger than the other two; for the latter, all will be expected to be weak.

Tetrahedral complexes of $d^2$ transition metals are rare, but octahedral $V^{III}$ complexes, such as $V(H_2O)_6{}^{3+}$, are well known. Unfortunately, such species, as well as d-d transitions, show electronic bands from transitions of electrons from mainly metal to mainly ligand orbitals (**charge transfer bands**), and only two weak d-d bands are seen, at 17800 $cm^{-1}$ and 25700 $cm^{-1}$, due to the $^3T_{1g} \rightarrow {}^3T_{2g}$ and $^3T_{1g} \rightarrow {}^3T_{1g}$ transitions, respectively. The third ($^3T_{1g} \rightarrow {}^3A_{2g}$) is hidden by a very strong charge transfer absorption.

### Octahedral high-spin $d^5$ complexes

The ground state electronic configuration here is $(t_{2g})^3(e_g)^2$, of $^6A_{1g}$ symmetry. For any possible excited state, such as $(t_{2g})^2(e_g)^3$, there can be no states with a multiplicity as high as 6. Thus, there are no spin-allowed transitions. As all transitions are, of course, also symmetry forbidden, they are all 'doubly forbidden', and a high-spin, octahedral $d^5$ complex, such as $Mn(H_2O)_6{}^{2+}$, will only show extremely weak d-d bands in the visible and near-ultraviolet regions of the spectrum.

In similar ways, the expected numbers and approximate intensities of d-d transitions can be deduced for any transition metal complex, of any geometry, and for any number of d-electrons.

## EXERCISES

1 Using the energy level diagrams of $BH_3$ and $NH_3$ (see Figure 10.8), deduce the symmetries of the ground electronic states of these molecules and of their low-lying excited electronic states. Determine which transitions are spin and/or symmetry allowed.

2 Using the $\pi$ molecular orbitals for the allyl radical, $CH_2CHCH_2\cdot$ (see Chapter 10, Exercise 4), deduce the symmetry of its electronic ground state and of its $\pi^*$ excited states. Is any $\pi \rightarrow \pi^*$ transition allowed?

3 Is the $n \rightarrow \pi^*$ transition of the carbonate ion (see Chapter 10) allowed?

4 For a $d^3$ octahedral transition metal complex, with electronic configuration $(t_{2g})^3$, the symmetry of the ground state is $^4A_{2g}$. Work out the possible symmetries for the excited state configuration $(t_{2g})^2(e_g)^1$. Are there any spin-allowed transitions from the ground state to this excited state?

# 12

# Orbital symmetry and chemical reactions

The importance of the symmetry properties of atomic and molecular orbitals for explaining the equilibrium state properties of molecules was described in Chapter 10. It has now become well established that molecular transformations involved in chemical reactions are also determined by the symmetries of the orbitals involved. This observation was first made and verified by Woodward and Hoffman (see the Bibliography), and consequently the rules by which the effects of orbital symmetry on chemical reactions are summarised are frequently referred to as the **Woodward–Hoffman rules**.

The fundamental basis of these rules is that the orbital symmetry is conserved throughout the course of a reaction; that is, the symmetry properties of the orbitals remain the same. By deducing whether the resulting electronic configuration of the products is lower or higher in energy than that of the reactants, it is possible to predict whether a reaction is *allowed* or *forbidden*. In general, the course of a reaction involves changes in the point group between the reactants and products, and in such cases we must only consider those symmetry elements that persist throughout the reaction path, when dealing with the symmetry properties of the relevant orbitals.

The ideas of Woodward and Hoffman are of very general applicability, and so we will only be able to consider a very few examples – in particular, electrocyclic reactions and cycloaddition reactions.

## *12.1* Electrocyclic reactions

Electrocyclic reactions are those in which a non-cyclic, $\pi$-bonded organic molecule undergoes a cyclisation reaction with the formation of a $\sigma$-bond between the two end C atoms, or the converse of such a reaction (a ring-opening process) (Figure 12.1).

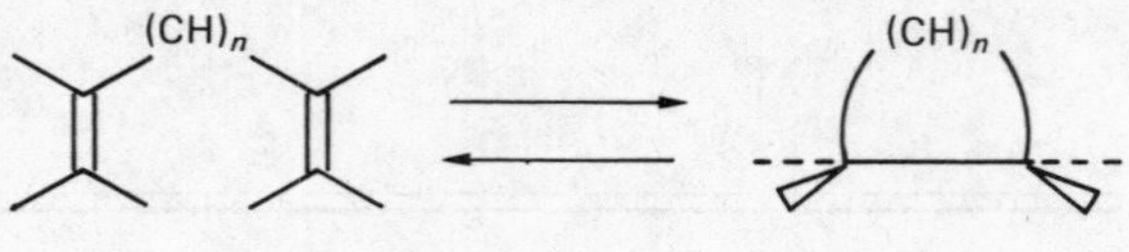


**Figure 12.1** *General form of electrocyclic reactions*

As a specific example of an electrocyclic reaction, let us look at the cyclisation of *cis*-butadiene to cyclobutene (Figure 12.2). For the cyclisation to take place, it is necessary to rotate the terminal $=CH_2$ groups of the butadiene by 90°. This can be done in two possible ways: conrotatory or disrotatory (Figure 12.3).

For unsubstituted butadiene and cyclobutene, the two mechanisms give the same products, but for alkyl-substituted derivatives this is not so. For example, *cis*,*trans*-dialkylbutadienes are converted by a thermal reaction into *cis*-dialkylcyclobutenes, but by a photochemical process to

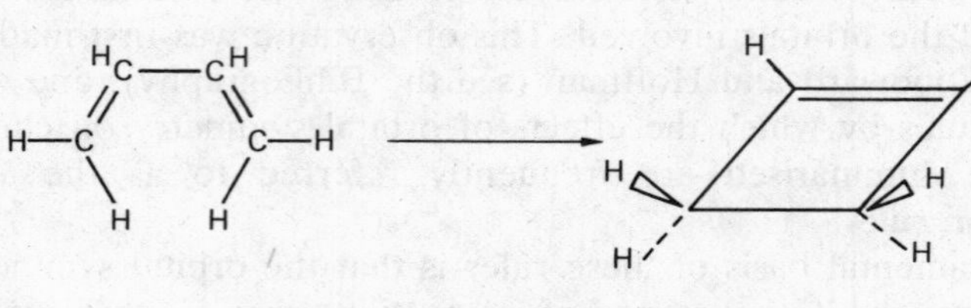

**Figure 12.2** *Cyclisation of* cis-*butadiene*

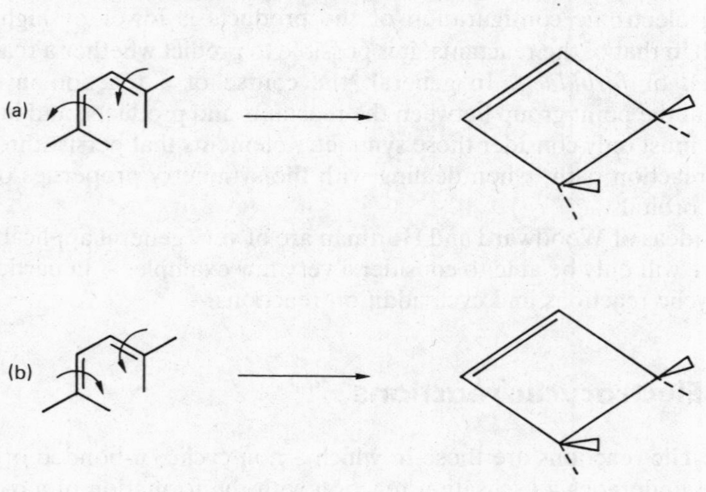


**Figure 12.3** *Conrotatory* (a) *and disrotatory* (b) *mechanisms for the cyclisation of* cis-*butadiene*

*trans*-dialkylcyclobutenes (Figure 12.4). As the figure shows, a conrotatory mechanism is needed to explain the result for the thermal reaction, but a disrotatory mechanism for the photochemical product. How can we account for these observations in terms of the orbital symmetries?

To do so, it is necessary to look at the $\pi$ molecular orbitals of *cis*-butadiene to see how they can be transformed into suitable molecular orbitals of cyclobutene. In Chapter 10, we looked at the $\pi$ molecular orbitals of *trans*-butadiene. The *cis* isomer will also have four $\pi$ molecular orbitals of analogous form, and these are shown in Figure 12.5, with their symmetries in the $\mathbf{C}_{2v}$ point group of the molecule.

The orbitals of cyclobutene into which these are transformed are shown in Figure 12.6. The irreducible representations to which these give rise are also shown, and it appears that there is a problem in conserving orbital symmetry because the symmetries of the orbitals for the two molecules do not all correspond. The reason for this is that during the cyclisation process, by either a conrotatory or a disrotatory mechanism, the symmetry of the reacting system is less than $\mathbf{C}_{2v}$. As Figure 12.7 shows, the conrotatory process produces a transition state of $\mathbf{C}_2$ symmetry (that is, both planes of symmetry are lost), while the disrotatory process destroys the two-fold axis and one symmetry plane, leaving $\mathbf{C}_s$ symmetry for the system. Thus, we only need to consider the symmetries of the molecular orbitals for $\mathbf{C}_2$ symmetry (conrotatory) or $\mathbf{C}_s$ symmetry (disrotatory).

Use of the correlation tables for $\mathbf{C}_{2v} \rightarrow \mathbf{C}_2$ or $\mathbf{C}_{2v} \rightarrow \mathbf{C}_s$ shows that the symmetries of the orbitals are as follows:

Butadiene ($\mathbf{C}_2$): $\psi_1$, b; $\psi_2$, a; $\psi_3$, b; $\psi_4$, a
($\mathbf{C}_s$): $\psi_1$, a′; $\psi_2$, a″; $\psi_3$, a′; $\psi_4$, a″

Cyclobutene ($\mathbf{C}_2$): $\sigma$, a; $\pi$, b; $\pi^*$, a; $\sigma^*$, b
($\mathbf{C}_s$): $\sigma$, a′; $\pi$, a′; $\pi^*$, a″; $\sigma^*$, a″

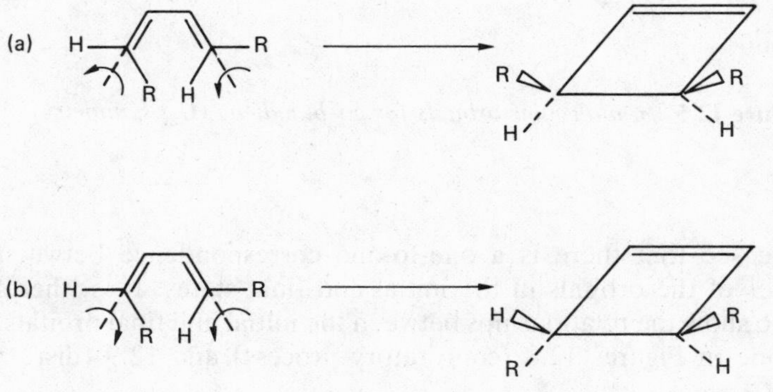


**Figure 12.4** *Thermal* (a) *and photochemical* (b) *cyclisation reactions of* cis,trans-*dialkylbutadienes*

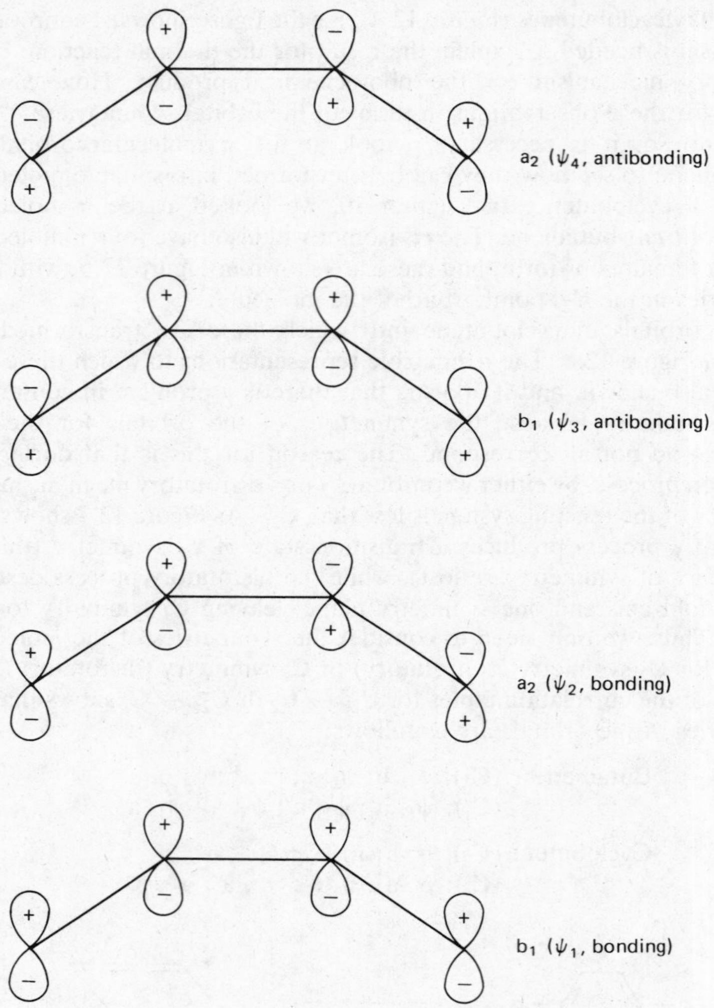


**Figure 12.5** *π molecular orbitals for* cis-*butadiene* (**$C_{2v}$** *symmetry*)

Hence we see that there is a one-to-one correspondence between the symmetries of the orbitals in the initial and final states. It is, therefore, possible to show the relationships between the initial and final orbitals, and this is done in Figures 12.8 (conrotatory process) and 12.9 (disrotatory process).

There is always a correlation between corresponding orbitals of the same symmetry, and by a general quantum–mechanical principle (the

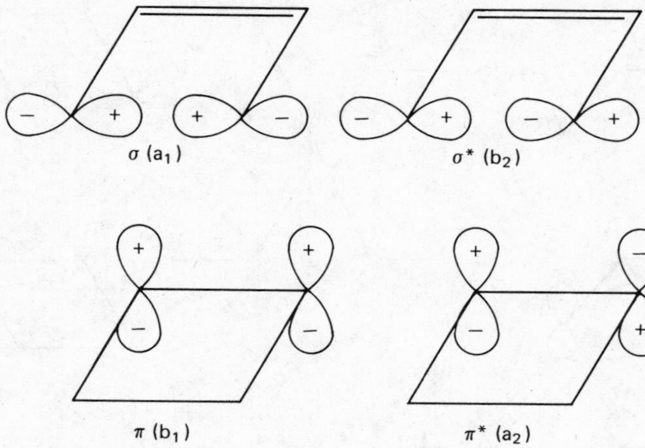


**Figure 12.6** *Some molecular orbitals of cyclobutene* ($\mathbf{C}_{2v}$ *symmetry)*

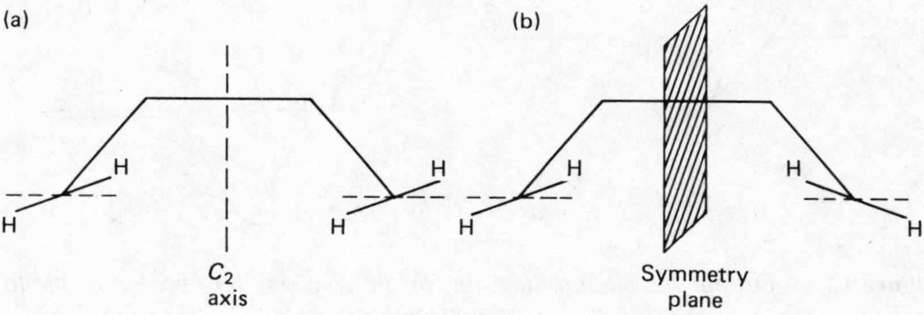


**Figure 12.7** *Symmetries of the transition states of* cis-*butadiene involving* (a) *conrotary or* (b) *disrotatory motion of the* $CH_2$ *groups*

**non-crossing rule**), there is no crossing-over of energy levels of the same symmetry. Thus, we see from Figure 12.8 that the conrotatory mechanism converts the two bonding molecular orbitals of butadiene to the two bonding molecular orbitals of cyclobutene. The ground state of butadiene, $(\psi_1)^2(\psi_2)^2$, hence goes to the ground state of cyclobutene, $(\sigma)^2(\pi)^2$, and so the conrotatory mechanism is *symmetry allowed*. The symmetry of the bonding molecular orbitals of the reactant is preserved in the product.

For the disrotatory mechanism, however, correlation of the molecular orbitals (see Figure 12.9) shows that the ground state of butadiene produces an excited state of cyclobutene, $(\sigma)^2(\pi^*)^2$. There is, therefore, a considerable energy barrier to the process, which is *symmetry forbidden*.

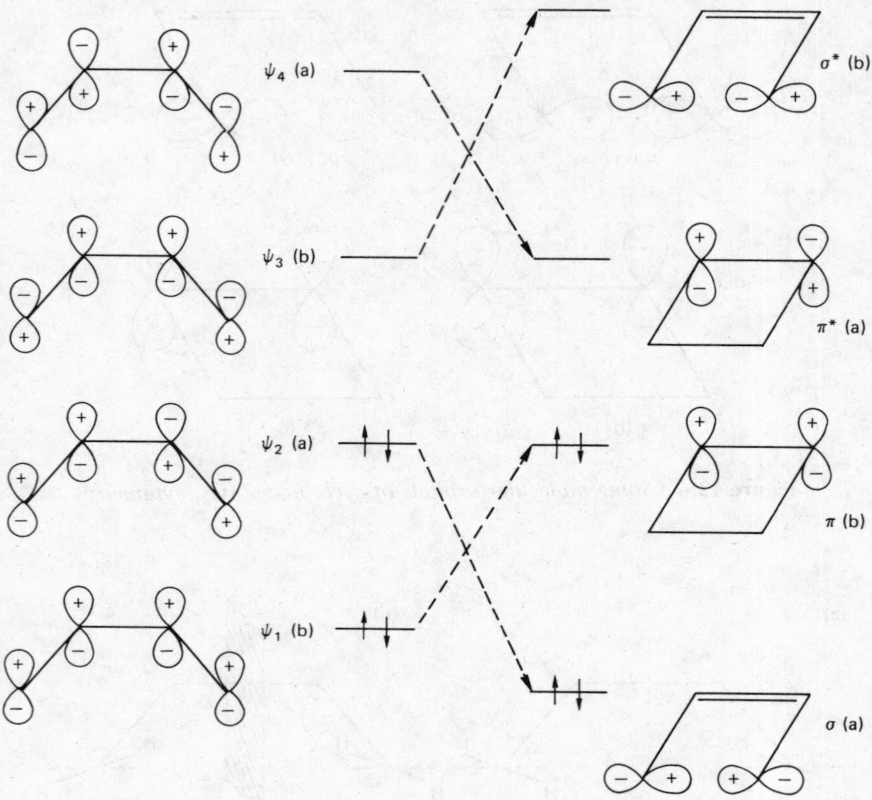


**Figure 12.8** *Orbital correlation diagram for the conversion of* cis-*butadiene to cyclobutene by a conrotatory process*

This result confirms the experimental observation that the thermal cyclisation of butadienes proceeds by a conrotatory mechanism. Why, on the other hand, does the photochemical process involve disrotatory motion? The photochemical reaction involves the initial formation of an excited state of butadiene – $(\psi_1)^2(\psi_2)^1(\psi_3)^1$ – as a result of absorption of incident radiation. If we now see how this correlates with the cyclobutene molecular orbitals, we have (conrotatory) $(\sigma)^1(\pi)^2(\sigma^*)^1$ or (disrotatory) $(\sigma)^2(\pi)^1(\pi^*)^1$. In this case, the disrotatory process yields a very much lower energy state than does the conrotatory one. Hence, the photochemical disrotatory mechanism is *symmetry allowed*.

Other electrocyclic reactions can be dealt with in a similar way. Consider, for example, the cyclisation of the allyl cation, $CH_2CHCH_2^+$, to the cyclopropyl cation. Figures 12.10 and 12.11 show the appropriate

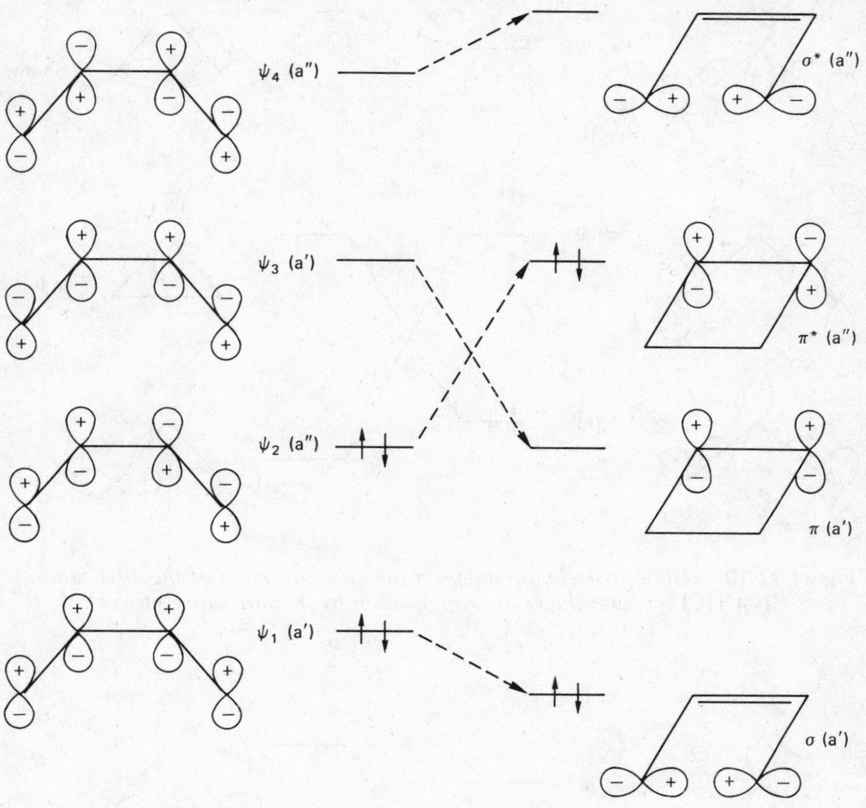


**Figure 12.9** *Orbital correlation diagram for the conversion of* cis-*butadiene to cyclobutene by a disrotatory process*

molecular orbitals and their symmetries for conrotatory ($\mathbf{C}_2$) and disrotatory ($\mathbf{C}_s$) motion of the terminal $CH_2$ groups. There are two $\pi$-electrons in the allyl cation (ground state $(\pi)^2$) and the orbital correlation diagrams show that the conrotatory mechanism produces an excited state of the cyclopropyl cation. This is, therefore, *symmetry forbidden*. Disrotatory motion, however, on this occasion gives a product in the ground state, and so is *symmetry allowed*. A photochemical reaction, involving an excited state, $(\pi)^1(\pi^0)^1$, of the allyl cation would clearly give the reverse results.

Thus, we see that an electrocyclic reaction involving four $\pi$-electrons is thermally allowed for a conrotatory mechanism and photochemically allowed for a disrotatory mechanism. For two $\pi$-electrons, the reverse situation applies. We can generalise these observations to say that for $4n$ $\pi$-electrons, where $n$ is an integer, an electrocyclic reaction will be

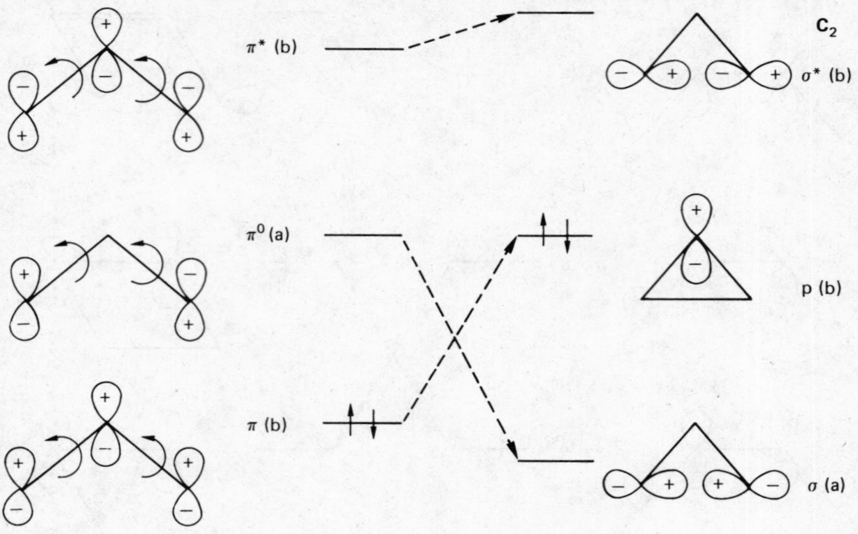


**Figure 12.10** *Orbital correlation diagram for the conversion of the allyl cation,* $CH_2CHCH_2^+$*, into the cyclopropyl cation by a conrotatory process*

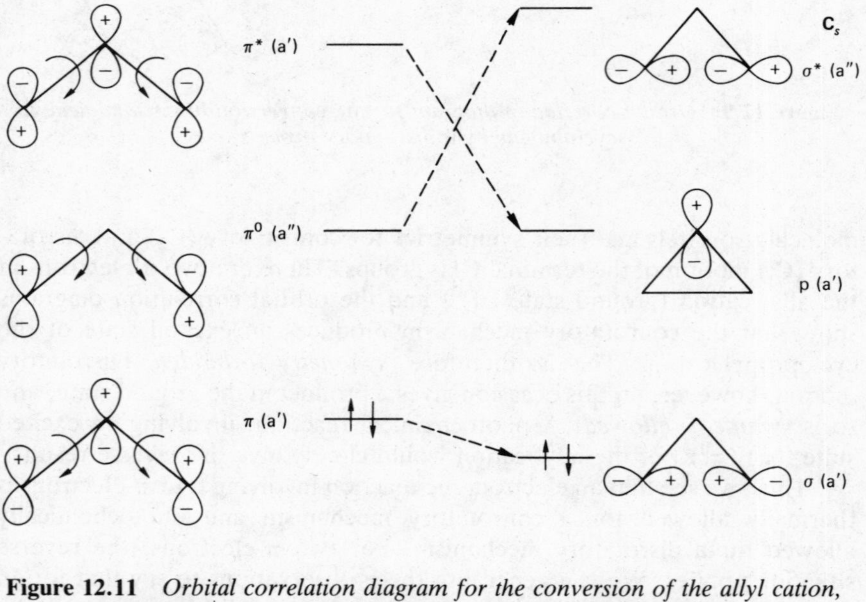


**Figure 12.11** *Orbital correlation diagram for the conversion of the allyl cation,* $CH_2CHCH_2^+$*, into the cyclopropyl cation by a disrotatory process*

thermally allowed for a conrotatory mechanism and photochemically allowed for a disrotatory mechanism. In any system with $(4n + 2)$ $\pi$-electrons, the reverse is true.

## 12.2 Cycloaddition reactions

These are similar to the electrocyclic reactions, except that the $\pi$-electrons from two reactants are used to form $\sigma$-bonds in the cyclic reaction product. A very important class of cycloaddition reactions are the **Diels–Alder reactions**, for which the prototype is the addition of ethene to butadiene, to form cyclohexene (Figure 12.12). The only symmetry operation of the constituent molecules that persists throughout the reaction is the plane of symmetry shown in Figure 12.12. We, therefore, consider the symmetries of the $\pi$ orbitals of the reacting fragments under $\mathbf{C}_s$ symmetry.

The orbitals of butadiene have a′ ($\psi_1$, $\psi_3$) or a″ ($\psi_2$, $\psi_4$) symmetry, while those of ethene are a′ ($\pi$) and a″ ($\pi^*$). The new $\sigma$-bonds of cyclohexene are formed from the highest occupied molecular orbitals (HOMOs) and lowest unoccupied molecular orbitals (LUMOs) of the butadiene and ethene, and in particular by an interaction of the butadiene HOMO ($\psi_2$) with the ethene LUMO ($\pi^*$), and of the ethene HOMO ($\pi$) with the butadiene LUMO ($\psi_3$). The former pair are both of a″ symmetry, while the latter are of a′ symmetry (Figure 12.13). Each of these interactions will give a bonding (in-phase) and an antibonding (out-of-phase) $\sigma$ molecular orbital, and the qualitative molecular orbital diagram (Figure 12.14) shows that this is a symmetry-allowed process, leading to a stabilisation of the whole system.

This cycloaddition reaction, described as a [4 + 2]-cycloaddition, due to the fact that the butadiene has four and the ethene two $\pi$-electrons, is symmetry allowed because the required HOMO–LUMO interactions involve pairs of orbitals of matching symmetries.

Let us examine another possible cycloaddition process, the dimerisation of ethene to cyclobutane, a [2 + 2]-cycloaddition. In this case, no

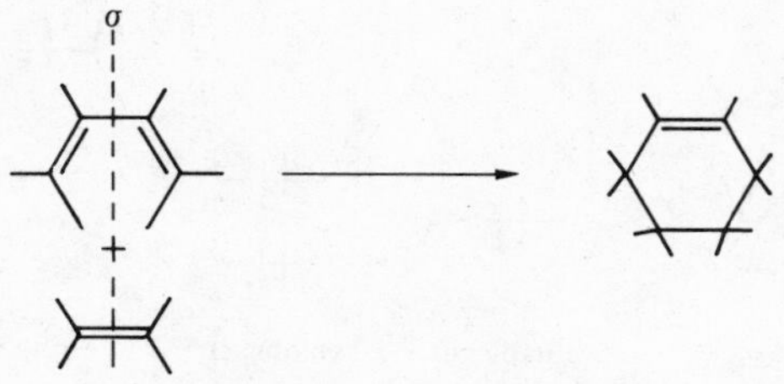


**Figure 12.12** *Diels–Alder addition of ethene to butadiene*

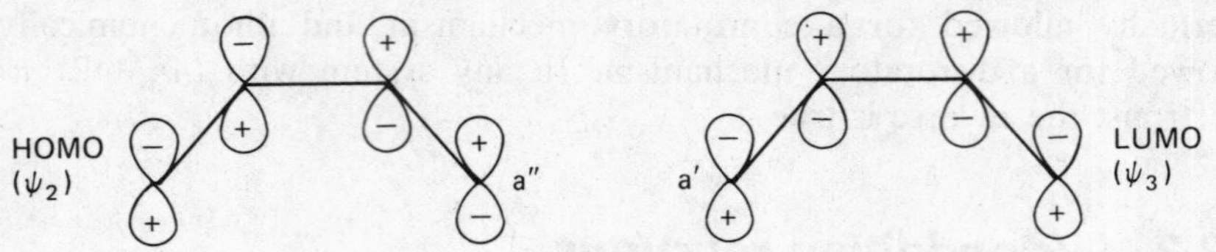

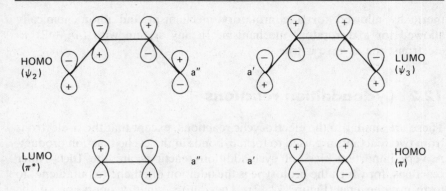

**Figure 12.13** *Formation of σ-bonds from HOMO and LUMO interactions of ethene and* cis-*butadiene*

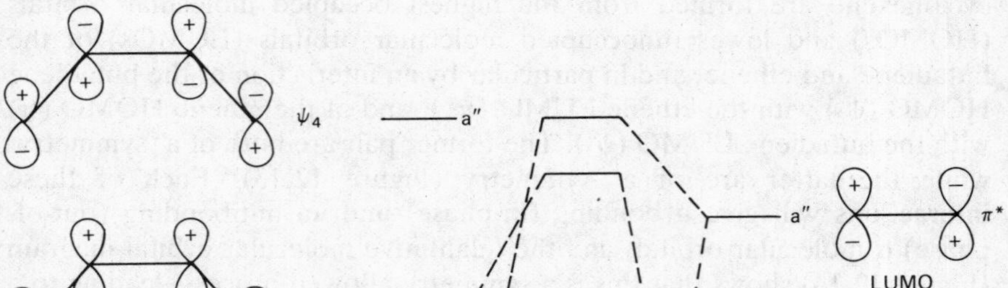

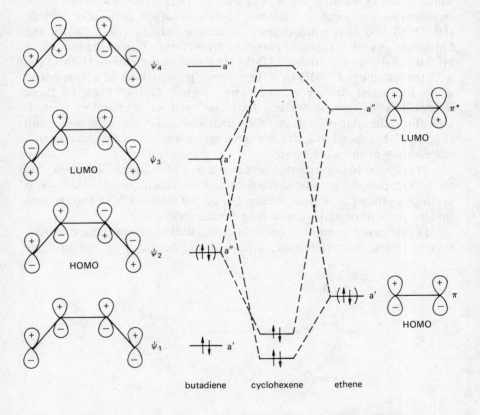

**Figure 12.14** *Energy level diagram for the molecular orbitals of cyclohexene, derived from butadiene and ethene*

HOMO–LUMO interaction can occur, because the HOMO and LUMO are of different symmetries. The only possible interactions are HOMO–HOMO and LUMO–LUMO. Each of these will give a bonding and an antibonding combination, with an energy level diagram summarised in Figure 12.15. Note that the symmetries are classified in terms of $\mathbf{C}_s$ symmetry, with a plane of symmetry passing through the centres of the ethene CC bonds. The resulting cyclobutane molecular orbitals are shown in Figure 12.16. The resultant electronic configuration for the cyclobutane product corresponds to an excited state, and there has been no net gain in energy. Thus, the thermal dimerisation of ethene is symmetry forbidden.

The examples of electrocyclic reactions and cycloadditions show that the symmetry properties of orbitals participating in chemical reactions are crucial for determining whether or not chemical reactions can occur. We have only chosen a few examples, but there are very many other cases where such symmetry relationships can tell us a great deal about the possible courses of reactions.

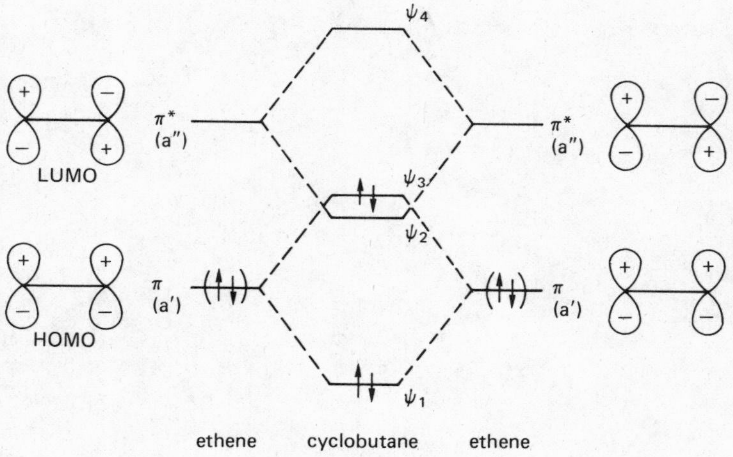


**Figure 12.15** [2 + 2]-*cycloaddition–dimerisation of ethene to cyclobutane*

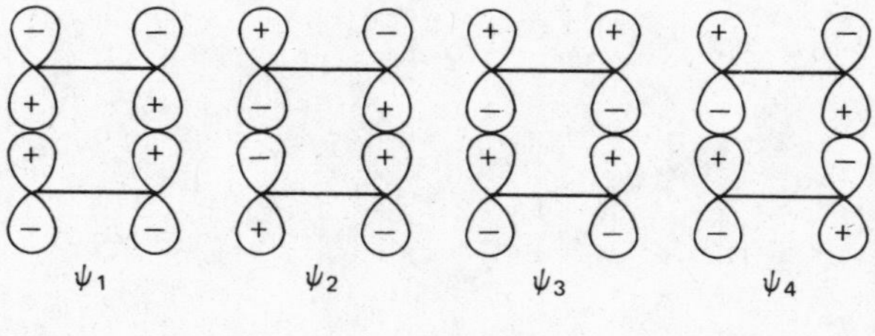


**Figure 12.16** *Cyclobutane molecular orbitals derived from the π and π* molecular orbitals of two ethene molecules*

## EXERCISES

1 Use the method of orbital symmetry correlation to determine the predicted mechanisms of cyclisation of the allyl anion, $CH_2CHCH_2^-$, under thermal and photochemical conditions.

2 Determine whether the dimerisation of ethene is allowed in a photochemical reaction.

# Appendix A

## Character and correlation tables and multiplication properties of irreducible representations

### A.1 Character tables for some chemically important symmetry groups

| $C_s$ | $E$ | $\sigma_h$ | | |
|---|---|---|---|---|
| A′ | 1 | 1 | $\mathbf{T_x}, \mathbf{T_y}, \mathbf{R_z}$ | $x^2, y^2$ $z^2, xy$ |
| A″ | 1 | −1 | $\mathbf{T_z}, \mathbf{R_x}, \mathbf{R_y}$ | $yz, zx$ |

| $C_i$ | $E$ | $i$ | | |
|---|---|---|---|---|
| $A_g$ | 1 | 1 | $\mathbf{R_x}, \mathbf{R_y}, \mathbf{R_z}$ | $x^2, y^2, z^2$ $xy, zx, yz$ |
| $A_u$ | 1 | −1 | $\mathbf{T_x}, \mathbf{T_y}, \mathbf{T_z}$ | |

**The $C_n$ groups**

| $C_2$ | $E$ | $C_2$ | | |
|---|---|---|---|---|
| A | 1 | 1 | $\mathbf{T_z}, \mathbf{R_z}$, | $x^2, y^2, z^2, xy$ |
| B | 1 | −1 | $\mathbf{T_x}, \mathbf{T_y}, \mathbf{R_x}, \mathbf{R_y}$ | $yz, zx$ |

| $C_3$ | $E$ | $C_3$ | $C_3^2$ | | $\epsilon = \exp(2\pi i/3)$ |
|---|---|---|---|---|---|
| A | 1 | 1 | 1 | $\mathbf{T_z}, \mathbf{R_z}$ | $x^2 + y^2, z^2$ |
| E | $\left\{\begin{matrix} 1 \\ 1 \end{matrix}\right.$ | $\begin{matrix} \epsilon \\ \epsilon^* \end{matrix}$ | $\left.\begin{matrix} \epsilon^* \\ \epsilon \end{matrix}\right\}$ | $(\mathbf{T_x}, \mathbf{T_y}), (\mathbf{R_x}, \mathbf{R_y})$ | $(x^2 - y^2, xy), (yz, zx)$ |

| $C_4$ | $E$ | $C_4$ | $C_2$ | $C_4^3$ | | |
|---|---|---|---|---|---|---|
| A | 1 | 1 | 1 | 1 | $\mathbf{T_z}, \mathbf{R_z}$ | $x^2 + y^2, z^2$ |
| B | 1 | −1 | 1 | −1 | | $x^2 - y^2, xy$ |
| E | $\left\{\begin{matrix} 1 \\ 1 \end{matrix}\right.$ | $\begin{matrix} i \\ -i \end{matrix}$ | $\begin{matrix} -1 \\ -1 \end{matrix}$ | $\left.\begin{matrix} -i \\ i \end{matrix}\right\}$ | $(\mathbf{T_x}, \mathbf{T_y}), (\mathbf{R_x}, \mathbf{R_y})$ | $(yz, zx)$ |

| $C_5$ | $E$ | $C_5$ | $C_5^2$ | $C_5^3$ | $C_5^4$ | | $\epsilon = \exp(2\pi i/5)$ |
|---|---|---|---|---|---|---|---|
| A | 1 | 1 | 1 | 1 | 1 | $\mathbf{T_z}, \mathbf{R_z}$ | $x^2 + y^2, z^2$ |
| $E_1$ | $\left\{\begin{matrix} 1 \\ 1 \end{matrix}\right.$ | $\begin{matrix} \epsilon \\ \epsilon^* \end{matrix}$ | $\begin{matrix} \epsilon^2 \\ \epsilon^{2*} \end{matrix}$ | $\begin{matrix} \epsilon^{2*} \\ \epsilon^2 \end{matrix}$ | $\left.\begin{matrix} \epsilon^* \\ \epsilon \end{matrix}\right\}$ | $(\mathbf{T_x}, \mathbf{T_y}), (\mathbf{R_x}, \mathbf{R_y})$ | $(yz, zx)$ |
| $E_2$ | $\left\{\begin{matrix} 1 \\ 1 \end{matrix}\right.$ | $\begin{matrix} \epsilon^2 \\ \epsilon^{2*} \end{matrix}$ | $\begin{matrix} \epsilon^* \\ \epsilon \end{matrix}$ | $\begin{matrix} \epsilon \\ \epsilon^* \end{matrix}$ | $\left.\begin{matrix} \epsilon^{2*} \\ \epsilon^2 \end{matrix}\right\}$ | | $(x^2 - y^2, xy)$ |

| $\mathbf{C_6}$ | $E$ | $C_6$ | $C_3$ | $C_2$ | $C_3^2$ | $C_6^5$ | | $\epsilon = \exp(2\pi i/6)$ |
|---|---|---|---|---|---|---|---|---|
| A | 1 | 1 | 1 | 1 | 1 | 1 | $\mathbf{T_z}, \mathbf{R_z}$ | $x^2 + y^2, z^2$ |
| B | 1 | −1 | 1 | −1 | 1 | −1 | | |
| $E_1$ | 1 | $\epsilon$ | $-\epsilon^*$ | −1 | $-\epsilon$ | $\epsilon^*$ | $(\mathbf{T_x}, \mathbf{T_y})$, | $(yz, zx)$ |
| | 1 | $\epsilon^*$ | $-\epsilon$ | −1 | $-\epsilon^*$ | $\epsilon$ | $(\mathbf{R_x}, \mathbf{R_y})$ | |
| $E_2$ | 1 | $-\epsilon^*$ | $-\epsilon$ | 1 | $-\epsilon^*$ | $-\epsilon$ | | $(x^2 - y^2, xy)$ |
| | 1 | $-\epsilon$ | $-\epsilon^*$ | 1 | $-\epsilon$ | $-\epsilon^*$ | | |

| $\mathbf{C_7}$ | $E$ | $C_7$ | $C_7^2$ | $C_7^3$ | $C_7^4$ | $C_7^5$ | $C_7^6$ | | $\epsilon = \exp(2\pi i/7)$ |
|---|---|---|---|---|---|---|---|---|---|
| A | 1 | 1 | 1 | 1 | 1 | 1 | 1 | $\mathbf{T_z}, \mathbf{R_z}$ | $x^2 + y^2, z^2$ |
| $E_1$ | 1 | $\epsilon$ | $\epsilon^2$ | $\epsilon^3$ | $\epsilon^{3*}$ | $\epsilon^{2*}$ | $\epsilon^*$ | $(\mathbf{T_x}, \mathbf{T_y})$ | $(yz, zx)$ |
| | 1 | $\epsilon^*$ | $\epsilon^{2*}$ | $\epsilon^{3*}$ | $\epsilon^3$ | $\epsilon^2$ | $\epsilon$ | $(\mathbf{R_x}, \mathbf{R_y})$ | |
| $E_2$ | 1 | $\epsilon^2$ | $\epsilon^{3*}$ | $\epsilon^*$ | $\epsilon$ | $\epsilon^3$ | $\epsilon^{2*}$ | | $(x^2 - y^2, xy)$ |
| | 1 | $\epsilon^{2*}$ | $\epsilon^3$ | $\epsilon$ | $\epsilon^*$ | $\epsilon^{3*}$ | $\epsilon^2$ | | |
| $E_3$ | 1 | $\epsilon^3$ | $\epsilon^*$ | $\epsilon^2$ | $\epsilon^{2*}$ | $\epsilon$ | $\epsilon^{3*}$ | | |
| | 1 | $\epsilon^{3*}$ | $\epsilon$ | $\epsilon^{2*}$ | $\epsilon^2$ | $\epsilon^*$ | $\epsilon^3$ | | |

| $\mathbf{C_8}$ | $E$ | $C_8$ | $C_4$ | $C_2$ | $C_4^3$ | $C_8^3$ | $C_8^5$ | $C_8^7$ | | $\epsilon = \exp(2\pi i/8)$ |
|---|---|---|---|---|---|---|---|---|---|---|
| A | 1 | 1 | 1 | 1 | 1 | 1 | 1 | 1 | $\mathbf{T_z}, \mathbf{R_z}$ | $x^2 + y^2, z^2$ |
| B | 1 | −1 | 1 | 1 | 1 | −1 | −1 | −1 | | |
| $E_1$ | 1 | $\epsilon$ | $i$ | −1 | $-i$ | $-\epsilon^*$ | $-\epsilon$ | $\epsilon^*$ | $(\mathbf{T_x}, \mathbf{T_y})$, | $(yz, zx)$ |
| | 1 | $\epsilon^*$ | $-i$ | −1 | $i$ | $-\epsilon$ | $-\epsilon^*$ | $\epsilon$ | $(\mathbf{R_x}, \mathbf{R_y})$ | |
| $E_2$ | 1 | $i$ | −1 | 1 | −1 | $-i$ | $i$ | $-i$ | | $(x^2 - y^2, xy)$ |
| | 1 | $-i$ | −1 | 1 | −1 | $i$ | $-i$ | $i$ | | |
| $E_3$ | 1 | $-\epsilon$ | $i$ | −1 | $-i$ | $\epsilon^*$ | $\epsilon$ | $-\epsilon^*$ | | |
| | 1 | $-\epsilon^*$ | $-i$ | −1 | $i$ | $\epsilon$ | $\epsilon^*$ | $-\epsilon$ | | |

### The $\mathbf{D}_n$ groups

| $\mathbf{D_2}$ | $E$ | $C_2(z)$ | $C_2(y)$ | $C_2(x)$ | | |
|---|---|---|---|---|---|---|
| A | 1 | 1 | 1 | 1 | | $x^2, y^2, z^2$ |
| $B_1$ | 1 | 1 | −1 | −1 | $\mathbf{T_z}, \mathbf{R_z}$ | $xy$ |
| $B_2$ | 1 | −1 | 1 | −1 | $\mathbf{T_y}, \mathbf{R_y}$ | $zx$ |
| $B_3$ | 1 | −1 | −1 | 1 | $\mathbf{T_x}, \mathbf{R_x}$ | $yz$ |

| $\mathbf{D_3}$ | $E$ | $2C_3$ | $3C_2$ | | |
|---|---|---|---|---|---|
| $A_1$ | 1 | 1 | 1 | | $x^2 + y^2, z^2$ |
| $A_2$ | 1 | 1 | −1 | $\mathbf{T_z}, \mathbf{R_z}$ | |
| E | 2 | −1 | 0 | $(\mathbf{T_x}, \mathbf{T_y}), (\mathbf{R_x}, \mathbf{R_y})$ | $(x^2 - y^2, xy), (yz, zx)$ |

| $\mathbf{D_4}$ | $E$ | $2C_4$ | $C_2(=C_4^2)$ | $2C_2'$ | $2C_2''$ | | |
|---|---|---|---|---|---|---|---|
| $A_1$ | 1 | 1 | 1 | 1 | 1 | | $x^2 + y^2, z^2$ |
| $A_2$ | 1 | 1 | 1 | −1 | −1 | $\mathbf{T_z}, \mathbf{R_z}$ | |
| $B_1$ | 1 | −1 | 1 | 1 | −1 | | $x^2 - y^2$ |
| $B_2$ | 1 | −1 | 1 | −1 | 1 | | $xy$ |
| E | 2 | 0 | −2 | 0 | 0 | $(\mathbf{T_x}, \mathbf{T_y}), (\mathbf{R_x}, \mathbf{R_y})$ | $(yz, zx)$ |

| $D_5$ | $E$ | $2C_5$ | $2C_5^2$ | $5C_2$ | | |
|---|---|---|---|---|---|---|
| $A_1$ | 1 | 1 | 1 | 1 | | $x^2 + y^2, z^2$ |
| $A_2$ | 1 | 1 | 1 | −1 | $\mathbf{T_z}, \mathbf{R_z}$ | |
| $E_1$ | 2 | 2 cos 72° | 2 cos 144° | 0 | $(\mathbf{T_x}, \mathbf{T_y}), (\mathbf{R_x}, \mathbf{R_y})$ | $(yz, zx)$ |
| $E_2$ | 2 | 2 cos 144° | 2 cos 72° | 0 | | $(x^2 - y^2, xy)$ |

| $D_6$ | $E$ | $2C_6$ | $2C_3$ | $C_2$ | $3C_2'$ | $3C_2''$ | | |
|---|---|---|---|---|---|---|---|---|
| $A_1$ | 1 | 1 | 1 | 1 | 1 | 1 | | $x^2 + y^2, z^2$ |
| $A_2$ | 1 | 1 | 1 | 1 | −1 | −1 | $\mathbf{T_z}, \mathbf{R_z}$ | |
| $B_1$ | 1 | −1 | 1 | −1 | 1 | −1 | | |
| $B_2$ | 1 | −1 | 1 | −1 | −1 | 1 | | |
| $E_1$ | 2 | 1 | −1 | −2 | 0 | 0 | $(\mathbf{T_x}, \mathbf{T_y}), (\mathbf{R_x}, \mathbf{R_y})$ | $(yz, zx)$ |
| $E_2$ | 2 | −1 | −1 | 2 | 0 | 0 | | $(x^2 - y^2, xy)$ |

## The $C_{nv}$ groups

| $C_{2v}$ | $E$ | $C_2$ | $\sigma_v(xz)$ | $\sigma_v'(yz)$ | | |
|---|---|---|---|---|---|---|
| $A_1$ | 1 | 1 | 1 | 1 | $\mathbf{T_z}$ | $x^2, y^2, z^2$ |
| $A_2$ | 1 | 1 | −1 | −1 | $\mathbf{R_z}$ | $xy$ |
| $B_1$ | 1 | −1 | 1 | −1 | $\mathbf{T_x}, \mathbf{R_y}$ | $zx$ |
| $B_2$ | 1 | −1 | −1 | 1 | $\mathbf{T_y}, \mathbf{R_x}$ | $yz$ |

| $C_{3v}$ | $E$ | $2C_3$ | $3\sigma_v$ | | |
|---|---|---|---|---|---|
| $A_1$ | 1 | 1 | 1 | $\mathbf{T_z}$ | $x^2 + y^2, z^2$ |
| $A_2$ | 1 | 1 | −1 | $\mathbf{R_z}$ | |
| $E$ | 2 | −1 | 0 | $(\mathbf{T_x}, \mathbf{T_y}); (\mathbf{R_x}, \mathbf{R_y})$ | $(x^2 - y^2, xy), (yz, zx)$ |

| $C_{4v}$ | $E$ | $2C_4$ | $C_2$ | $2\sigma_v$ | $2\sigma_d$ | | |
|---|---|---|---|---|---|---|---|
| $A_1$ | 1 | 1 | 1 | 1 | 1 | $\mathbf{T_z}$ | $x^2 + y^2, z^2$ |
| $A_2$ | 1 | 1 | 1 | −1 | −1 | $\mathbf{R_z}$ | |
| $B_1$ | 1 | −1 | 1 | 1 | −1 | | $x^2 - y^2$ |
| $B_2$ | 1 | −1 | 1 | −1 | 1 | | $xy$ |
| $E$ | 2 | 0 | −2 | 0 | 0 | $(\mathbf{T_x}, \mathbf{T_y}), (\mathbf{R_x}, \mathbf{R_y})$ | $(yz, zx)$ |

| $C_{5v}$ | $E$ | $2C_5$ | $2C_5^2$ | $5\sigma_v$ | | |
|---|---|---|---|---|---|---|
| $A_1$ | 1 | 1 | 1 | 1 | $\mathbf{T_z}$ | $x^2 + y^2, z^2$ |
| $A_2$ | 1 | 1 | 1 | −1 | $\mathbf{R_z}$ | |
| $E_1$ | 2 | 2 cos 72° | 2 cos 144° | 0 | $(\mathbf{T_x}, \mathbf{T_y}), (\mathbf{R_x}, \mathbf{R_y})$ | $(yz, zx)$ |
| $E_2$ | 2 | 2 cos 144° | 2 cos 72° | 0 | | $(x^2 - y^2, xy)$ |

| $C_{6v}$ | $E$ | $2C_6$ | $2C_3$ | $C_2$ | $3\sigma_v$ | $3\sigma_d$ | | |
|---|---|---|---|---|---|---|---|---|
| $A_1$ | 1 | 1 | 1 | 1 | 1 | 1 | $\mathbf{T_z}$ | $x^2 + y^2, z^2$ |
| $A_2$ | 1 | 1 | 1 | 1 | −1 | −1 | $\mathbf{R_z}$ | |
| $B_1$ | 1 | −1 | 1 | −1 | 1 | −1 | | |
| $B_2$ | 1 | −1 | 1 | −1 | −1 | 1 | | |
| $E_1$ | 2 | 1 | −1 | −2 | 0 | 0 | $(\mathbf{T_x}, \mathbf{T_y}), (\mathbf{R_x}, \mathbf{R_y})$ | $(yz, zx)$ |
| $E_2$ | 2 | −1 | −1 | 2 | 0 | 0 | | $(x^2 - y^2, xy)$ |

**The $\mathbf{C}_{nh}$ groups**

| $\mathbf{C}_{2h}$ | $E$ | $C_2$ | $i$ | $\sigma_h$ | | |
|---|---|---|---|---|---|---|
| $A_g$ | 1 | 1 | 1 | 1 | $\mathbf{R_z}$ | $x^2, y^2, z^2, xy$ |
| $B_g$ | 1 | −1 | 1 | −1 | $\mathbf{R_x}, \mathbf{R_y}$ | $yz, zx$ |
| $A_u$ | 1 | 1 | −1 | −1 | $\mathbf{T_z}$ | |
| $B_u$ | 1 | −1 | −1 | 1 | $\mathbf{T_x}, \mathbf{T_y}$ | |

| $\mathbf{C}_{3h}$ | $E$ | $C_3$ | $C_3^2$ | $\sigma_h$ | $S_3$ | $S_3^2$ | | $\epsilon = \exp(2\pi i/3)$ |
|---|---|---|---|---|---|---|---|---|
| $A'$ | 1 | 1 | 1 | 1 | 1 | 1 | $\mathbf{R_z}$ | $x^2 + y^2, z^2$ |
| $E'$ | 1 | $\epsilon$ | $\epsilon^*$ | 1 | $\epsilon$ | $\epsilon^*$ | $(\mathbf{T_x}, \mathbf{T_y})$ | $(x^2 - y^2, xy)$ |
| | 1 | $\epsilon^*$ | $\epsilon$ | 1 | $\epsilon^*$ | $\epsilon$ | | |
| $A''$ | 1 | 1 | 1 | −1 | −1 | −1 | $\mathbf{T_z}$ | |
| $E''$ | 1 | $\epsilon$ | $\epsilon^*$ | −1 | $-\epsilon$ | $-\epsilon^*$ | $(\mathbf{R_x}, \mathbf{R_y})$ | $(yz, zx)$ |
| | 1 | $\epsilon^*$ | $\epsilon$ | −1 | $-\epsilon^*$ | $-\epsilon$ | | |

| $\mathbf{C}_{4h}$ | $E$ | $C_4$ | $C_2$ | $C_4^3$ | $i$ | $S_4^3$ | $\sigma_h$ | $S_4$ | | |
|---|---|---|---|---|---|---|---|---|---|---|
| $A_g$ | 1 | 1 | 1 | 1 | 1 | 1 | 1 | 1 | $\mathbf{R_z}$ | $x^2 + y^2, z^2$ |
| $B_g$ | 1 | −1 | 1 | −1 | 1 | −1 | 1 | −1 | | $x^2 - y^2, xy$ |
| $E_g$ | 1 | $i$ | −1 | $-i$ | 1 | $i$ | −1 | $-i$ | $(\mathbf{R_x}, \mathbf{R_y})$ | $(yz, zx)$ |
| | 1 | $-i$ | −1 | $i$ | 1 | $-i$ | −1 | $i$ | | |
| $A_u$ | 1 | 1 | 1 | 1 | −1 | −1 | −1 | −1 | $\mathbf{T_z}$ | |
| $B_u$ | 1 | −1 | 1 | −1 | −1 | 1 | −1 | 1 | | |
| $E_u$ | 1 | $i$ | −1 | $-i$ | −1 | $-i$ | 1 | $i$ | $(\mathbf{T_x}, \mathbf{T_y})$ | |
| | 1 | $-i$ | −1 | $i$ | −1 | $i$ | 1 | $-i$ | | |

| $\mathbf{C}_{5h}$ | $E$ | $C_5$ | $C_5^2$ | $C_5^3$ | $C_5^4$ | $\sigma_h$ | $S_5$ | $S_5^7$ | $S_5^3$ | $S_5^9$ | | $\epsilon = \exp(2\pi i/5)$ |
|---|---|---|---|---|---|---|---|---|---|---|---|---|
| $A'$ | 1 | 1 | 1 | 1 | 1 | 1 | 1 | 1 | 1 | 1 | $\mathbf{R_z}$ | $x^2 + y^2, z^2$ |
| $E_1'$ | 1 | $\epsilon$ | $\epsilon^2$ | $\epsilon^{2*}$ | $\epsilon^*$ | 1 | $\epsilon$ | $\epsilon^2$ | $\epsilon^{2*}$ | $\epsilon^*$ | $(\mathbf{T_x}, \mathbf{T_y})$ | |
| | 1 | $\epsilon^*$ | $\epsilon^{2*}$ | $\epsilon^2$ | $\epsilon$ | 1 | $\epsilon^*$ | $\epsilon^{2*}$ | $\epsilon^2$ | $\epsilon$ | | |
| $E_2'$ | 1 | $\epsilon^2$ | $\epsilon^*$ | $\epsilon$ | $\epsilon^{2*}$ | 1 | $\epsilon^2$ | $\epsilon^*$ | $\epsilon$ | $\epsilon^{2*}$ | | $(x^2 - y^2, xy)$ |
| | 1 | $\epsilon^{2*}$ | $\epsilon$ | $\epsilon^*$ | $\epsilon^2$ | 1 | $\epsilon^{2*}$ | $\epsilon$ | $\epsilon^*$ | $\epsilon^2$ | | |
| $A''$ | 1 | 1 | 1 | 1 | 1 | −1 | −1 | −1 | −1 | −1 | $\mathbf{T_z}$ | |
| $E_1''$ | 1 | $\epsilon$ | $\epsilon^2$ | $\epsilon^{2*}$ | $\epsilon^*$ | −1 | $-\epsilon$ | $-\epsilon^2$ | $-\epsilon^{2*}$ | $-\epsilon^*$ | $(\mathbf{R_x}, \mathbf{R_y})$ | $(yz, zx)$ |
| | 1 | $\epsilon^*$ | $\epsilon^{2*}$ | $\epsilon^2$ | $\epsilon$ | −1 | $-\epsilon^*$ | $-\epsilon^{2*}$ | $-\epsilon^2$ | $-\epsilon$ | | |
| $E_2''$ | 1 | $\epsilon^2$ | $\epsilon^*$ | $\epsilon$ | $\epsilon^{2*}$ | −1 | $-\epsilon^2$ | $-\epsilon^*$ | $-\epsilon$ | $-\epsilon^{2*}$ | | |
| | 1 | $\epsilon^{2*}$ | $\epsilon$ | $\epsilon^*$ | $\epsilon^2$ | −1 | $-\epsilon^{2*}$ | $-\epsilon$ | $-\epsilon^*$ | $-\epsilon^2$ | | |

| $\mathbf{C}_{6h}$ | $E$ | $C_6$ | $C_3$ | $C_2$ | $C_3^2$ | $C_6^5$ | $i$ | $S_3^5$ | $S_6^5$ | $\sigma_h$ | $S_6$ | $S_3$ | | $\epsilon = \exp(2\pi i/6)$ |
|---|---|---|---|---|---|---|---|---|---|---|---|---|---|---|
| $A_g$ | 1 | 1 | 1 | 1 | 1 | 1 | 1 | 1 | 1 | 1 | 1 | 1 | $\mathbf{R_z}$ | $x^2 + y^2, z^2$ |
| $B_g$ | 1 | −1 | 1 | −1 | 1 | −1 | 1 | −1 | 1 | −1 | 1 | −1 | | |
| $E_{1g}$ | 1 | $\epsilon$ | $-\epsilon^*$ | −1 | $-\epsilon$ | $\epsilon^*$ | 1 | $\epsilon$ | $-\epsilon^*$ | −1 | $-\epsilon$ | $\epsilon^*$ | $(\mathbf{R_x}, \mathbf{R_y})$ | $(yz, zx)$ |
| | 1 | $\epsilon^*$ | $-\epsilon$ | −1 | $-\epsilon^*$ | $\epsilon$ | 1 | $\epsilon^*$ | $-\epsilon$ | −1 | $-\epsilon^*$ | $\epsilon$ | | |
| $E_{2g}$ | 1 | $-\epsilon^*$ | $-\epsilon$ | 1 | $-\epsilon^*$ | $-\epsilon$ | 1 | $-\epsilon^*$ | $-\epsilon$ | 1 | $-\epsilon^*$ | $-\epsilon$ | | $(x^2 - y^2, xy)$ |
| | 1 | $-\epsilon$ | $-\epsilon^*$ | 1 | $-\epsilon$ | $-\epsilon^*$ | 1 | $-\epsilon$ | $-\epsilon^*$ | 1 | $-\epsilon$ | $-\epsilon^*$ | | |
| $A_u$ | 1 | 1 | 1 | 1 | 1 | 1 | −1 | −1 | −1 | −1 | −1 | −1 | $\mathbf{T_z}$ | |
| $B_u$ | 1 | −1 | 1 | −1 | 1 | −1 | −1 | 1 | −1 | 1 | −1 | 1 | | |
| $E_{1u}$ | 1 | $\epsilon$ | $-\epsilon^*$ | −1 | $-\epsilon$ | $\epsilon^*$ | −1 | $-\epsilon$ | $\epsilon^*$ | 1 | $\epsilon$ | $-\epsilon^*$ | $(\mathbf{T_x}, \mathbf{T_y})$ | |
| | 1 | $\epsilon^*$ | $-\epsilon$ | −1 | $-\epsilon^*$ | $\epsilon$ | −1 | $-\epsilon^*$ | $\epsilon$ | 1 | $\epsilon^*$ | $-\epsilon$ | | |
| $E_{2u}$ | 1 | $-\epsilon^*$ | $-\epsilon$ | 1 | $-\epsilon^*$ | $-\epsilon$ | −1 | $\epsilon^*$ | $\epsilon$ | −1 | $\epsilon^*$ | $\epsilon$ | | |
| | 1 | $-\epsilon$ | $-\epsilon^*$ | 1 | $-\epsilon$ | $-\epsilon^*$ | −1 | $\epsilon$ | $\epsilon^*$ | −1 | $\epsilon$ | $\epsilon^*$ | | |

**The $D_{nh}$ groups**

| $D_{2h}$ | $E$ | $C_2(z)$ | $C_2(y)$ | $C_2(x)$ | $i$ | $\sigma(xy)$ | $\sigma(xz)$ | $\sigma(yz)$ | | |
|---|---|---|---|---|---|---|---|---|---|---|
| $A_g$ | 1 | 1 | 1 | 1 | 1 | 1 | 1 | 1 | | $x^2, y^2, z^2$ |
| $B_{1g}$ | 1 | 1 | −1 | −1 | 1 | 1 | −1 | −1 | $R_z$ | $xy$ |
| $B_{2g}$ | 1 | −1 | 1 | −1 | 1 | −1 | 1 | −1 | $R_y$ | $zx$ |
| $B_{3g}$ | 1 | −1 | −1 | 1 | 1 | −1 | −1 | 1 | $R_x$ | $yz$ |
| $A_u$ | 1 | 1 | 1 | 1 | −1 | −1 | −1 | −1 | | |
| $B_{1u}$ | 1 | 1 | −1 | −1 | −1 | −1 | 1 | 1 | $T_z$ | |
| $B_{2u}$ | 1 | −1 | 1 | −1 | −1 | 1 | −1 | 1 | $T_y$ | |
| $B_{3u}$ | 1 | −1 | −1 | 1 | −1 | 1 | 1 | −1 | $T_x$ | |

| $D_{3h}$ | $E$ | $2C_3$ | $3C_2$ | $\sigma_h$ | $2S_3$ | $3\sigma_v$ | | |
|---|---|---|---|---|---|---|---|---|
| $A_1'$ | 1 | 1 | 1 | 1 | 1 | 1 | | $x^2 + y^2, z^2$ |
| $A_2'$ | 1 | 1 | −1 | 1 | 1 | −1 | $R_z$ | |
| $E'$ | 2 | −1 | 0 | 2 | −1 | 0 | $(T_x, T_y)$ | $(x^2 - y^2, xy)$ |
| $A_1''$ | 1 | 1 | 1 | −1 | −1 | −1 | | |
| $A_2''$ | 1 | 1 | −1 | −1 | −1 | 1 | $T_z$ | |
| $E''$ | 2 | −1 | 0 | −2 | 1 | 0 | $(R_x, R_y)$ | $(yz, zx)$ |

| $D_{4h}$ | $E$ | $2C_4$ | $C_2$ | $2C_2'$ | $2C_2''$ | $i$ | $2S_4$ | $\sigma_h$ | $2\sigma_v$ | $2\sigma_d$ | | |
|---|---|---|---|---|---|---|---|---|---|---|---|---|
| $A_{1g}$ | 1 | 1 | 1 | 1 | 1 | 1 | 1 | 1 | 1 | 1 | | $x^2 + y^2, z^2$ |
| $A_{2g}$ | 1 | 1 | 1 | −1 | −1 | 1 | 1 | 1 | −1 | −1 | $R_z$ | |
| $B_{1g}$ | 1 | −1 | 1 | 1 | −1 | 1 | −1 | 1 | 1 | −1 | | $x^2 - y^2$ |
| $B_{2g}$ | 1 | −1 | 1 | −1 | 1 | 1 | −1 | 1 | −1 | 1 | | $xy$ |
| $E_g$ | 2 | 0 | −2 | 0 | 0 | 2 | 0 | −2 | 0 | 0 | $(R_x, R_y)$ | $(yz, zx)$ |
| $A_{1u}$ | 1 | 1 | 1 | 1 | 1 | −1 | −1 | −1 | −1 | −1 | | |
| $A_{2u}$ | 1 | 1 | 1 | −1 | −1 | −1 | −1 | −1 | 1 | 1 | $T_z$ | |
| $B_{1u}$ | 1 | −1 | 1 | 1 | −1 | −1 | 1 | −1 | −1 | 1 | | |
| $B_{2u}$ | 1 | −1 | 1 | −1 | 1 | −1 | 1 | −1 | 1 | −1 | | |
| $E_u$ | 2 | 0 | −2 | 0 | 0 | −2 | 0 | 2 | 0 | 0 | $(T_x, T_y)$ | |

| $D_{5h}$ | $E$ | $2C_5$ | $2C_5^2$ | $5C_2$ | $\sigma_h$ | $2S_5$ | $2S_5^3$ | $5\sigma_v$ | | |
|---|---|---|---|---|---|---|---|---|---|---|
| $A_1'$ | 1 | 1 | 1 | 1 | 1 | 1 | 1 | 1 | | $x^2 + y^2, z^2$ |
| $A_2'$ | 1 | 1 | 1 | −1 | 1 | 1 | 1 | −1 | $R_z$ | |
| $E_1'$ | 2 | 2 cos 72° | 2 cos 144° | 0 | 2 | 2 cos 72° | 2 cos 144° | 0 | $(T_x, T_y)$ | |
| $E_2'$ | 2 | 2 cos 144° | 2 cos 72° | 0 | 2 | 2 cos 144° | 2 cos 72° | 0 | | $(x^2 - y^2, xy)$ |
| $A_1''$ | 1 | 1 | 1 | 1 | −1 | −1 | −1 | −1 | | |
| $A_2''$ | 1 | 1 | 1 | −1 | −1 | −1 | −1 | 1 | $T_z$ | |
| $E_1''$ | 2 | 2 cos 72° | 2 cos 144° | 0 | −2 | −2 cos 72° | −2 cos 144° | 0 | $(R_x, R_y)$ | $(yz, zx)$ |
| $E_2''$ | 2 | 2 cos 144° | 2 cos 72° | 0 | −2 | −2 cos 144° | −2 cos 72° | 0 | | |

| $D_{6h}$ | $E$ | $2C_6$ | $2C_3$ | $C_2$ | $3C_2'$ | $3C_2''$ | $i$ | $2S_3$ | $2S_6$ | $\sigma_h$ | $3\sigma_d$ | $3\sigma_v$ | | |
|---|---|---|---|---|---|---|---|---|---|---|---|---|---|---|
| $A_{1g}$ | 1 | 1 | 1 | 1 | 1 | 1 | 1 | 1 | 1 | 1 | 1 | 1 | | $x^2 + y^2, z^2$ |
| $A_{2g}$ | 1 | 1 | 1 | 1 | −1 | −1 | 1 | 1 | 1 | 1 | −1 | −1 | $R_z$ | |
| $B_{1g}$ | 1 | −1 | 1 | −1 | 1 | −1 | 1 | −1 | 1 | −1 | 1 | −1 | | |
| $B_{2g}$ | 1 | −1 | 1 | −1 | −1 | 1 | 1 | −1 | 1 | −1 | −1 | 1 | | |
| $E_{1g}$ | 2 | 1 | −1 | −2 | 0 | 0 | 2 | 1 | −1 | −2 | 0 | 0 | $(R_x, R_y)$ | $(yz, zx)$ |
| $E_{2g}$ | 2 | −1 | −1 | 2 | 0 | 0 | 2 | −1 | −1 | 2 | 0 | 0 | | $(x^2 - y^2, xy)$ |
| $A_{1u}$ | 1 | 1 | 1 | 1 | 1 | 1 | −1 | −1 | −1 | −1 | −1 | −1 | | |
| $A_{2u}$ | 1 | 1 | 1 | 1 | −1 | −1 | −1 | −1 | −1 | −1 | 1 | 1 | $T_z$ | |
| $B_{1u}$ | 1 | −1 | 1 | −1 | 1 | −1 | −1 | 1 | −1 | 1 | −1 | 1 | | |
| $B_{2u}$ | 1 | −1 | 1 | −1 | −1 | 1 | −1 | 1 | −1 | 1 | 1 | −1 | | |
| $E_{1u}$ | 2 | 1 | −1 | −2 | 0 | 0 | −2 | −1 | 1 | 2 | 0 | 0 | $(T_x, T_y)$ | |
| $E_{2u}$ | 2 | −1 | −1 | 2 | 0 | 0 | −2 | 1 | 1 | −2 | 0 | 0 | | |

**The $D_{nd}$ groups**

| $D_{2d}$ | $E$ | $2S_4$ | $C_2$ | $2C_2'$ | $2\sigma_d$ | | |
|---|---|---|---|---|---|---|---|
| $A_1$ | 1 | 1 | 1 | 1 | 1 | | $x^2 + y^2, z^2$ |
| $A_2$ | 1 | 1 | 1 | −1 | −1 | $R_z$ | |
| $B_1$ | 1 | −1 | 1 | 1 | −1 | | $x^2 - y^2$ |
| $B_2$ | 1 | −1 | 1 | −1 | 1 | $T_z$ | $xy$ |
| E | 2 | 0 | −2 | 0 | 0 | $(T_x, T_y), (R_x, R_y)$ | $(yz, zx)$ |

| $D_{3d}$ | $E$ | $2C_3$ | $3C_2$ | $i$ | $2S_6$ | $3\sigma_d$ | | |
|---|---|---|---|---|---|---|---|---|
| $A_{1g}$ | 1 | 1 | 1 | 1 | 1 | 1 | | $x^2 + y^2, z^2$ |
| $A_{2g}$ | 1 | 1 | −1 | 1 | 1 | −1 | $R_z$ | |
| $E_g$ | 2 | −1 | 0 | 2 | −1 | 0 | $(R_x, R_y)$ | $(x^2 - y^2, xy), (yz, zx)$ |
| $A_{1u}$ | 1 | 1 | 1 | −1 | −1 | −1 | | |
| $A_{2u}$ | 1 | 1 | −1 | −1 | −1 | 1 | $T_z$ | |
| $E_u$ | 2 | −1 | 0 | −2 | 1 | 0 | $(T_x, T_y)$ | |

| $D_{4d}$ | $E$ | $2S_8$ | $2C_4$ | $2S_8^3$ | $C_2$ | $4C_2'$ | $4\sigma_d$ | | |
|---|---|---|---|---|---|---|---|---|---|
| $A_1$ | 1 | 1 | 1 | 1 | 1 | 1 | 1 | | $x^2 + y^2, z^2$ |
| $A_2$ | 1 | 1 | 1 | 1 | 1 | −1 | −1 | $R_z$ | |
| $B_1$ | 1 | −1 | 1 | −1 | 1 | 1 | −1 | | |
| $B_2$ | 1 | −1 | 1 | −1 | 1 | −1 | 1 | $T_z$ | |
| $E_1$ | 2 | $\sqrt{2}$ | 0 | $-\sqrt{2}$ | −2 | 0 | 0 | $(T_x, T_y)$ | |
| $E_2$ | 2 | 0 | −2 | 0 | 2 | 0 | 0 | | $(x^2 - y^2, xy)$ |
| $E_3$ | 2 | $-\sqrt{2}$ | 0 | $\sqrt{2}$ | −2 | 0 | 0 | $(R_x, R_y)$ | $(yz, zx)$ |

| $D_{5d}$ | $E$ | $2C_5$ | $2C_5^2$ | $5C_2$ | $i$ | $2S_{10}^3$ | $2S_{10}$ | $5\sigma_d$ | | |
|---|---|---|---|---|---|---|---|---|---|---|
| $A_{1g}$ | 1 | 1 | 1 | 1 | 1 | 1 | 1 | 1 | | $x^2 + y^2, z^2$ |
| $A_{2g}$ | 1 | 1 | 1 | −1 | 1 | 1 | 1 | −1 | $R_z$ | |
| $E_{1g}$ | 2 | 2 cos 72° | 2 cos 144° | 0 | 2 | 2 cos 72° | 2 cos 144° | 0 | $(R_x, R_y)$ | $(yz, zx)$ |
| $E_{2g}$ | 2 | 2 cos 144° | 2 cos 72° | 0 | 2 | 2 cos 144° | 2 cos 72° | 0 | | $(x^2 - y^2, xy)$ |
| $A_{1u}$ | 1 | 1 | 1 | 1 | −1 | −1 | −1 | −1 | | |
| $A_{2u}$ | 1 | 1 | 1 | −1 | −1 | −1 | −1 | 1 | $T_z$ | |
| $E_{1u}$ | 2 | 2 cos 72° | 2 cos 144° | 0 | −2 | −2 cos 72° | −2 cos 144° | 0 | $(T_x, T_y)$ | |
| $E_{2u}$ | 2 | 2 cos 144° | 2 cos 72° | 0 | −2 | −2 cos 144° | −2 cos 72° | 0 | | |

| $D_{6d}$ | $E$ | $2S_{12}$ | $2C_6$ | $2S_4$ | $2C_3$ | $2S_{12}^5$ | $C_2$ | $6C_2'$ | $6\sigma_d$ | | |
|---|---|---|---|---|---|---|---|---|---|---|---|
| $A_1$ | 1 | 1 | 1 | 1 | 1 | 1 | 1 | 1 | 1 | | $x^2 + y^2, z^2$ |
| $A_2$ | 1 | 1 | 1 | 1 | 1 | 1 | 1 | −1 | −1 | $R_z$ | |
| $B_1$ | 1 | −1 | 1 | −1 | 1 | −1 | 1 | 1 | −1 | | |
| $B_2$ | 1 | −1 | 1 | −1 | 1 | −1 | 1 | −1 | 1 | $T_z$ | |
| $E_1$ | 2 | $\sqrt{3}$ | 1 | 0 | −1 | $-\sqrt{3}$ | −2 | 0 | 0 | $(T_x, T_y)$ | |
| $E_2$ | 2 | 1 | −1 | −2 | −1 | 1 | 2 | 0 | 0 | | $(x^2 - y^2, xy)$ |
| $E_3$ | 2 | 0 | −2 | 0 | 2 | 0 | −2 | 0 | 0 | | |
| $E_4$ | 2 | −1 | −1 | 2 | −1 | −1 | 2 | 0 | 0 | | |
| $E_5$ | 2 | $-\sqrt{3}$ | 1 | 0 | −1 | $\sqrt{3}$ | −2 | 0 | 0 | $(R_x, R_y)$ | $(yz, zx)$ |

## The $S_n$ groups

| $\mathbf{S_4}$ | $E$ | $S_4$ | $C_2$ | $S_4^3$ | | |
|---|---|---|---|---|---|---|
| A | 1 | 1 | 1 | 1 | $\mathbf{R_z}$ | $x^2+y^2, z^2$ |
| B | 1 | −1 | 1 | −1 | $\mathbf{T_z}$ | $x^2-y^2, xy$ |
| E | 1 | $i$ | −1 | $-i$ | $(\mathbf{T_x}, \mathbf{T_y}), (\mathbf{R_x}, \mathbf{R_y})$ | $(yz, zx)$ |
| | 1 | $-i$ | −1 | $i$ | | |

| $\mathbf{S_6}$ | $E$ | $C_3$ | $C_3^2$ | $i$ | $S_6^5$ | $S_6$ | | $\epsilon = \exp(2\pi i/3)$ |
|---|---|---|---|---|---|---|---|---|
| $A_g$ | 1 | 1 | 1 | 1 | 1 | 1 | $\mathbf{R_z}$ | $x^2+y^2, z^2$ |
| $E_g$ | 1 | $\epsilon$ | $\epsilon^*$ | 1 | $\epsilon$ | $\epsilon^*$ | $(\mathbf{R_x}, \mathbf{R_y})$ | $(x^2-y^2, xy)$ |
| | 1 | $\epsilon^*$ | $\epsilon$ | 1 | $\epsilon^*$ | $\epsilon$ | | $(yz, zx)$ |
| $A_u$ | 1 | 1 | 1 | −1 | −1 | −1 | $\mathbf{T_z}$ | |
| $E_u$ | 1 | $\epsilon$ | $\epsilon^*$ | −1 | $-\epsilon$ | $-\epsilon^*$ | $(\mathbf{T_x}, \mathbf{T_y})$ | |
| | 1 | $\epsilon^*$ | $\epsilon$ | −1 | $-\epsilon^*$ | $-\epsilon$ | | |

| $\mathbf{S_8}$ | $E$ | $S_8$ | $C_4$ | $S_8^3$ | $C_2$ | $S_8^5$ | $C_4^3$ | $S_8^7$ | | $\epsilon = \exp(2\pi i/8)$ |
|---|---|---|---|---|---|---|---|---|---|---|
| A | 1 | 1 | 1 | 1 | 1 | 1 | 1 | 1 | $\mathbf{R_z}$ | $x^2+y^2, z^2$ |
| B | 1 | −1 | 1 | −1 | 1 | −1 | 1 | −1 | $\mathbf{T_z}$ | |
| $E_1$ | 1 | $\epsilon$ | $i$ | $-\epsilon^*$ | −1 | $-\epsilon$ | $-i$ | $\epsilon^*$ | $(\mathbf{T_x}, \mathbf{T_y})$ | |
| | 1 | $\epsilon^*$ | $-i$ | $-\epsilon$ | −1 | $-\epsilon^*$ | $i$ | $\epsilon$ | $(\mathbf{R_x}, \mathbf{R_y})$ | |
| $E_2$ | 1 | $i$ | −1 | $-i$ | 1 | $i$ | −1 | $-i$ | | $(x^2-y^2, xy)$ |
| | 1 | $-i$ | −1 | $i$ | 1 | $-i$ | −1 | $i$ | | |
| $E_3$ | 1 | $-\epsilon^*$ | $-i$ | $\epsilon$ | −1 | $\epsilon^*$ | $i$ | $-\epsilon$ | | $(yz, xz)$ |
| | 1 | $-\epsilon$ | $i$ | $\epsilon^*$ | −1 | $\epsilon$ | $-i$ | $-\epsilon^*$ | | |

## The cubic groups

| $\mathbf{T_d}$ | $E$ | $8C_3$ | $3C_2$ | $6S_4$ | $6\sigma_d$ | | |
|---|---|---|---|---|---|---|---|
| $A_1$ | 1 | 1 | 1 | 1 | 1 | | $x^2+y^2+z^2$ |
| $A_2$ | 1 | 1 | 1 | −1 | −1 | | |
| E | 2 | −1 | 2 | 0 | 0 | | $(2z^2-x^2-y^2, x^2-y^2)$ |
| $T_1$ | 3 | 0 | −1 | 1 | −1 | $(\mathbf{R_x}, \mathbf{R_y}, \mathbf{R_z})$ | |
| $T_2$ | 3 | 0 | −1 | −1 | 1 | $(\mathbf{T_x}, \mathbf{T_y}, \mathbf{T_z})$ | $(xy, yz, zx)$ |

| $\mathbf{O_h}$ | $E$ | $8C_3$ | $6C_2$ | $6C_4$ | $3C_2(=C_4^2)$ | $i$ | $6S_4$ | $8S_6$ | $3\sigma_h$ | $6\sigma_d$ | | |
|---|---|---|---|---|---|---|---|---|---|---|---|---|
| $A_{1g}$ | 1 | 1 | 1 | 1 | 1 | 1 | 1 | 1 | 1 | 1 | | $x^2+y^2+z^2$ |
| $A_{2g}$ | 1 | 1 | −1 | −1 | 1 | 1 | −1 | 1 | 1 | −1 | | |
| $E_g$ | 2 | −1 | 0 | 0 | 2 | 2 | 0 | −1 | 2 | 0 | | $(2z^2-x^2-y^2, x^2-y^2)$ |
| $T_{1g}$ | 3 | 0 | −1 | 1 | −1 | 3 | 1 | 0 | −1 | −1 | $(\mathbf{R_x}, \mathbf{R_y}, \mathbf{R_z})$ | |
| $T_{2g}$ | 3 | 0 | 1 | −1 | −1 | 3 | −1 | 0 | −1 | 1 | | $(xy, yz, zx)$ |
| $A_{1u}$ | 1 | 1 | 1 | 1 | 1 | −1 | −1 | −1 | −1 | −1 | | |
| $A_{2u}$ | 1 | 1 | −1 | −1 | 1 | −1 | 1 | −1 | −1 | 1 | | |
| $E_u$ | 2 | −1 | 0 | 0 | 2 | −2 | 0 | 1 | −2 | 0 | | |
| $T_{1u}$ | 3 | 0 | −1 | 1 | −1 | −3 | −1 | 0 | 1 | 1 | $(\mathbf{T_x}, \mathbf{T_y}, \mathbf{T_z})$ | |
| $T_{2u}$ | 3 | 0 | 1 | −1 | −1 | −3 | 1 | 0 | 1 | −1 | | |

**The $C_{\infty v}$ and $D_{\infty h}$ groups for linear molecules**

| $C_{\infty v}$ | $E$ | $2C_{\infty}^{\Phi}$ | . . . | $\infty\sigma_v$ | | |
|---|---|---|---|---|---|---|
| $A_1 = \Sigma+$ | 1 | 1 | . . . | 1 | $T_z$ | $x^2 + y^2, z^2$ |
| $A_2 = \Sigma-$ | 1 | 1 | . . . | −1 | $R_z$ | |
| $E_1 = \Pi$ | 2 | 2 cos Φ | . . . | 0 | $(T_x, T_y), (R_x, R_y)$ | |
| $E_2 = \Delta$ | 2 | 2 cos 2Φ | . . . | 0 | | $(yz, zx)$ |
| $E_3 = \Phi$ | 2 | 2 cos 3Φ | . . . | 0 | | $(x^2 - y^2, xy)$ |
| . . . | . . . | . . . | . . . | . . . | | |

| $D_{\infty h}$ | $E$ | $2C_{\infty}^{\Phi}$ | . . . | $\infty\sigma_v$ | $i$ | $2S_{\infty}^{\Phi}$ | . . . | $\infty C_2$ | | |
|---|---|---|---|---|---|---|---|---|---|---|
| $\Sigma_g^+$ | 1 | 1 | . . . | 1 | 1 | 1 | . . . | 1 | | $x^2 + y^2, z^2$ |
| $\Sigma_g^-$ | 1 | 1 | . . . | −1 | 1 | 1 | . . . | −1 | $R_z$ | |
| $\Pi_g$ | 2 | 2 cos Φ | . . . | 0 | 2 | −2 cos φ | . . . | 0 | $(R_x, R_y)$ | $(yz, zx)$ |
| $\Delta_g$ | 2 | 2 cos 2Φ | . . . | 0 | 2 | 2 cos2Φ | . . . | 0 | | $(x^2 - y^2, xy)$ |
| . | . | . | . | . | . | . | . | . | | |
| . | . | . | . | . | . | . | . | . | | |
| . | . | . | . | . | . | . | . | . | | |
| $\Sigma_u^+$ | 1 | 1 | . . . | 1 | −1 | −1 | . . . | −1 | $T_z$ | |
| $\Sigma_u^-$ | 1 | 1 | . . . | −1 | −1 | −1 | . . . | 1 | | |
| $\Pi_u$ | 2 | 2 cos Φ | . . . | 0 | −2 | 2 cos Φ | . . . | 0 | $(T_x, T_y)$ | |
| $\Delta_u$ | 2 | 2 cos 2Φ | . . . | 0 | −2 | −2 cos 2Φ | . . . | 0 | | |
| . . . | . . . | . . . | . . . | . . . | . . . | | . . . | . . . | | |

## A.2 Multiplication properties of irreducible representations

### General rules

A × A = A, B × B = A, A × B = B, A × E = E, B × E = E, A × T = T;
B × T = T;

g × g = g, u × u = g, u × g = u;
′ × ′ = ′, ″ × ″ = ′, ′ × ″ = ″;
$A \times E_1 = E_1$, $A \times E_2 = E_2$, $B \times E_1 = E_2$, $B \times E_2 = E_1$

### Subscripts on A or B

1 × 1 = 1, 2 × 2 = 1, 1 × 2 = 2. except for $\mathbf{D}_2$ and $\mathbf{D}_{2h}$, where 1 × 2 = 3, 2 × 3 = 1, 1 × 3 = 2

### Doubly-degenerate representations

For $\mathbf{C}_3$, $\mathbf{C}_{3h}$, $\mathbf{C}_{3v}$, $\mathbf{D}_3$, $\mathbf{D}_{3h}$, $\mathbf{D}_{3d}$, $\mathbf{C}_6$, $\mathbf{C}_{6h}$, $\mathbf{C}_{6v}$, $\mathbf{D}_6$, $\mathbf{D}_{6h}$, $\mathbf{S}_6$, $\mathbf{O}_h$, $\mathbf{T}_d$,:

$$E_1 \times E_1 = E_2 \times E_2 = A_1 + A_2 + E_2$$
$$E_1 \times E_2 = B_1 + B_2 + E_1$$

For $C_4$, $C_{4v}$, $C_{4h}$, $D_{2d}$, $D_4$, $D_{4h}$, $S_4$:

$$E \times E = A_1 + A_2 + B_1 + B_2$$

For groups in above lists that have symbols A, B or E without subscripts, read $A_1 = A_2 = A$, etc.

**Triply-degenerate representations:**

For $T_d$, $O_h$:

$$E \times T_1 = E \times T_2 = T_1 + T_2$$
$$T_1 \times T_1 = T_2 \times T_2 = A_1 + E + T_1 + T_2$$
$$T_1 \times T_2 = A_2 + E + T_1 + T_2$$

**Linear molecules ($C_{\infty v}$ and $D_{\infty h}$):**

$$\Sigma^+ \times \Sigma^+ = \Sigma^- \times \Sigma^- = \Sigma^+; \qquad \Sigma^+ \times \Sigma^- = \Sigma^-$$
$$\Sigma^+ \times \Pi = \Sigma^- \times \Pi = \Pi; \qquad \Sigma^+ \times \Delta = \Sigma^- \times \Delta = \Delta; \text{ etc.}$$
$$\Pi \times \Pi = \Sigma^+ + \Sigma^- + \Delta$$
$$\Delta \times \Delta = \Sigma^+ + \Sigma^- + \Gamma$$
$$\Pi \times \Delta = \Pi + \Phi$$

## A.3 Correlation tables for the species of a group and its subgroups

| $C_4$ | $C_2$ |
|---|---|
| A | A |
| B | A |
| E | 2B |

| $C_6$ | $C_3$ | $C_2$ |
|---|---|---|
| A | A | A |
| B | A | B |
| $E_1$ | E | 2B |
| $E_2$ | E | 2A |

| $D_2$ | $C_2$ | $C_2$ | $C_2$ |
|---|---|---|---|
| A | A | A | A |
| $B_1$ | A | B | B |
| $B_2$ | B | A | B |
| $B_3$ | B | B | A |

| $D_3$ | $C_3$ | $C_2$ |
|---|---|---|
| $A_1$ | A | A |
| $A_2$ | A | B |
| E | E | A + B |

| $D_4$ | $C_4$ | $C_2$ | $C_2'$<br>$C_2$ | $C_2''$<br>$C_2$ |
|---|---|---|---|---|
| $A_1$ | A | A | A | A |
| $A_2$ | A | A | B | B |
| $B_1$ | B | A | A | B |
| $B_2$ | B | A | B | A |
| E | E | 2B | A + B | A + B |

| $D_5$ | $C_5$ | $C_2$ |
|---|---|---|
| $A_1$ | A | A |
| $A_2$ | A | B |
| $E_1$ | $E_1$ | A + B |
| $E_2$ | $E_2$ | A + B |

| $\mathbf{D}_6$ | $\mathbf{C}_6$ | $\mathbf{D}_3$ ($C_2'$) | $\mathbf{D}_3$ ($C_2''$) | $\mathbf{D}_2$ | $\mathbf{C}_3$ | $\mathbf{C}_2$ | $\mathbf{C}_2$ ($C_2'$) | $\mathbf{C}_2$ ($C_2''$) |
|---|---|---|---|---|---|---|---|---|
| $A_1$ | A | $A_1$ | $A_1$ | A | A | A | A | A |
| $A_2$ | A | $A_2$ | $A_2$ | $B_1$ | A | A | B | B |
| $B_1$ | B | $A_1$ | $A_2$ | $B_2$ | A | B | A | B |
| $B_2$ | B | $A_2$ | $A_1$ | $B_3$ | A | B | B | A |
| $E_1$ | $E_1$ | E | E | $B_2 + B_3$ | E | 2B | A + B | A + B |
| $E_2$ | $E_2$ | E | E | $A + B_1$ | E | 2A | A + B | A + B |

| $\mathbf{C}_{2v}$ | $\mathbf{C}_2$ | $\mathbf{C}_s$ ($\sigma(zx)$) | $\mathbf{C}_s$ ($\sigma(yz)$) |
|---|---|---|---|
| $A_1$ | A | $A'$ | $A'$ |
| $A_2$ | A | $A''$ | $A''$ |
| $B_1$ | B | $A'$ | $A''$ |
| $B_2$ | B | $A''$ | $A'$ |

| $\mathbf{C}_{3v}$ | $\mathbf{C}_3$ | $\mathbf{C}_s$ |
|---|---|---|
| $A_1$ | A | $A'$ |
| $A_2$ | A | $A''$ |
| E | E | $A' + A''$ |

| $\mathbf{C}_{4v}$ | $\mathbf{C}_4$ | $\mathbf{C}_{2v}$ ($\sigma_v$) | $\mathbf{C}_{2v}$ ($\sigma_d$) | $\mathbf{C}_2$ | $\mathbf{C}_s$ ($\sigma_v$) | $\mathbf{C}_s$ ($\sigma_d$) |
|---|---|---|---|---|---|---|
| $A_1$ | A | $A_1$ | $A_1$ | A | $A'$ | $A'$ |
| $A_2$ | A | $A_2$ | $A_2$ | A | $A''$ | $A''$ |
| $B_1$ | B | $A_1$ | $A_2$ | A | $A'$ | $A''$ |
| $B_2$ | B | $A_2$ | $A_1$ | A | $A''$ | $A'$ |
| E | E | $B_1 + B_2$ | $B_1 + B_2$ | 2B | $A' + A''$ | $A' + A''$ |

| $\mathbf{C}_{5v}$ | $\mathbf{C}_5$ | $\mathbf{C}_s$ |
|---|---|---|
| $A_1$ | A | $A'$ |
| $A_2$ | A | $A''$ |
| $E_1$ | $E_1$ | $A' + A''$ |
| $E_2$ | $E_2$ | $A' + A''$ |

| $\mathbf{C}_{6v}$ | $\mathbf{C}_6$ | $\mathbf{C}_{3v}$ ($\sigma_v$) | $\mathbf{C}_{3v}$ ($\sigma_d$) | $\mathbf{C}_{2v}$ ($\sigma_v \to \sigma(zx)$) | $\mathbf{C}_3$ | $\mathbf{C}_2$ | $\mathbf{C}_s$ ($\sigma_v$) | $\mathbf{C}_s$ ($\sigma_d$) |
|---|---|---|---|---|---|---|---|---|
| $A_1$ | A | $A_1$ | $A_1$ | $A_1$ | A | A | $A'$ | $A'$ |
| $A_2$ | A | $A_2$ | $A_2$ | $A_2$ | A | A | $A''$ | $A''$ |
| $B_1$ | B | $A_1$ | $A_2$ | $B_1$ | A | B | $A'$ | $A''$ |
| $B_2$ | B | $A_2$ | $A_1$ | $B_2$ | A | B | $A''$ | $A'$ |
| $E_1$ | $E_1$ | E | E | $B_1 + B_2$ | E | 2B | $A' + A''$ | $A' + A''$ |
| $E_2$ | $E_2$ | E | E | $A_1 + A_2$ | E | 2A | $A' + A''$ | $A' + A''$ |

| $\mathbf{C}_{2h}$ | $\mathbf{C}_2$ | $\mathbf{C}_s$ | $\mathbf{C}_i$ |
|---|---|---|---|
| $A_g$ | A | $A'$ | $A_g$ |
| $B_g$ | B | $A''$ | $A_g$ |
| $A_u$ | A | $A''$ | $A_u$ |
| $B_u$ | B | $A'$ | $A_u$ |

| $\mathbf{C}_{3h}$ | $\mathbf{C}_3$ | $\mathbf{C}_s$ |
|---|---|---|
| $A'$ | A | $A'$ |
| $E'$ | E | $2A'$ |
| $A''$ | A | $A''$ |
| $E''$ | E | $2A''$ |

| $\mathbf{C}_{4h}$ | $\mathbf{C}_4$ | $\mathbf{S}_4$ | $\mathbf{C}_{2h}$ | $\mathbf{C}_2$ | $\mathbf{C}_s$ | $\mathbf{C}_i$ |
|---|---|---|---|---|---|---|
| $A_g$ | A | A | $A_g$ | A | $A'$ | $A_g$ |
| $B_g$ | B | B | $A_g$ | A | $A'$ | $A_g$ |
| $E_g$ | E | E | $2B_g$ | 2B | $2A''$ | $2A_g$ |
| $A_u$ | A | B | $A_u$ | A | $A''$ | $A_u$ |
| $B_u$ | B | A | $A_u$ | A | $A''$ | $A_u$ |
| $E_u$ | E | E | $2B_u$ | 2B | $2A'$ | $2A_u$ |

| $\mathbf{C}_{5h}$ | $\mathbf{C}_5$ | $\mathbf{C}_s$ |
|---|---|---|
| $A'$ | A | $A'$ |
| $E_1'$ | $E_1$ | $2A'$ |
| $E_2'$ | $E_2$ | $2A'$ |
| $A''$ | A | $A''$ |
| $E_1''$ | $E_1$ | $2A''$ |
| $E_2''$ | $E_2$ | $2A''$ |

| $\mathbf{C}_{6h}$ | $\mathbf{C}_6$ | $\mathbf{C}_{3h}$ | $\mathbf{S}_6$ | $\mathbf{C}_{2h}$ | $\mathbf{C}_3$ | $\mathbf{C}_2$ | $\mathbf{C}_s$ | $\mathbf{C}_i$ |
|---|---|---|---|---|---|---|---|---|
| $A_g$ | A | $A'$ | $A_g$ | $A_g$ | A | A | $A'$ | $A_g$ |
| $B_g$ | B | $A''$ | $A_g$ | $B_g$ | A | B | $A''$ | $A_g$ |
| $E_{1g}$ | $E_1$ | $E''$ | $E_g$ | $2B_g$ | E | 2B | $2A''$ | $2A_g$ |
| $E_{2g}$ | $E_2$ | $E'$ | $E_g$ | $2A_g$ | E | 2A | $2A'$ | $2A_g$ |
| $A_u$ | A | $A''$ | $A_u$ | $A_u$ | A | A | $A''$ | $A_u$ |
| $B_u$ | B | $A'$ | $A_u$ | $B_u$ | A | A | $A'$ | $A_u$ |
| $E_{1u}$ | $E_1$ | $E'$ | $E_u$ | $2B_u$ | E | 2B | $2A'$ | $2A_u$ |
| $E_{2u}$ | $E_2$ | $E''$ | $E_u$ | $2A_u$ | E | 2A | $2A''$ | $2A_u$ |

| | | $C_2(z)$ | $C_2(y)$ | $C_2(x)$ | $C_2(z)$ | $C_2(y)$ | $C_2(x)$ | $C_2(z)$ | $C_2(y)$ | $C_2(x)$ | $\sigma(xy)$ | $\sigma(zx)$ | $\sigma(yz)$ |
|---|---|---|---|---|---|---|---|---|---|---|---|---|---|
| $\mathbf{D}_{2h}$ | $\mathbf{D}_2$ | $\mathbf{C}_{2v}$ | $\mathbf{C}_{2v}$ | $\mathbf{C}_{2v}$ | $\mathbf{C}_{2h}$ | $\mathbf{C}_{2h}$ | $\mathbf{C}_{2h}$ | $\mathbf{C}_2$ | $\mathbf{C}_2$ | $\mathbf{C}_2$ | $\mathbf{C}_s$ | $\mathbf{C}_s$ | $\mathbf{C}_s$ |
| $A_g$ | A | $A_1$ | $A_1$ | $A_1$ | $A_g$ | $A_g$ | $A_g$ | A | A | A | $A'$ | $A'$ | $A'$ |
| $B_{1g}$ | $B_1$ | $A_2$ | $B_2$ | $B_1$ | $A_g$ | $B_g$ | $B_g$ | A | B | B | $A'$ | $A''$ | $A''$ |
| $B_{2g}$ | $B_2$ | $B_1$ | $A_2$ | $B_2$ | $B_g$ | $A_g$ | $B_g$ | B | A | B | $A''$ | $A'$ | $A''$ |
| $B_{3g}$ | $B_3$ | $B_2$ | $B_1$ | $A_2$ | $B_g$ | $B_g$ | $A_g$ | B | B | A | $A''$ | $A''$ | $A'$ |
| $A_u$ | A | $A_2$ | $A_2$ | $A_2$ | $A_u$ | $A_u$ | $A_u$ | A | A | A | $A''$ | $A''$ | $A''$ |
| $B_{1u}$ | $B_1$ | $A_1$ | $B_1$ | $B_2$ | $A_u$ | $B_u$ | $B_u$ | A | B | B | $A''$ | $A'$ | $A'$ |
| $B_{2u}$ | $B_2$ | $B_2$ | $A_1$ | $B_1$ | $B_u$ | $A_u$ | $B_u$ | B | A | B | $A'$ | $A''$ | $A'$ |
| $B_{3u}$ | $B_3$ | $B_1$ | $B_2$ | $A_1$ | $B_u$ | $B_u$ | $A_u$ | B | B | A | $A'$ | $A'$ | $A''$ |

| | | | | $\sigma_h \to \sigma_v(zy)$ | | | $\sigma_h$ | $\sigma_v$ |
|---|---|---|---|---|---|---|---|---|
| $\mathbf{D}_{3h}$ | $\mathbf{C}_{3h}$ | $\mathbf{D}_3$ | $\mathbf{C}_{3v}$ | $\mathbf{C}_{2v}$ | $\mathbf{C}_3$ | $\mathbf{C}_2$ | $\mathbf{C}_s$ | $\mathbf{C}_s$ |
| $A_1'$ | $A'$ | $A_1$ | $A_1$ | $A_1$ | A | A | $A'$ | $A'$ |
| $A_2'$ | $A'$ | $A_2$ | $A_2$ | $B_2$ | A | B | $A'$ | $A''$ |
| $E'$ | $E'$ | E | E | $A_1 + B_2$ | E | A + B | $2A'$ | $A' + A''$ |
| $A_1''$ | $A''$ | $A_1$ | $A_2$ | $A_2$ | A | A | $A''$ | $A''$ |
| $A_2''$ | $A''$ | $A_2$ | $A_1$ | $B_1$ | A | B | $A''$ | $A'$ |
| $E''$ | $E''$ | E | E | $A_2 + B_1$ | E | A + B | $2A''$ | $A' + A''$ |

| | | $C_2' \to C_2'$ | $C_2'' \to C_2'$ | | | $C_2'$ | $C_2''$ | | |
|---|---|---|---|---|---|---|---|---|---|
| $\mathbf{D}_{4h}$ | $\mathbf{D}_4$ | $\mathbf{D}_{2d}$ | $\mathbf{D}_{2d}$ | $\mathbf{C}_{4v}$ | $\mathbf{C}_{4h}$ | $\mathbf{D}_{2h}$ | $\mathbf{D}_{2h}$ | $\mathbf{C}_4$ | $\mathbf{S}_4$ |
| $A_{1g}$ | $A_1$ | $A_1$ | $A_1$ | $A_1$ | $A_g$ | $A_g$ | $A_g$ | A | A |
| $A_{2g}$ | $A_2$ | $A_2$ | $A_2$ | $A_2$ | $A_g$ | $B_{1g}$ | $B_{1g}$ | A | A |
| $B_{1g}$ | $B_1$ | $B_1$ | $B_2$ | $B_1$ | $B_g$ | $A_g$ | $B_{1g}$ | B | B |
| $B_{2g}$ | $B_2$ | $B_2$ | $B_1$ | $B_2$ | $B_g$ | $B_{1g}$ | $A_g$ | B | B |
| $E_g$ | E | E | E | E | $E_g$ | $B_{2g} + B_{3g}$ | $B_{2g} + B_{3g}$ | E | E |
| $A_{1u}$ | $A_1$ | $B_1$ | $B_1$ | $A_2$ | $A_u$ | $A_u$ | $A_u$ | A | B |
| $A_{2u}$ | $A_2$ | $B_2$ | $B_2$ | $A_1$ | $A_u$ | $B_{1u}$ | $B_{1u}$ | A | B |
| $B_{1u}$ | $B_1$ | $A_1$ | $A_2$ | $B_2$ | $B_u$ | $A_u$ | $B_{1u}$ | B | A |
| $B_{2u}$ | $B_2$ | $A_2$ | $A_1$ | $B_1$ | $B_u$ | $B_{1u}$ | $A_u$ | B | A |
| $E_u$ | E | E | E | E | $E_u$ | $B_{2u} + B_{3u}$ | $B_{2u} + B_{3u}$ | E | E |

| | $C_2'$ | $C_2''$ | $C_2, \sigma_v$ | $C_2, \sigma_d$ | $C_2'$ | $C_2''$ |
|---|---|---|---|---|---|---|
| $\mathbf{D}_{4h}$ (cont.) | $\mathbf{D}_2$ | $\mathbf{D}_2$ | $\mathbf{C}_{2v}$ | $\mathbf{C}_{2v}$ | $\mathbf{C}_{2v}$ | $\mathbf{C}_{2v}$ |
| $A_{1g}$ | A | A | $A_1$ | $A_1$ | $A_1$ | $A_1$ |
| $A_{2g}$ | $B_1$ | $B_1$ | $A_2$ | $A_2$ | $B_1$ | $B_1$ |
| $B_{1g}$ | A | $B_1$ | $A_1$ | $A_2$ | $A_1$ | $B_1$ |
| $B_{2g}$ | $B_1$ | A | $A_2$ | $A_1$ | $B_1$ | $A_1$ |
| $E_g$ | $B_2 + B_3$ | $B_2 + B_3$ | $B_1 + B_2$ | $B_1 + B_2$ | $A_2 + B_2$ | $A_2 + B_2$ |
| $A_{1u}$ | A | A | $A_2$ | $A_2$ | $A_2$ | $A_2$ |
| $A_{2u}$ | $B_1$ | $B_1$ | $A_1$ | $A_1$ | $B_2$ | $B_2$ |
| $B_{1u}$ | A | $B_1$ | $A_2$ | $A_1$ | $A_2$ | $B_2$ |
| $B_{2u}$ | $B_1$ | A | $A_1$ | $A_2$ | $B_2$ | $A_2$ |
| $E_u$ | $B_2 + B_3$ | $B_2 + B_3$ | $B_1 + B_2$ | $B_1 + B_2$ | $A_1 + B_1$ | $A_1 + B_1$ |

| | $C_2$ | $C_2'$ | $C_2''$ | $C_2$ | $C_2'$ | $C_2''$ | $\sigma_h$ | $\sigma_v$ | $\sigma_d$ | |
|---|---|---|---|---|---|---|---|---|---|---|
| $\mathbf{D}_{4h}$ (cont.) | $\mathbf{C}_{2h}$ | $\mathbf{C}_{2h}$ | $\mathbf{C}_{2h}$ | $\mathbf{C}_2$ | $\mathbf{C}_2$ | $\mathbf{C}_2$ | $\mathbf{C}_s$ | $\mathbf{C}_s$ | $\mathbf{C}_s$ | $\mathbf{C}_i$ |
| $A_{1g}$ | $A_g$ | $A_g$ | $A_g$ | A | A | A | A′ | A′ | A′ | $A_g$ |
| $A_{2g}$ | $A_g$ | $B_g$ | $B_g$ | A | B | B | A′ | A″ | A″ | $A_g$ |
| $B_{1g}$ | $A_g$ | $A_g$ | $B_g$ | A | A | B | A′ | A′ | A″ | $A_g$ |
| $B_{2g}$ | $A_g$ | $B_g$ | $A_g$ | A | B | A | A′ | A″ | A′ | $A_g$ |
| $E_g$ | $2B_g$ | $A_g + B_g$ | $A_g + B_g$ | 2B | A + B | A + B | 2A″ | A′ + A″ | A′ + A″ | $2A_g$ |
| $A_{1u}$ | $A_u$ | $A_u$ | $A_u$ | A | A | A | A″ | A″ | A″ | $A_u$ |
| $A_{2u}$ | $A_u$ | $B_u$ | $B_u$ | A | B | B | A″ | A′ | A′ | $A_u$ |
| $B_{1u}$ | $A_u$ | $A_u$ | $B_u$ | A | A | B | A″ | A″ | A′ | $A_u$ |
| $B_{2u}$ | $A_u$ | $B_u$ | $A_u$ | A | B | A | A″ | A′ | A″ | $A_u$ |
| $E_u$ | $2B_u$ | $A_u + B_u$ | $A_u + B_u$ | 2B | A + B | A + B | 2A′ | A′ + A″ | A′ + A″ | $2A_u$ |

| | | | | | $\sigma_h \rightarrow \sigma(zx)$ | | $\sigma_h$ | $\sigma_v$ |
|---|---|---|---|---|---|---|---|---|
| $\mathbf{D}_{5h}$ | $\mathbf{D}_5$ | $\mathbf{C}_{5v}$ | $\mathbf{C}_{5h}$ | $\mathbf{C}_5$ | $\mathbf{C}_{2v}$ | $\mathbf{C}_2$ | $\mathbf{C}_s$ | $\mathbf{C}_s$ |
| $A_1'$ | $A_1$ | $A_1$ | A′ | A | $A_1$ | A | A′ | A′ |
| $A_2'$ | $A_2$ | $A_2$ | A′ | A | $B_1$ | B | A′ | A″ |
| $E_1'$ | $E_1$ | $E_1$ | $E_1'$ | $E_1$ | $A_1 + B_1$ | A + B | 2A′ | A′ + A″ |
| $E_2'$ | $E_2$ | $E_2$ | $E_2'$ | $E_2$ | $A_1 + B_1$ | A + B | 2A′ | A′ + A″ |
| $A_1''$ | $A_1$ | $A_2$ | A″ | A | $A_2$ | A | A″ | A″ |
| $A_2''$ | $A_2$ | $A_1$ | A″ | A | $B_2$ | B | A″ | A′ |
| $E_1''$ | $E_1$ | $E_1$ | $E_1''$ | $E_1$ | $A_2 + B_2$ | A + B | 2A″ | A′ + A″ |
| $E_2''$ | $E_2$ | $E_2$ | $E_2''$ | $E_2$ | $A_2 + B_2$ | A + B | 2A″ | A′ + A″ |

| | | $C_2'$ | $C_2''$ | | | $C_2''$ | $C_2'$ | $\sigma_h \rightarrow \sigma(xy)$, $\sigma_v \rightarrow \sigma(yz)$ | | | $C_2'$ | $C_2''$ | $\sigma_v$ | $\sigma_d$ | | |
|---|---|---|---|---|---|---|---|---|---|---|---|---|---|---|---|---|
| $\mathbf{D}_{6h}$ | $\mathbf{D}_6$ | $\mathbf{D}_{3h}$ | $\mathbf{D}_{3h}$ | $\mathbf{C}_{6v}$ | $\mathbf{C}_{6h}$ | $\mathbf{D}_{3d}$ | $\mathbf{D}_{3d}$ | $\mathbf{D}_{2h}$ | $\mathbf{C}_6$ | $\mathbf{C}_{3h}$ | $\mathbf{D}_3$ | $\mathbf{D}_3$ | $\mathbf{C}_{3v}$ | $\mathbf{C}_{3v}$ | $\mathbf{S}_6$ | $\mathbf{D}_2$ |
| $A_{1g}$ | $A_1$ | $A_1'$ | $A_1'$ | $A_1$ | $A_g$ | $A_{1g}$ | $A_{1g}$ | $A_g$ | A | $A'$ | $A_1$ | $A_1$ | $A_1$ | $A_1$ | $A_g$ | A |
| $A_{2g}$ | $A_2$ | $A_2'$ | $A_2'$ | $A_2$ | $A_g$ | $A_{2g}$ | $A_{2g}$ | $B_{1g}$ | A | $A'$ | $A_2$ | $A_2$ | $A_2$ | $A_2$ | $A_g$ | $B_1$ |
| $B_{1g}$ | $B_1$ | $A_1''$ | $A_2''$ | $B_2$ | $B_g$ | $A_{2g}$ | $A_{1g}$ | $B_{2g}$ | B | $A''$ | $A_1$ | $A_2$ | $A_2$ | $A_1$ | $A_g$ | $B_2$ |
| $B_{2g}$ | $B_2$ | $A_2''$ | $A_1''$ | $B_1$ | $B_g$ | $A_{1g}$ | $A_{2g}$ | $B_{3g}$ | B | $A''$ | $A_2$ | $A_1$ | $A_1$ | $A_2$ | $A_g$ | $B_3$ |
| $E_{1g}$ | $E_1$ | $E''$ | $E''$ | $E_1$ | $E_{1g}$ | $E_g$ | $E_g$ | $B_{2g} + B_{3g}$ | $E_1$ | $E''$ | E | E | E | E | $E_g$ | $B_2 + B_3$ |
| $E_{2g}$ | $E_2$ | $E'$ | $E'$ | $E_2$ | $E_{2g}$ | $E_g$ | $E_g$ | $A_g + B_{1g}$ | $E_2$ | $E'$ | E | E | E | E | $E_g$ | $A + B_1$ |
| $A_{1u}$ | $A_1$ | $A_1''$ | $A_1''$ | $A_2$ | $A_u$ | $A_{1u}$ | $A_{1u}$ | $A_u$ | A | $A''$ | $A_1$ | $A_1$ | $A_2$ | $A_2$ | $A_u$ | A |
| $A_{2u}$ | $A_2$ | $A_2''$ | $A_2''$ | $A_1$ | $A_u$ | $A_{2u}$ | $A_{2u}$ | $B_{1u}$ | A | $A''$ | $A_2$ | $A_2$ | $A_1$ | $A_1$ | $A_u$ | $B_1$ |
| $B_{1u}$ | $B_1$ | $A_1'$ | $A_2'$ | $B_1$ | $B_u$ | $A_{2u}$ | $A_{1u}$ | $B_{2u}$ | B | $A'$ | $A_1$ | $A_2$ | $A_1$ | $A_2$ | $A_u$ | $B_2$ |
| $B_{2u}$ | $B_2$ | $A_2'$ | $A_1'$ | $B_2$ | $B_u$ | $A_{1u}$ | $A_{2u}$ | $B_{3u}$ | B | $A'$ | $A_2$ | $A_1$ | $A_2$ | $A_1$ | $A_u$ | $B_3$ |
| $E_{1u}$ | $E_1$ | $E'$ | $E'$ | $E_1$ | $E_{1u}$ | $E_u$ | $E_u$ | $B_{2u} + B_{3u}$ | $E_1$ | $E'$ | E | E | E | E | $E_u$ | $B_2 + B_3$ |
| $E_{2u}$ | $E_2$ | $E''$ | $E''$ | $E_2$ | $E_{2u}$ | $E_u$ | $E_u$ | $A_u + B_{1u}$ | $E_2$ | $E''$ | E | E | E | E | $E_u$ | $A + B_1$ |

| | $C_2'$ | $C_2''$ | $C_2$ | $C_2'$ | $C_2''$ | | $C_2$ |
|---|---|---|---|---|---|---|---|
| $\mathbf{D}_{6h}$ (cont.) | $\mathbf{C}_{2v}$ | $\mathbf{C}_{2v}$ | $\mathbf{C}_{2h}$ | $\mathbf{C}_{2h}$ | $\mathbf{C}_{2h}$ | $\mathbf{C}_3$ | $\mathbf{C}_2$ |
| $A_{1g}$ | $A_1$ | $A_1$ | $A_g$ | $A_g$ | $A_g$ | A | A |
| $A_{2g}$ | $B_1$ | $B_1$ | $A_g$ | $B_g$ | $B_g$ | A | A |
| $B_{1g}$ | $A_2$ | $B_2$ | $B_g$ | $A_g$ | $B_g$ | A | B |
| $B_{2g}$ | $B_2$ | $A_2$ | $B_g$ | $B_g$ | $A_g$ | A | B |
| $E_{1g}$ | $A_2 + B_2$ | $A_2 + B_2$ | $2B_g$ | $A_g + B_g$ | $A_g + B_g$ | E | 2B |
| $E_{2g}$ | $A_1 + B_1$ | $A_1 + B_1$ | $2A_g$ | $A_g + B_g$ | $A_g + B_g$ | E | 2A |
| $A_{1u}$ | $A_2$ | $A_2$ | $A_u$ | $A_u$ | $A_u$ | A | A |
| $A_{2u}$ | $B_2$ | $B_2$ | $A_u$ | $B_u$ | $B_u$ | A | A |
| $B_{1u}$ | $A_1$ | $B_1$ | $B_u$ | $A_u$ | $B_u$ | A | B |
| $B_{2u}$ | $B_1$ | $A_1$ | $B_u$ | $B_u$ | $A_u$ | A | B |
| $E_{1u}$ | $A_1 + B_1$ | $A_1 + B_1$ | $2B_u$ | $A_u + B_u$ | $A_u + B_u$ | E | 2B |
| $E_{2u}$ | $A_2 + B_2$ | $A_2 + B_2$ | $2A_u$ | $A_u + B_u$ | $A_u + B_u$ | E | 2A |

| | $C_2'$ | $C_2''$ | $\sigma_h$ | $\sigma_d$ | $\sigma_v$ | |
|---|---|---|---|---|---|---|
| $\mathbf{D}_{6h}$ (cont.) | $\mathbf{C}_2$ | $\mathbf{C}_2$ | $\mathbf{C}_s$ | $\mathbf{C}_s$ | $\mathbf{C}_s$ | $\mathbf{C}_i$ |
| $A_{1g}$ | A | A | $A'$ | $A'$ | $A'$ | $A_g$ |
| $A_{2g}$ | B | B | $A'$ | $A''$ | $A''$ | $A_g$ |
| $B_{1g}$ | A | B | $A''$ | $A'$ | $A''$ | $A_g$ |
| $B_{2g}$ | B | A | $A''$ | $A''$ | $A'$ | $A_g$ |
| $E_{1g}$ | A + B | A + B | $2A''$ | $A' + A''$ | $A' + A''$ | $2A_g$ |
| $E_{2g}$ | A + B | A + B | $2A'$ | $A' + A''$ | $A' + A''$ | $2A_g$ |
| $A_{1u}$ | A | A | $A''$ | $A''$ | $A''$ | $A_u$ |
| $A_{2u}$ | B | B | $A''$ | $A'$ | $A'$ | $A_u$ |
| $B_{1u}$ | A | B | $A'$ | $A''$ | $A'$ | $A_u$ |
| $B_{2u}$ | B | A | $A'$ | $A'$ | $A''$ | $A_u$ |
| $E_{1u}$ | A + B | A + B | $2A'$ | $A' + A''$ | $A' + A''$ | $2A_u$ |
| $E_{2u}$ | A + B | A + B | $2A''$ | $A' + A''$ | $A' + A''$ | $2A_u$ |

| | | $C_2 \rightarrow C_2(z)$ | | $C_2$ | $C_2'$ | |
|---|---|---|---|---|---|---|
| $\mathbf{D}_{2d}$ | $\mathbf{S}_4$ | $\mathbf{D}_2$ | $\mathbf{C}_{2v}$ | $\mathbf{C}_2$ | $\mathbf{C}_2$ | $\mathbf{C}_s$ |
| $A_1$ | A | A | $A_1$ | A | A | A′ |
| $A_2$ | A | $B_1$ | $A_2$ | A | B | A″ |
| $B_1$ | B | A | $A_2$ | A | A | A″ |
| $B_2$ | B | $B_1$ | $A_1$ | A | B | A′ |
| E | E | $B_2 + B_3$ | $B_1 + B_2$ | 2B | A + B | A′ + A″ |

| $\mathbf{D}_{3d}$ | $\mathbf{D}_3$ | $\mathbf{C}_{3v}$ | $\mathbf{S}_6$ | $\mathbf{C}_3$ | $\mathbf{C}_{2h}$ | $\mathbf{C}_2$ | $\mathbf{C}_s$ | $\mathbf{C}_i$ |
|---|---|---|---|---|---|---|---|---|
| $A_{1g}$ | $A_1$ | $A_1$ | $A_g$ | A | $A_g$ | A | A′ | $A_g$ |
| $A_{2g}$ | $A_2$ | $A_2$ | $A_g$ | A | $B_g$ | B | A″ | $A_g$ |
| $E_g$ | E | E | $E_g$ | E | $A_g + B_g$ | A + B | A′ + A″ | $2A_g$ |
| $A_{1u}$ | $A_1$ | $A_2$ | $A_u$ | A | $A_u$ | A | A″ | $A_u$ |
| $A_{2u}$ | $A_2$ | $A_1$ | $A_u$ | A | $B_u$ | B | A′ | $A_u$ |
| $E_u$ | E | E | $E_u$ | E | $A_u + B_u$ | A + B | A′ + A″ | $2A_u$ |

| | | | | | | $C_2$ | $C_2'$ | |
|---|---|---|---|---|---|---|---|---|
| $\mathbf{D}_{4d}$ | $\mathbf{D}_4$ | $\mathbf{C}_{4v}$ | $\mathbf{S}_8$ | $\mathbf{C}_4$ | $\mathbf{C}_{2v}$ | $\mathbf{C}_2$ | $\mathbf{C}_2$ | $\mathbf{C}_s$ |
| $A_1$ | $A_1$ | $A_1$ | A | A | $A_1$ | A | A | A′ |
| $A_2$ | $A_2$ | $A_2$ | A | A | $A_2$ | A | B | A″ |
| $B_1$ | $A_1$ | $A_2$ | B | A | $A_2$ | A | A | A″ |
| $B_2$ | $A_2$ | $A_1$ | B | A | $A_1$ | A | B | A′ |
| $E_1$ | E | E | $E_1$ | E | $B_1 + B_2$ | 2B | A + B | A′ + A″ |
| $E_2$ | $B_1 + B_2$ | $B_1 + B_2$ | $E_2$ | 2B | $A_1 + A_2$ | 2A | A + B | A′ + A″ |
| $E_3$ | E | E | $E_3$ | E | $B_1 + B_2$ | 2B | A + B | A′ + A″ |

| $\mathbf{D}_{5d}$ | $\mathbf{D}_5$ | $\mathbf{C}_{5v}$ | $\mathbf{C}_5$ | $\mathbf{C}_2$ | $\mathbf{C}_s$ | $\mathbf{C}_i$ |
|---|---|---|---|---|---|---|
| $A_{1g}$ | $A_1$ | $A_1$ | A | A | A′ | $A_g$ |
| $A_{2g}$ | $A_2$ | $A_2$ | A | B | A″ | $A_g$ |
| $E_{1g}$ | $E_1$ | $E_1$ | $E_1$ | A + B | A′ + A″ | $2A_g$ |
| $E_{2g}$ | $E_2$ | $E_2$ | $E_2$ | A + B | A′ + A″ | $2A_g$ |
| $A_{1u}$ | $A_1$ | $A_2$ | A | A | A″ | $A_u$ |
| $A_{2u}$ | $A_2$ | $A_1$ | A | B | A′ | $A_u$ |
| $E_{1u}$ | $E_1$ | $E_1$ | $E_1$ | A + B | A′ + A″ | $2A_u$ |
| $E_{2u}$ | $E_2$ | $E_2$ | $E_2$ | A + B | A′ + A″ | $2A_u$ |

| $\mathbf{D}_{6d}$ | $\mathbf{D}_6$ | $\mathbf{C}_{6v}$ | $\mathbf{C}_6$ | $\mathbf{D}_{2d}$ | $\mathbf{D}_3$ | $\mathbf{C}_{3v}$ |
|---|---|---|---|---|---|---|
| $A_1$ | $A_1$ | $A_1$ | A | $A_1$ | $A_1$ | $A_1$ |
| $A_2$ | $A_2$ | $A_2$ | A | $A_2$ | $A_2$ | $A_2$ |
| $B_1$ | $A_1$ | $A_2$ | A | $B_1$ | $A_1$ | $A_2$ |
| $B_2$ | $A_2$ | $A_1$ | A | $B_2$ | $A_2$ | $A_1$ |
| $E_1$ | $E_1$ | $E_1$ | $E_1$ | E | E | E |
| $E_2$ | $E_2$ | $E_2$ | $E_2$ | $B_1 + B_2$ | E | E |
| $E_3$ | $B_1 + B_2$ | $B_1 + B_2$ | 2B | E | $A_1 + A_2$ | $A_1 + A_2$ |
| $E_4$ | $E_2$ | $E_2$ | $E_2$ | $A_1 + A_2$ | E | E |
| $E_5$ | $E_1$ | $E_1$ | $E_1$ | E | E | E |

| $\mathbf{D}_{6d}$ (cont.) | $\mathbf{D}_2$ | $\mathbf{C}_{2v}$ | $\mathbf{S}_4$ | $\mathbf{C}_3$ | $C_2$ <br> $\mathbf{C}_2$ | $C_2'$ <br> $\mathbf{C}_2$ | $\mathbf{C}_s$ |
|---|---|---|---|---|---|---|---|
| $A_1$ | A | $A_1$ | A | A | A | A | A′ |
| $A_2$ | $B_1$ | $A_2$ | A | A | A | B | A″ |
| $B_1$ | A | $A_2$ | B | A | A | A | A″ |
| $B_2$ | $B_1$ | $A_1$ | B | A | A | B | A′ |
| $E_1$ | $B_2 + B_3$ | $B_1 + B_2$ | E | E | 2B | A + B | A′ + A″ |
| $E_2$ | $A + B_1$ | $A_1 + A_2$ | 2B | E | 2A | A + B | A′ + A″ |
| $E_3$ | $B_2 + B_3$ | $B_1 + B_2$ | E | 2A | 2B | A + B | A′ + A″ |
| $E_4$ | $A + B_1$ | $A_1 + A_2$ | 2A | E | 2A | A + B | A′ + A″ |
| $E_5$ | $B_2 + B_3$ | $B_1 + B_2$ | E | E | 2B | A + B | A′ + A″ |

| $\mathbf{S}_4$ | $\mathbf{C}_2$ |
|---|---|
| A | A |
| B | A |
| E | 2B |

| $\mathbf{S}_6$ | $\mathbf{C}_3$ | $\mathbf{C}_i$ |
|---|---|---|
| $A_g$ | A | $A_g$ |
| $E_g$ | E | $2A_g$ |
| $A_u$ | A | $A_u$ |
| $E_u$ | E | $2A_u$ |

| $\mathbf{S}_8$ | $\mathbf{C}_4$ | $\mathbf{C}_2$ |
|---|---|---|
| A | A | A |
| B | A | A |
| $E_1$ | E | 2B |
| $E_2$ | 2B | 2A |
| $E_3$ | E | 2B |

| $\mathbf{T}_d$ | $\mathbf{D}_{2d}$ | $\mathbf{C}_{3v}$ | $\mathbf{S}_4$ | $\mathbf{D}_2$ | $\mathbf{C}_{2v}$ | $\mathbf{C}_3$ | $\mathbf{C}_2$ | $\mathbf{C}_s$ |
|---|---|---|---|---|---|---|---|---|
| $A_1$ | $A_1$ | $A_1$ | A | A | $A_1$ | A | A | A′ |
| $A_2$ | $B_1$ | $A_2$ | B | A | $A_2$ | A | A | A″ |
| E | $A_1 + B_1$ | E | A + B | 2A | $A_1 + A_2$ | E | 2A | A′ + A″ |
| $T_1$ | $A_2 + E$ | $A_2 + E$ | A + E | $B_1 + B_2 + B_3$ | $A_2 + B_1 + B_2$ | A + E | A + 2B | A′ + 2A″ |
| $T_2$ | $B_2 + E$ | $A_1 + E$ | B + E | $B_1 + B_2 + B_3$ | $A_1 + B_1 + B_2$ | A + E | A + 2B | 2A′ + A″ |

| $\mathbf{O}_h$ | $\mathbf{T}_d$ | $\mathbf{D}_{4h}$ | $\mathbf{D}_{3d}$ |
|---|---|---|---|
| $A_{1g}$ | $A_1$ | $A_{1g}$ | $A_{1g}$ |
| $A_{2g}$ | $A_2$ | $B_{1g}$ | $A_{2g}$ |
| $E_g$ | E | $A_{1g} + B_{1g}$ | $E_g$ |
| $T_{1g}$ | $T_1$ | $A_{2g} + E_g$ | $A_{2g} + E_g$ |
| $T_{2g}$ | $T_2$ | $B_{2g} + E_g$ | $A_{1g} + E_g$ |
| $A_{1u}$ | $A_2$ | $A_{1u}$ | $A_{1u}$ |
| $A_{2u}$ | $A_1$ | $B_{1u}$ | $A_{2u}$ |
| $E_u$ | E | $A_{1u} + B_{1u}$ | $E_u$ |
| $T_{1u}$ | $T_2$ | $A_{2u} + E_u$ | $A_{2u} + E_u$ |
| $T_{2u}$ | $T_1$ | $B_{2u} + E_u$ | $A_{1u} + E_u$ |

# Appendix B

## Some useful properties of square matrices

### B.1 A proof

Here, we will prove that carrying out a similarity transformation:

$$\mathbf{CAC^{-1} = B}$$

does not alter the character of any matrix.

We need to prove that $\chi(\mathbf{A}) = \chi(\mathbf{B})$. The proof is as follows:

$$\chi(\mathbf{B}) = \chi(\mathbf{CAC^{-1}})$$

but the multiplication of matrices is associative, which means that we can bracket off any pair in any way we choose. Therefore:

$$\mathbf{CAC^{-1}} = (\mathbf{CA})\mathbf{C^{-1}} = \mathbf{C}(\mathbf{AC^{-1}})$$

(This property is also possessed by symmetry operations – see Chapter 2.) Therefore:

$$\chi(\mathbf{B}) = \chi[\mathbf{C}(\mathbf{AC^{-1}})]$$

but as:

$$\chi[\mathbf{C}(\mathbf{AC^{-1}})] = \chi[(\mathbf{AC^{-1}})\mathbf{C}] \qquad \text{(see page 61)}$$

Therefore:

$$\chi(\mathbf{B}) = \chi[(\mathbf{AC^{-1}})\mathbf{C}] = \chi[\mathbf{A}(\mathbf{C^{-1}C})]$$

and hence:

$$\chi(\mathbf{B}) = \chi(\mathbf{A})$$

This proves the desired result. The last step follows from the fact that $\mathbf{C^{-1}C = E}$ where $\mathbf{E}$ is the unit matrix, which has a value of +1 for every diagonal element and zero for all other elements. Multiplying **A** by **E**, therefore, does not change any of the diagonal elements of **A**, and hence does not alter $\chi(\mathbf{A})$.

### B.2 Irreducible representations

Here, we look at some of the important properties of the characters of irreducible representation matrices, and a derivation of the equation showing the number of times each irreducible representation is present in a reducible representation.

**1** The sum of the squares of the characters of any irreducible representation equals the number of symmetry operations of the group ($g$):

$$\sum_R [\chi_i(R)]^2 = g$$

where $R$ is any symmetry operation of the group and $\chi_i(R)$ is the character of that operation in the irreducible representation $i$. As an example, consider the characters of the $A_2$ representation of $\mathbf{C}_{3v}$ (using the Mulliken symbol for the irreducible representation generated by the $\mathbf{R}_z$ vector – see the character tables in Appendix A):

$$\begin{aligned}[\chi(E)]^2 + [\chi(C_3^1)]^2 + [\chi(C_3^2)]^2 + 3[\chi(\sigma_v)]^2 \\ = 1^2 + 1^2 + 1^2 + (-1)^2 + (-1)^2 + (-1)^2 \\ = 6 \quad \text{(the total number of symmetry operations of } \mathbf{C}_{3v})\end{aligned}$$

**2** The sum (over all $R$) of the products of the characters of any symmetry operation in *different* irreducible representations is zero; that is:

$$\sum_R \chi_i(R)\chi_j(R) = 0$$

where $i$ and $j$ are two different irreducible representations. Using the $A_2$ and E representations of $\mathbf{C}_{3v}$ as examples:

$$(1 \times 2) + (1 \times -1) + (1 \times -1) + (-1 \times 0) + (-1 \times 0) + (-1 \times 0) = 0$$

The two equations from 1 and 2 may be summarised as:

$$\sum_R \chi_i(R)\chi_j(R) = g\delta_{ij}$$

where $\delta_{ij}$ is the Kronecker delta symbol, which has the value +1 when $i = j$, but zero when $i \neq j$. If we use this equation, together with the result of B.1 (p.188), we can determine which irreducible representations contribute to any reducible one (this equation also limits the possible combinations of characters permissible in any irreducible representation).

Let the character of a given operation in any representation be $\chi(R)$. Let the character of the same operation in the irreducible representation $q$ be $\chi_q(R)$. By the result of B.1, the following relationship holds:

$$\chi(R) = \sum_q a_q\chi_q(R)$$

where the sum is taken over all irreducible representations of the group and $a_q$ is the number of times that the irreducible representation $q$ is present.

Now multiply both sides by $\chi_p(R)$, the character of $R$ in the irreducible representation $p$, and sum both sides over all the symmetry operations of the group:

$$\sum_R \chi(R)\chi_p(R) = \sum_R \sum_q a_q\chi_q(R)\chi_p(R)$$

$$= \sum_q \sum_R a_q\chi_q(R)\chi_p(R)$$

(the order of summations is not significant). But:

$$\sum_R a_q\chi_q(R)\chi_p(R) = a_q\delta_{pq}$$

and so this term vanishes unless $p = q$. Therefore, when this is summed over all $q$, the only term that does not vanish is:

$$\sum_R a_p \chi_p(R) \chi_p(R)$$

which equals $a_p g$. Therefore:

$$\sum_R \chi(R) \chi_p(R) = a_p g$$

By rearrangement, we can see that the number of times that the irreducible representation $p$ appears in any reducible representation is:

$$a_p = \left(\frac{1}{g}\right) \sum_R \chi(R) \chi_p(R)$$

# Appendix C

## Additional useful information

### Procedure for assignment to point groups

**1** Determine whether the molecule is linear, or belongs to the highly symmetrical cubic or icosahedral point groups (**T**$_d$, **O**$_h$ or **I**$_h$). If not, proceed to step 2.

**2** Find the proper rotation axis of highest order ($C_n$). In the absence of such an axis, look for (a) a plane of symmetry (**C**$_s$), (b) a centre of symmetry (**C**$_i$) or (c) no symmetry other than $E$ (**C**$_1$).

**3** If an axis $C_n$ is found, look for a set of $n$ $C_2$ axes perpendicular to it. If these are present, proceed to step 4. If they are absent, look for (a) a horizontal plane (**C**$_{nh}$), (b) $n$ vertical planes (**C**$_{nv}$), (c) an $S_{2n}$ axis coincident with $C_n$ (**S**$_{2n}$) or (d) no symmetry planes or other axes (**C**$_n$).

**4** If a $C_n$ axis and $n$ perpendicular axes are present, check on the presence of (a) a horizontal plane (**D**$_{nh}$), (b) $n$ vertical planes and no horizontal plane (**D**$_{nd}$) or (c) no symmetry planes or other axes (**D**$_n$).

### The reduction formula:

$$a_p = \left(\frac{1}{g}\right)\sum_R \chi(R)\chi_p(R)$$

### The projection operator equation:

$$[P^p]x = \left[\sum_R \{\chi_p(R)\cdot R\}\right]x$$

### Contribution to character per unshifted atom

| $R$ | $\chi(R)$ |
|---|---|
| $E$ | +3 |
| $i$ | −3 |
| $\sigma$ | +1 |
| $C_2$ | −1 |
| $C_3^1$, $C_3^2$ | 0 |
| $C_4^1$, $C_4^3$ | +1 |
| $C_6^1$, $C_6^5$ | +2 |
| $S_3^1$, $S_3^5$ | −2 |
| $S_4^1$, $S_4^3$ | −1 |
| $S_6^1$, $S_6^5$ | 0 |

# Answers to exercises

## Chapter 1

**1** (a) A $C_4$ axis (coincident with the F—W—Cl direction); two $\sigma_v$ planes each one including the W and Cl atoms, the axial F and two *trans* equatorial F′ atoms); and two $\sigma_d$ planes (bisecting the angles between the $\sigma_v$ planes).

(b) A $C_4$ axis (passing through the Pt perpendicular to the molecular plane); two $C_2'$ axes (along the Cl—Pt—Cl bond directions); two $C_2''$ axes (bisecting the angle between the $C_2'$ axes); a $\sigma_h$; two $\sigma_v$ planes (including the $C_2'$ axes); two $\sigma_d$ planes (including the $C_2''$ axes); an $i$ (at the Pt atom); and an $S_4$ (coincident with $C_4$).

(c) A $C_3$ axis (along the Si—C—N direction); and three $\sigma_v$ planes (each containing the Si, C, N and one H).

(d) A $C_2$ axis (through the Cl atom and the opposite C); and two $\sigma_v$ planes (one in the molecular plane and one perpendicular to it, passing through the Cl atom).

(e) A $C_2$ axis (along the C═C═C direction); two $C_2'$ axes (perpendicular to $C_2$, each at 45° to the planes defined by the $CH_2$ groups); two $\sigma_d$ planes (bisecting the angles between the $C_2$ axes); and an $S_4$ (coincident with $C_2$).

(f) Four $C_3$ axes (one along each Ni—C—O direction); three $C_2$ axes (each one bisecting two opposite edges of the tetrahedron defined by the O atoms); three $S_4$ axes (coincident with the $C_2$ axes); and six $\sigma_d$ planes (each one containing one edge of the tetrahedron).

(g) A $C_3$ axis (perpendicular to the molecular plane); three $C_2'$ axes (one passing along each C—O bond); a $\sigma_h$; three $\sigma_v$ planes (each containing a $C_2'$); and an $S_3$ (coincident with $C_3$).

(h) A $C_3$ axis (passing through the ring centre); three $C_2'$ axes (each one passing through opposite B and N atoms); a $\sigma_h$; three $\sigma_v$ planes (each containing one $C_2'$); and an $S_3$ (coincident with $C_3$).

**2** (a) $C_5^1$, $C_5^2$, $C_5^3$, $C_5^4$, $C_5^5 = E$

(b) $C_6^1$, $C_6^2 = C_3^1$, $C_6^3 = C_2^1$, $C_6^4 = C_3^2$, $C_6^5$, $C_6^6 = E$

(c) $S_3^1$, $S_3^2 = C_3^2$, $S_3^3 = \sigma_h$, $S_3^4 = C_3^1$, $S_3^5$, $S_3^6 = E$

(d) $S_8^1$, $S_8^2 = C_8^2 = C_4^1$, $S_8^3$, $S_8^4 = C_8^4 = C_2^1$, $S_8^5$, $S_8^6 = C_8^6 = C_4^3$, $S_8^7$, $S_8^8 = E$

**3** (a) $\sigma_v(3)$
(b) $C_3^1$
(c) $\sigma_v(1)$
(d) $C_3^1$

**4** (a) $\sigma_v(1)$
(b) $C_2'(1)$
(c) $S_3^5$
(d) $C_3^2$

## Chapter 2

**1** Remember that $E = E^{-1}$, $\sigma(xz) = \sigma(xz)^{-1}$, $\sigma(yz) = \sigma(yz)^{-1}$ and $C_2 = C_2^{-1}$. Work through all the possible similarity transformations; for example:

$EC_2E = EEC_2 = C_2$
$C_2C_2C_2 = C_2E = C_2$
$\sigma(xz)C_2\sigma(xz) = \sigma(xz)\sigma(xz)C_2 = EC_2 = C_2$ (show that $C_2$ and $\sigma(xz)$ commute)
$\sigma(yz)C_2\sigma(yz) = \sigma(yz)\sigma(yz)C_2 = EC_2 = C_2$

Therefore, $C_2$ is in a class by itself.

**2** (a) $\mathbf{C}_1$
(b) $\mathbf{C}_s$
(c) $\mathbf{C}_s$
(d) $\mathbf{C}_{2v}$
(e) $\mathbf{C}_{2v}$
(f) $\mathbf{C}_{3v}$
(g) $\mathbf{C}_{4v}$
(h) $\mathbf{D}_{4h}$
(i) $\mathbf{D}_{2h}$
(j) $\mathbf{T}_d$
(k) $\mathbf{D}_{3h}$
(l) $\mathbf{D}_{5h}$
(m) $\mathbf{O}_h$
(n) $\mathbf{D}_{\infty h}$
(o) $\mathbf{C}_{\infty v}$

## Chapter 3

**1** (a) $\begin{bmatrix} 10 & 7 \\ 4 & -2 \\ -6 & 3 \end{bmatrix}$

(b) Not possible

(c) $\begin{bmatrix} 0 & 3 \\ 4 & 2 \end{bmatrix}$

**2** (a) $\begin{bmatrix} 16 & 0 & 2 \\ 1 & 2 & 1 \\ 17 & 2 & 3 \end{bmatrix}$

(b) Not possible

(c) $\begin{bmatrix} -2 & -4 \\ 7 & -6 \end{bmatrix}$

(d) $\begin{bmatrix} 0 & 10 \\ -4 & -8 \end{bmatrix}$

(e) $\begin{bmatrix} 2 & 0 \\ 0 & 2 \end{bmatrix}$

(f) $\begin{bmatrix} 2 & 0 \\ 0 & 2 \end{bmatrix}$

**3** $\begin{bmatrix} 0 & -1 \\ 1 & 0 \end{bmatrix} \begin{bmatrix} 0 & 1 \\ -1 & 0 \end{bmatrix} = \begin{bmatrix} 1 & 0 \\ 0 & 1 \end{bmatrix} = \mathbf{E}$

## Chapter 4

**1** (a)

| $\mathbf{D}_{4h}$ | $E$ | $2C_4$ | $C_2$ | $2C_2'$ | $2C_2''$ | $i$ | $2S_4$ | $\sigma_h$ | $2\sigma_v$ | $2\sigma_d$ |
|---|---|---|---|---|---|---|---|---|---|---|
| | +1 | +1 | +1 | −1 | −1 | −1 | −1 | −1 | +1 | +1 |

(b) The $\mathbf{R_z}$ vector is:

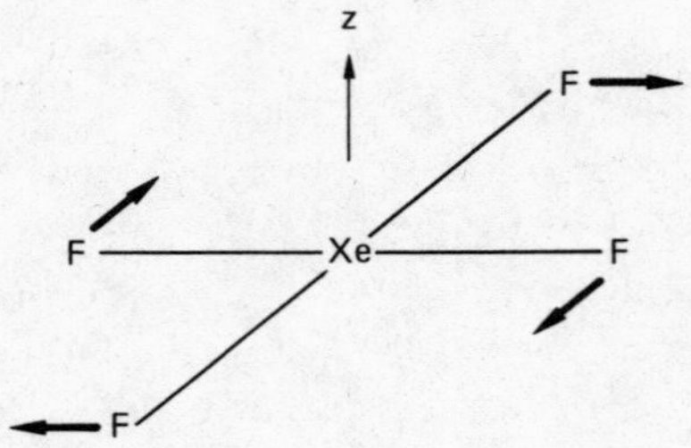


| $\mathbf{D}_{4h}$ | $E$ | $2C_4$ | $C_2$ | $2C_2'$ | $2C_2''$ | $i$ | $2S_4$ | $\sigma_h$ | $2\sigma_v$ | $2\sigma_d$ |
|---|---|---|---|---|---|---|---|---|---|---|
| | +1 | +1 | +1 | −1 | −1 | +1 | +1 | +1 | −1 | −1 |

**2**

| $\mathbf{C}_{4v}$ | $E$ | $C_4^1$ | $C_2$ | $C_4^3$ |
|---|---|---|---|---|
| | $\begin{bmatrix} 1 & 0 \\ 0 & 1 \end{bmatrix}$ | $\begin{bmatrix} 0 & -1 \\ 1 & 0 \end{bmatrix}$ | $\begin{bmatrix} -1 & 0 \\ 0 & -1 \end{bmatrix}$ | $\begin{bmatrix} 0 & 1 \\ -1 & 0 \end{bmatrix}$ |

| $C_{4v}$ (cont.) | $\sigma_v$ | $\sigma_v$ | $\sigma_d$ | $\sigma_d$ |
|---|---|---|---|---|
| | $\begin{bmatrix} 1 & 0 \\ 0 & -1 \end{bmatrix}$ | $\begin{bmatrix} -1 & 0 \\ 0 & 1 \end{bmatrix}$ | $\begin{bmatrix} 0 & 1 \\ 1 & 0 \end{bmatrix}$ | $\begin{bmatrix} 0 & -1 \\ -1 & 0 \end{bmatrix}$ |

3 (a)

| $C_{4v}$ | $E$ | $C_4^1$ | $C_2$ | $C_4^3$ | $\sigma_v$ | $\sigma_v$ | $\sigma_d$ | $\sigma_d$ |
|---|---|---|---|---|---|---|---|---|
| | +1 | −1 | +1 | −1 | +1 | +1 | −1 | −1 |

(b) These orbitals will give the same representation as the $\mathbf{T_x}$ and $\mathbf{T_y}$ vectors (see Exercise 2).

## Chapter 5

1

$$\mathbf{C} = \begin{bmatrix} 4 & -1 & 7 \\ 7 & 1 & 10 \\ 2 & 6 & 8 \end{bmatrix} \quad \text{therefore } \chi(\mathbf{C}) = 13$$

$$\mathbf{D} = \begin{bmatrix} 4 & 1 & 6 \\ -4 & 0 & 1 \\ 12 & 3 & 9 \end{bmatrix} \quad \text{therefore } \chi(\mathbf{D}) = 13$$

2

$$\mathbf{B} = \mathbf{CAC}^{-1} = \begin{bmatrix} 0 & -1 \\ 1 & 0 \end{bmatrix} \begin{bmatrix} 2 & 3 \\ 4 & 5 \end{bmatrix} \begin{bmatrix} 0 & 1 \\ -1 & 0 \end{bmatrix}$$

$$= \begin{bmatrix} 5 & -4 \\ -3 & 2 \end{bmatrix} \quad \text{therefore } \chi(\mathbf{A}) = \chi(\mathbf{B}) = 7$$

3 (a) $1^2 + 2(-1)^2 + 1^2 + 2(-1)^2 + 2(1)^2 = 8$
(b) $(1 \times 2) + 2(-1 \times 0) + (1 \times -2) + 2(1 \times 0) + 2(-1 \times 0) = 0$
(c) $2^2 + 2(-1)^2 + 3(0)^2 + 2^2 + 2(-1)^2 + 3(0)^2 = 12$
(d) $(2 \times 1) + 2(-1 \times 1) + 3(0 \times -1) + (-2 \times 1) + 2(1 \times 1)$
$+ 3(0 \times -1) = 0$

4 (a) $2A_{1g} + A_{1u} + E_u$
(b) $A_2 + B_1 + E_2$
(c) $2A_1 + T_1 + T_2$

## Chapter 6

1 The irreducible components of $\Gamma_{3N}$ in each case are as follows:
(a) $3A_1 + A_2 + 4E$
(b) $5A_1 + A_2 + 2B_1 + B_2 + 6E$
(c) $A_1' + A_2' + 3E' + 2A_2'' + E''$
(d) $2A_{1g} + 2A_{2g} + 2B_{2g} + 2E_{1g} + 4E_{2g} + 2A_{2u} + 2B_{1u} + 2B_{2u} + 4E_{1u} + 2E_{2u}$
(e) $5A_g + 4B_g + 4A_u + 5B_u$
(f) $2A_1 + 2E + 2T_1 + 5T_2$

**2** $\mathbf{C}_{2v}$: $2A_1 + A_2 + B_1 + B_2$
$\mathbf{C}_{4v}$: $A_1 + B_1 + B_2 + E$
$\mathbf{D}_{3h}$: $A_1' + E' + E''$
$\mathbf{T}_d$: $E + T_2$

**3** $\mathbf{C}_{3v}$:

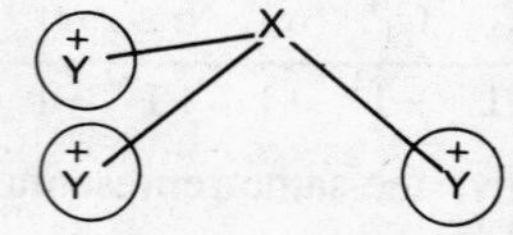


| $\mathbf{C}_{3v}$ | $E$ | $2C_3$ | $3\sigma_v$ | |
|---|---|---|---|---|
| | 3 | 0 | 1 | $= A_1 + E$ |

$\mathbf{D}_{3h}$:

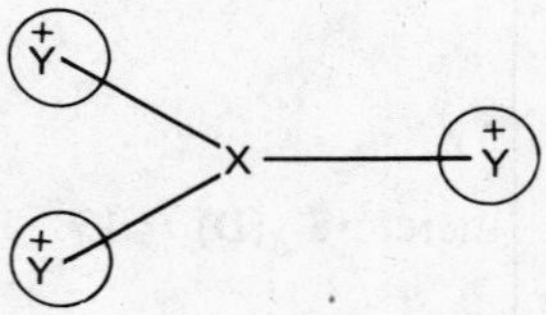


| $\mathbf{D}_{3h}$ | $E$ | $2C_3$ | $3C_2$ | $\sigma_h$ | $2S_3$ | $3\sigma_v$ | |
|---|---|---|---|---|---|---|---|
| | 3 | 0 | 1 | 3 | 0 | 1 | $= A_1' + E'$ |

**4** $\mathbf{D}_{3h}$:

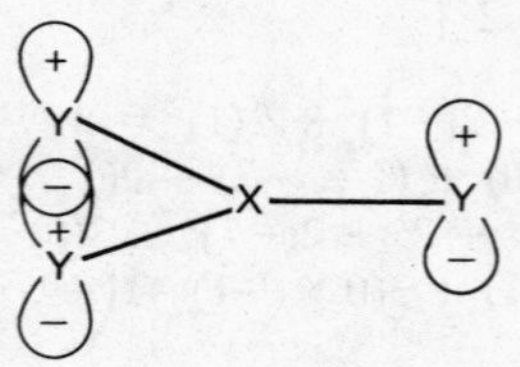


| $\mathbf{D}_{3h}$ | $E$ | $2C_3$ | $3C_2$ | $\sigma_h$ | $2S_3$ | $3\sigma_v$ | |
|---|---|---|---|---|---|---|---|
| | 3 | 0 | −1 | −3 | 0 | 1 | $= A_2'' + E''$ |

## Chapter 7

**1**

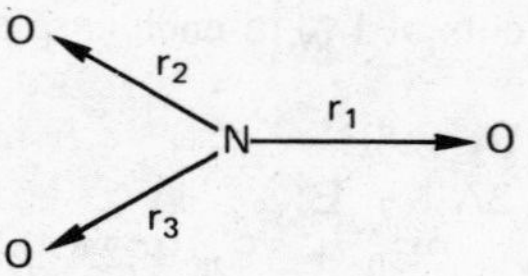


$\Gamma_{bond} = A_1' + E'$

SALCs:

$(1/\sqrt{3})\ (\mathbf{r}_1 + \mathbf{r}_2 + \mathbf{r}_3)\quad (A_1')$
$(1/\sqrt{6})\ (2\mathbf{r}_1 - \mathbf{r}_2 - \mathbf{r}_3)\quad (E')$
$(1/\sqrt{2})\ (\mathbf{r}_2 - \mathbf{r}_3)$

**2** $\Gamma_p = A_2'' + E''$

SALCs:

$(1/\sqrt{3})\ (\pi_1 + \pi_2 + \pi_3)\quad (A_2'')$
$(1/\sqrt{6})\ (2\pi_1 - \pi_2 - \pi_3)\quad (E'')$
$(1/\sqrt{2})\ (\pi_2 - \pi_3)$

**3** The procedure is as for the other examples. The only problem is defining the positions of the symmetry operations.

$\mathbf{T}_d$ (see Figure 7.8): $C_3^1(1)$, $C_3^2(1)$, etc.: $C_3$ axis along $\mathbf{r}_1$, etc; $C_2(12)$, etc.: $C_2$ axis bisecting the angle between $\mathbf{r}_1$ and $\mathbf{r}_2$, etc.; $S_4^1(12)$, $S_4^3(12)$, etc.: $S_4$ axis coincident with analogous $C_2$; $\sigma_d(12)$, etc.: plane containing $\mathbf{r}_1$ and $\mathbf{r}_2$ etc.

$\mathbf{O}_h$ (see Figure 7.9): $C_3^1(123)$, $C_3^2(123)$, etc.: $C_3$ axes forming equal angles with $\mathbf{r}_1$, $\mathbf{r}_2$ and $\mathbf{r}_3$, etc.; $C_2(12)$, etc.: $C_2$ axis bisecting angle between $\mathbf{r}_1$ and $\mathbf{r}_2$, etc.; $C_4^1(1)$, $C_4^3(1)$, $C_2(1)$, etc.: $C_4$ and $C_2$ axis along $\mathbf{r}_1$, etc.; $S_4^1(12)$, $S_4^3(12)$, etc.: $S_4$ axis bisecting angle between $\mathbf{r}_1$ and $\mathbf{r}_2$, etc.; $S_6^1(123)$, $S_6^5(123)$, etc.: $S_6$ axis coincident with $C_3$; $\sigma_h(1234)$, etc.: $\sigma_h$ containing $\mathbf{r}_1$, $\mathbf{r}_2$, $\mathbf{r}_3$ and $\mathbf{r}_4$, etc.; $\sigma_d(12)$, etc.: $\sigma_d$ bisecting angle between $\mathbf{r}_1$ and $\mathbf{r}_2$, etc.

## Chapter 8

**1** (a) $2A_1$ (R, pol.; i.r.) + $2E$ (R, depol.; i.r.)
(b) $4A_1$ (R, pol.; i.r.) + $2B_1$ (R, depol.) + $B_2$ (R, depol.) + $4E$ (R, depol.; i.r.)
(c) $A_1'$ (R, pol.) + $2E'$ (R, depol.; i.r.) + $A_2''$ (i.r.)
(d) $2A_{1g}$ (R, pol.) + $A_{2g}$ (inactive) + $2B_{2g}$ (inactive) + $E_{1g}$ (R, depol.) + $4E_{2g}$ (R, depol.) + $A_{2u}$ (i.r.) + $2B_{1u}$ (inactive) + $2B_{2u}$ (inactive) + $3E_{1u}$ (i.r.) + $2E_{2u}$ (inactive)
(e) $4A_g$ (R, pol.) + $2B_g$ (R, depol.) + $3A_u$ (i.r.) + $3B_u$ (i.r.)
(f) $2A_1$ (R, pol.) + $2E$ (R, depol.) + $T_1$ (inactive) + $4T_2$ (R, depol.; i.r.).

**2** $\nu_1$: 935 cm$^{-1}$: Cl—O symmetric stretch ($A_1$)
$\nu_2$: 462 cm$^{-1}$: deformation (E)
$\nu_3$: 1102/1111 cm$^{-1}$: Cl—O stretch ($T_2$)
$\nu_4$: 628/625 cm$^{-1}$: deformation ($T_2$)

**3** B—F stretches: $A_1'$ (R, pol.) + $E'$ (R, depol.; i.r.)
In-plane deformations: $E'$ (R, depol.; i.r.) [$A_1'$ is redundant]
Out-of-plane deformations: $A_2''$ (i.r.) [$E''$ is redundant – no $E''$ in $\Gamma_{vib}$]

$\nu_1$: 888 cm$^{-1}$: B—F symmetric stretch ($A_1'$)
$\nu_2$: 692 cm$^{-1}$: out-of-plane deformation ($A_2''$)
$\nu_3$: 1453/1454 cm$^{-1}$:B—F stretch ($E'$)
$\nu_4$: 481/479 cm$^{-1}$: in-plane deformation ($E'$)

**4** $\Gamma_{vib} = 2A_1' + 3E' + 2A_2'' + E''$

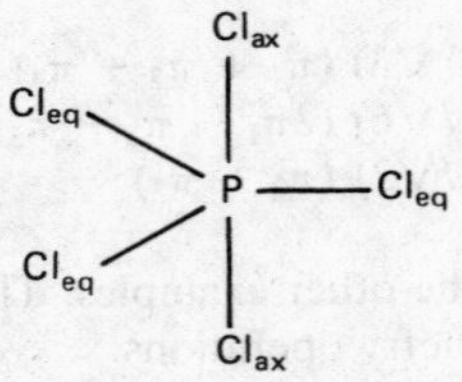


P—$Cl_{ax}$ stretches: $A_1'$ (R, pol.) + $A_2''$ (i.r.)
P—$Cl_{eq}$ stretches: $A_1'$ (R, pol.) + $E'$ (R, depol.; i.r.)
$Cl_{eq}$—P—$Cl_{eq}$ deformations: $E'$ (R, depol.; i.r.) [$A_1'$ is redundant]
$Cl_{ax}$—P—$Cl_{eq}$ deformations: $E'$ (R, depol.; i.r.) + $A_2''$ (i.r.) + $E''$ (R, depol.) [$A_1'$ is redundant]

$\nu_1$: 394 cm$^{-1}$ }
$\nu_2$: 385 cm$^{-1}$ }: P—$Cl_{ax}$, P—$Cl_{eq}$ stretches ($A_1'$)
$\nu_3$: 444 cm$^{-1}$: P—$Cl_{ax}$ stretch ($A_2''$)
$\nu_4$: 299 cm$^{-1}$: $Cl_{ax}$—P—$Cl_{eq}$ deformation ($A_2''$)
$\nu_5$: 579/581 cm$^{-1}$: P—$Cl_{eq}$ stretch ($E'$)
$\nu_6$: 279/277 cm$^{-1}$: $Cl_{ax}$—P—$Cl_{eq}$ deformation ($E'$)
$\nu_7$: 98 cm$^{-1}$: $Cl_{eq}$—P—$Cl_{eq}$ deformation ($E'$)
$\nu_8$: 261 cm$^{-1}$: $Cl_{ax}$—P—$Cl_{eq}$ deformation ($E''$)

## Chapter 9

**1** B—F stretches: ($A_1'$) $(1/\sqrt{3})\,(\mathbf{r_1} + \mathbf{r_2} + \mathbf{r_3})$
($E'$) $(1/\sqrt{6})\,(2\mathbf{r_1} - \mathbf{r_2} - \mathbf{r_3})$
$(1/\sqrt{2})\,(\mathbf{r_2} - \mathbf{r_3})$
In-plane deformations: ($E'$) $(1/\sqrt{6})\,(2\alpha_1 - \alpha_2 - \alpha_3)$
$(1/\sqrt{2})\,(\alpha_2 - \alpha_3)$
Out-of-plane deformations: ($A_2''$) $(1/\sqrt{3})\,(\beta_1 + \beta_2 + \beta_3)$

**2** The band can be assigned to $2\nu_3$, the first overtone of the $E'$ B—F stretch ($2 \times 1453 = 2906$). To determine the symmetry species of this overtone, use the equation on p. 114. For a first overtone, this is:

$$\chi_2(R) = \frac{1}{2}\left[\chi(R)\chi(R) + \chi(R^2)\right]$$

For $\mathbf{D}_{3h}$, we have:

| $R$ | $E$ | $C_3^1$ | $C_3^2$ | $C_2$ | $C_2$ | $C_2$ | $\sigma_h$ | $S_3^1$ | $S_3^5$ | $\sigma_v$ | $\sigma_v$ | $\sigma_v$ |
|---|---|---|---|---|---|---|---|---|---|---|---|---|
| $R^2$ | $E$ | $C_3^2$ | $C_3^1$ | $E$ | $E$ | $E$ | $E$ | $C_3^2$ | $C_3^1$ | $E$ | $E$ | $E$ |
| $x(R)$ | 2 | −1 | −1 | 0 | 0 | 0 | 2 | −1 | −1 | 0 | 0 | 0 |
| $x(R^2)$ | 2 | −1 | −1 | 2 | 2 | 2 | 2 | −1 | −1 | 2 | 2 | 2 |
| $x_2(R)$ | 3 | 0 | 0 | 1 | 1 | 1 | 3 | 0 | 0 | 1 | 1 | 1 |

The resulting representation is reducible to $A_1' + E'$. Hence, the first overtone of the $E'$ B—F stretch of $BF_3$ has symmetry species $A_1'$ and $E'$.

3 $\mathbf{D}_{3h} \rightarrow \mathbf{C}_{3v}$ $\mathbf{C}_{2v}$

| | | |
|---|---|---|
| $\mathbf{D}_{3h} \rightarrow \mathbf{C}_{3v}$ | | $\mathbf{C}_{2v}$ |
| $A_1' \rightarrow$ | $A_1$ | $A_1$ |
| $E' \rightarrow$ | $E$ | $A_1 + B_2$ |
| $A_2'' \rightarrow$ | $A_1$ | $B_1$ |
| $E'' \rightarrow$ | $E$ | $A_2 + B_1$ |

Therefore, $BF_2Cl$ ($\mathbf{C}_{2v}$) has stretches $2A_1 + B_2$. (NB: $BF_2$ stretches $A_1 + B_2$; BCl stretch $A_1$; in-plane bends $A_1 + B_2$; out-of-plane bend $B_1$.)

$PCl_4F$ (axial F; $\mathbf{C}_{3v}$) has stretches $3A_1 + E$ (that is, $A_1$ P—F, P—$Cl_{ax}$, P—$Cl_{eq}$; E $PCl_{3(eq)}$); 'equatorial' bends E; 'axial' bends $2A_1 + E$. $PCl_4F$ (equatorial F; $\mathbf{C}_{2v}$) has stretches $3A_1 + B_1 + B_2$ (that is, P—F $A_1$; $PCl_{2(eq)}$ $A_1 + B_2$; $PCl_{2(ax)}$, $A_1 + B_1$); 'equatorial' bends $2A_1 + B_2$; 'axial' bends $A_1 + A_2 + 2B_1 + B_2$.

## Chapter 10

1 (a) $a_{1g} + b_{1g} + e_u$

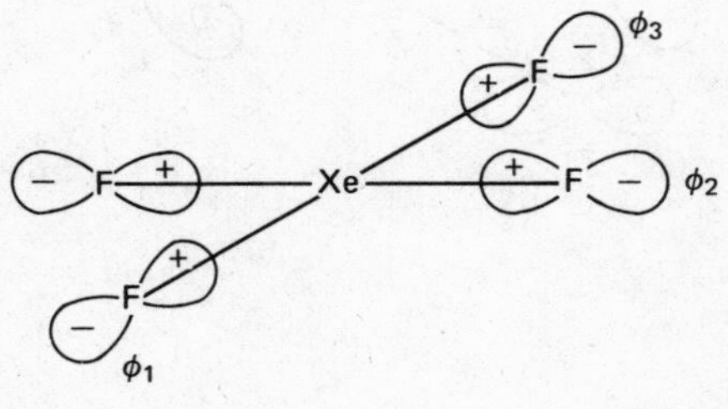


(b) 5s, $4d_{x2}$: $a_{1g}$
$5d_{x2-y2}$: $b_{1g}$
$5p_x$, $5p_y$: $e_u$

(c) $a_{1g}$: $(1/2)(\phi_1 + \phi_2 + \phi_3 + \phi_4)$
$b_{1g}$: $(1/2)(\phi_1 - \phi_2 + \phi_3 - \phi_4)$
$e_u$: $(1/\sqrt{2})(\phi_1 - \phi_3)$; $(1/\sqrt{2})(\phi_2 - \phi_4)$

(d)

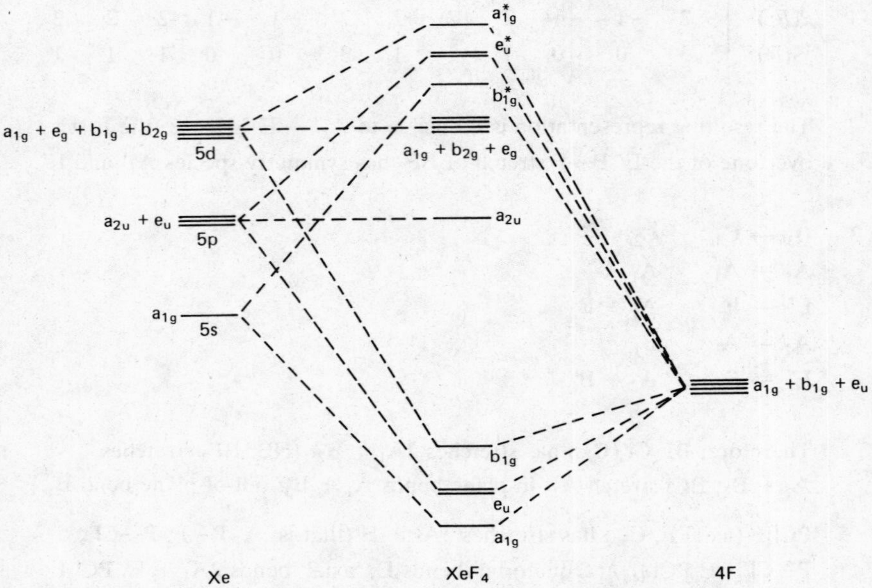


**2** π-bonding (in-plane): $\Gamma(\pi, \text{in-plane}) = a_{2g} + b_{2g} + e_u$

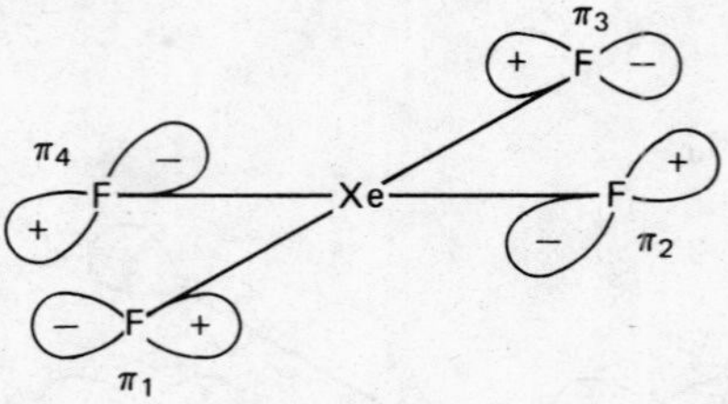

π-bonding (out-of-plane): $\Gamma(\pi, \text{out-of-plane}) = a_{2u} + b_{2u} + e_g$

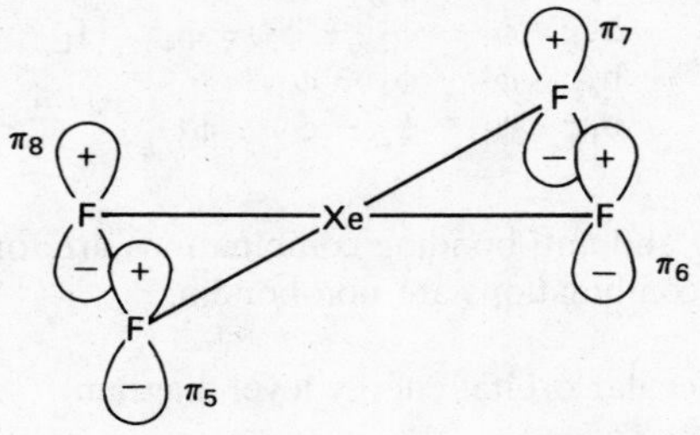


SALCs:

| | | |
|---|---|---|
| $\Gamma(\pi, \text{in-plane})$: | $a_{2g}$: | $(1/2)(\pi_1 + \pi_2 + \pi_3 + \pi_4)$ |
| | $b_{2g}$: | $(1/2)(\pi_1 - \pi_2 + \pi_3 - \pi_4)$ |
| | $e_u$: | $(1/\sqrt{2})(\pi_1 - \pi_3)$; $(1/\sqrt{2})(\pi_2 - \pi_4)$ |
| $\Gamma(\pi, \text{out-of-plane})$: | $a_{2u}$: | $(1/2)(\pi_5 + \pi_6 + \pi_7 + \pi_8)$ |
| | $b_{2u}$: | $(1/2)(\pi_5 - \pi_6 + \pi_7 - \pi_8)$ |
| | $e_g$: | $(1/\sqrt{2})(\pi_5 - \pi_7)$; $(1/\sqrt{2})(\pi_6 - \pi_8)$ |

Possible π-bonding interactions with:
$5d_{xy}$ ($b_{2g}$) (in-plane)
$5p_z$ ($a_{2u}$) and $5d_{yz}$, $5d_{zx}$ ($e_g$) (out-of-plane)

**3** $\Gamma_B = a_g + b_{2g} + b_{1u} + b_{3u}$
$\Gamma_H = a_g + b_{3u}$

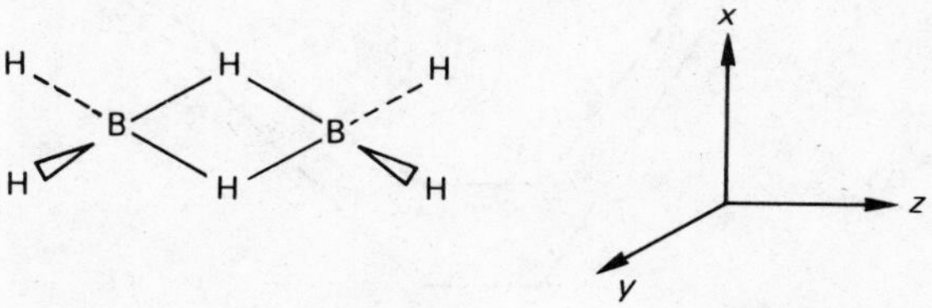


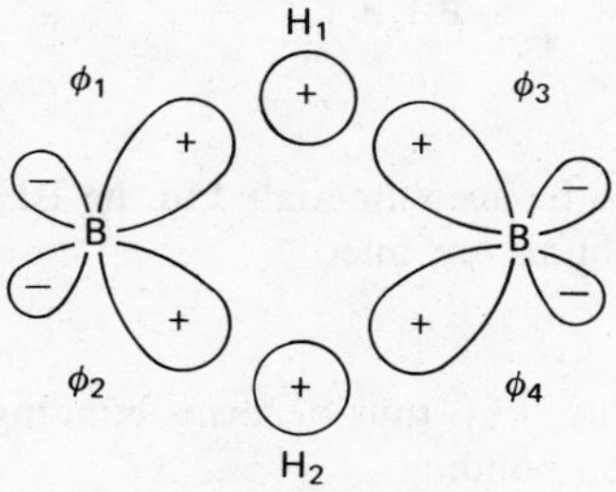

SALCs (un-normalised):

$a_g$: $\phi_1 + \phi_2 + \phi_3 + \phi_4$; $H_1 + H_2$
$b_{3u}$: $\phi_1 - \phi_2 + \phi_3 - \phi_4$; $H_1 - H_2$
$b_{2g}$: $\phi_1 - \phi_2 - \phi_3 + \phi_4$
$b_{1u}$: $\phi_1 + \phi_2 - \phi_3 - \phi_4$

Hence, bonding and anti-bonding combinations are formed for $a_g$ and $b_{3u}$; the $b_{2g}$ and $b_{1u}$ combinations are non-bonding.

Qualitative molecular orbital energy level diagram:

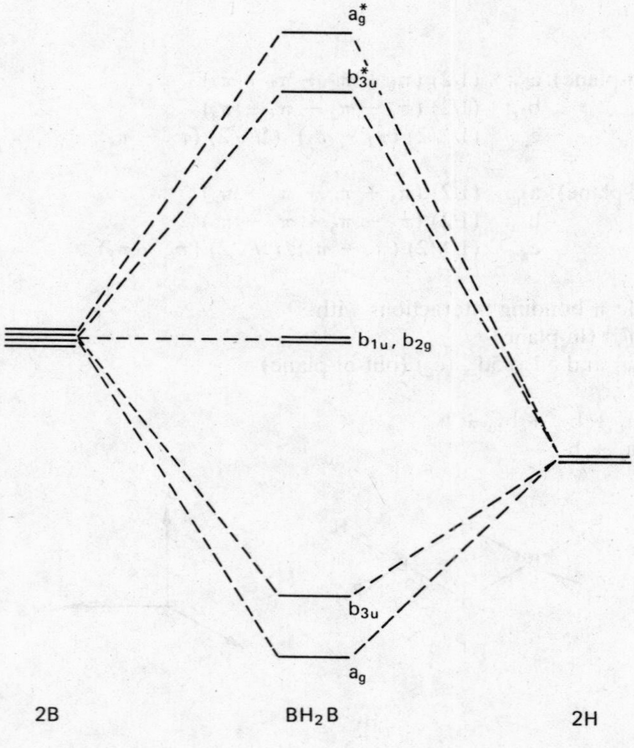


There are four electrons to be accommodated in the $BH_2B$ unit; that is, the two bonding molecular orbitals are filled.

**4** $C_{2v}$: Central C: $b_1$
$\Gamma(\pi$ – terminal C atoms): $a_2 + b_1$, thus $b_1$ forms bonding and anti-bonding combinations, and $a_2$ is non-bonding.

Molecular orbital energy level diagram:

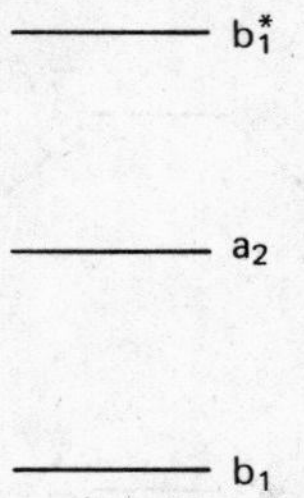


Number of $\pi$-electrons = 3; ground state $(b_1)^2(a_2)^1$

5 $C(CH_2)_3$

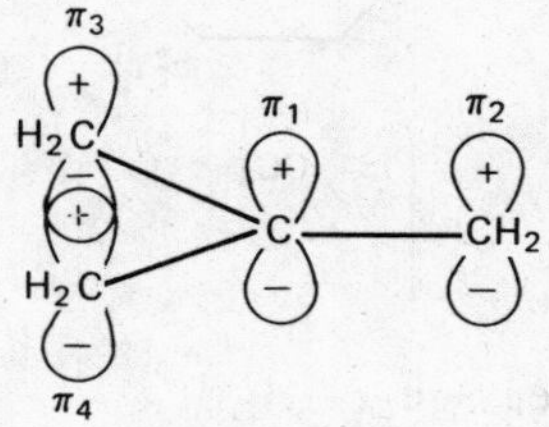


| $\mathbf{D}_{3h}$ | $E$ | $2C_3$ | $3C_2$ | $\sigma_h$ | $2S_3$ | $3\sigma_v$ | |
|---|---|---|---|---|---|---|---|
| Central C | 1 | 1 | −1 | −1 | −1 | 1 | i.e. $a_2''$ |
| Terminal C atoms ($\Gamma(\pi)$) | 3 | 0 | −1 | −3 | 0 | 1 | i.e. $a_2'' + e''$ |

SALCs for terminal C atoms:

$a_2''$: $(1/\sqrt{3})\,(\pi_2 + \pi_3 + \pi_4)$
$e''$: $(1/\sqrt{6})\,(2\pi_2 - \pi_3 - \pi_4)$
$(1/\sqrt{2})\,(\pi_3 - \pi_4)$

Bonding and anti-bonding $a_2''$ molecular orbitals formed, and $e''$ non-bonding.

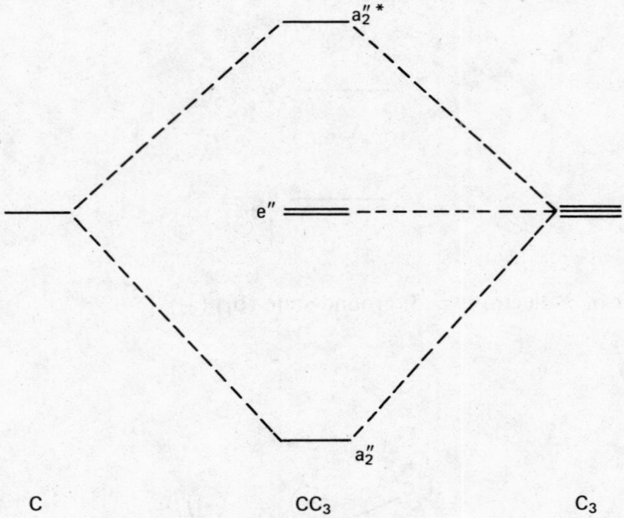


$C_6H_6$
$\Gamma_p(\pi) = a_{2u} + b_{2g} + e_{1g} + e_{2u}$:

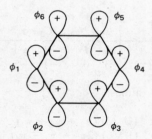

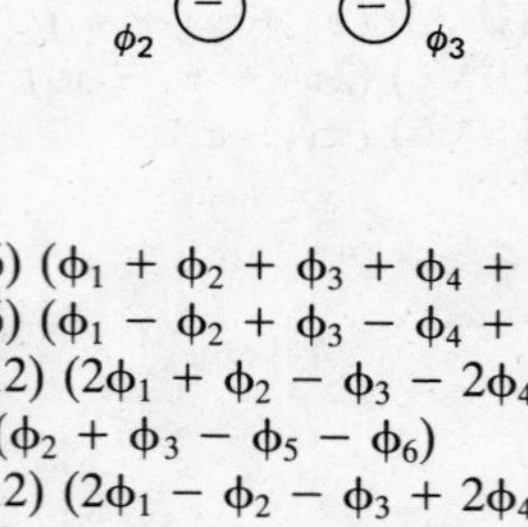


SALCs:

$$\begin{aligned}
a_{2u}&: (1/\sqrt{6})\,(\phi_1 + \phi_2 + \phi_3 + \phi_4 + \phi_5 + \phi_6)\\
b_{2g}&: (1/\sqrt{6})\,(\phi_1 - \phi_2 + \phi_3 - \phi_4 + \phi_5 - \phi_6)\\
e_{1g}&: (1/\sqrt{12})\,(2\phi_1 + \phi_2 - \phi_3 - 2\phi_4 - \phi_5 + \phi_6);\\
&\quad (1/2)\,(\phi_2 + \phi_3 - \phi_5 - \phi_6)\\
e_{2u}&: (1/\sqrt{12})\,(2\phi_1 - \phi_2 - \phi_3 + 2\phi_4 - \phi_5 - \phi_6);\\
&\quad (1/2)\,(\phi_2 - \phi_3 + \phi_5 - \phi_6)
\end{aligned}$$

$a_{2u}$ strongly bonding; $e_{1g}$ weakly bonding; $e_{2u}$ weakly anti-bonding; $b_{2g}$ strongly anti-bonding.

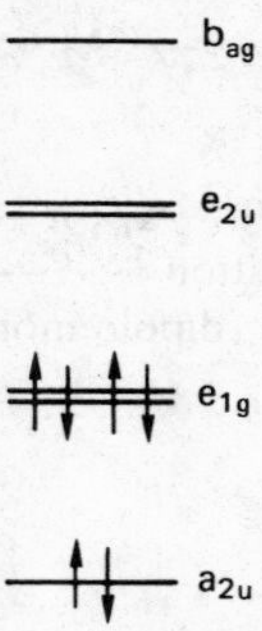


The six $\pi$-electrons fill all of the bonding molecular orbitals.

## Chapter 11

**1** Ground electronic states:

$BH_3$: $(a_1')^2(e')^2$: ${}^1A_1'$
$NH_3$: $(a_1)^2(e)^2$: ${}^1A_1$

Excited states:

$BH_3$: $(a_1')^2(e')^3(a_2'')^1$: ${}^1E''$ or ${}^3E''$
$(a_1')^2(e')^3(a_1{}^{*\prime})^2$: ${}^1E'$ or ${}^3E'$
$(a_1')^2(e')^3(e^{*\prime})^1$: ${}^1A_1' + {}^1A_2' + {}^1E'$ or ${}^3A_1' + {}^3A_2' + {}^3E'$
$NH_3$: $(a_1)^2(e)^3(e^*)^1$: ${}^1A_1 + {}^1A_2 + {}^1E$ or ${}^3A_1 + {}^3A_2 + {}^3E$
$(a_1)^2(e)^3(a_1{}^*)^1$: ${}^1E$ or ${}^3E$

All singlet $\rightarrow$ triplet transitions are spin forbidden. Singlet $\rightarrow$ singlet transitions are spin allowed. The symmetry selection rule gives the following results:

| | | | |
|---|---|---|---|
| $BH_3$: ${}^1A_1'$ | $\longrightarrow$ | ${}^1E''$ | forbidden |
| | $\longrightarrow$ | ${}^1E'$ | allowed |
| | $\longrightarrow$ | ${}^1A_1'$ | forbidden |
| | $\longrightarrow$ | ${}^1A_2'$ | forbidden |
| $NH_3$: ${}^1A_1$ | $\longrightarrow$ | ${}^1A_1$ | allowed |
| | $\longrightarrow$ | ${}^1A_2$ | forbidden |
| | $\longrightarrow$ | ${}^1E$ | allowed |

**2** Ground state of allyl radical:

$$(b_1)^2(a_2)^1\text{: } {}^2A_2$$

Possible $\pi^*$ excited states:

$$(b_1)^1(a_2)^1(b_1{}^*)^1\text{: } {}^2A_2 \text{ or } {}^4A_2$$
$$(b_1)^2(b_1{}^*)^1\text{: } {}^2B_1$$

The $\pi \rightarrow \pi^*$ transitions are $^2A_2 \rightarrow {}^2A_2$ (allowed), $^2A_2 \rightarrow {}^2B_1$ or $^2A_2 \rightarrow {}^4A_2$ (forbidden).

**3** $CO_3^{2-}$: Ground state $(a_2'')^2(e'')^4$: $^1A_1'$; $n \rightarrow \pi^*$ excited state $(a_2'')^2(e'')^3(a_2''^*)^1$: $^1E'$ or $^3E'$. The $n \rightarrow \pi^*$ transition $^1A_1' \rightarrow {}^3E'$ is spin forbidden; $^1A_1' \rightarrow {}^1E'$ is spin and symmetry allowed (dipole moment components are E′ and $A_2''$).

**4** $(t_{2g})^2(e_g)^1$
$(t_{2g})^2$: $^3T_{1g}$, $^1A_{1g}$, $^1E_g$, $^1T_{2g}$
$(e_g)^1$: $^2E_g$

Possible symmetries for $(t_{2g})^2(e_g)^1$:

$$^3T_{1g} \times {}^2E_g = {}^4T_{1g} + {}^4T_{2g}$$
$$^1A_{1g} \times {}^2E_g = {}^2E_g$$
$$^1E_g \times {}^2E_g = {}^2A_{1g} + {}^2A_{2g} + {}^2E_g$$
$$^1T_{2g} \times {}^2E_g = {}^2T_{1g} + {}^2T_{2g}$$

Ground state $^4A_{2g}$, hence the only spin-allowed transitions are $^4A_{2g} \rightarrow {}^4T_{1g}$ or $^4T_{2g}$. (Note that both are $g \rightarrow g$ and so are symmetry forbidden.)

## Chapter 12

**1** The ground state of the allyl anion, $CH_2CHCH_2^-$, is (see Figures 12.10 and 12.11) $(\pi)^2(\pi^\circ)^2$. Conrotatory motion gives a cyclic product with the electronic configuration $(\sigma)^2(p)^2$, while disrotatory motion gives the electronic configuration $(\sigma)^2(\sigma^*)^2$. Thus, the thermal cyclisation of $CH_2CHCH_2^-$ is predicted to proceed by a conrotatory mechanism.

For a photochemical reaction, the allyl anion will have the electronic configuration $(\pi)^2(\pi^\circ)^1(\pi^*)^1$. Conrotatory motion gives the product in the state $(\sigma)^1(p)^2(\sigma^*)^1$, disrotatory $(\sigma)^2(p)^1(\sigma^*)^1$, and so the latter is preferred.

**2** Photochemically excited $C_2H_4$ molecules will be in the electronic state $(\pi)^1(\pi^*)^1$. This (see Figure 12.15) would give the cyclobutane in the ground state, and so it will be a symmetry-allowed process.

# Bibliography


**Mathematical background**

R L Flurry, *Symmetry Groups*, Prentice-Hall (Englewood Cliffs), 1980.
E P Wigner, *Group Theory*, Academic Press (New York), 1959 (the definitive treatment).

**General applications (including theory)**

B E Douglas and C A Hollingsworth, *Symmetry in Bonding and Spectra*, Academic Press (Orlando), 1985.
L H Hall, *Group Theory and Symmetry in Chemistry*, McGraw-Hill (New York), 1969.
D S Schonland, *Molecular Symmetry*, D. Van Nostrand & Co. Ltd. (London), 1960.

**Spectroscopy (both theory and practice)**

C N Banwell, *Fundamentals of Modern Spectroscopy*, (3rd edn.), McGraw-Hill (London), 1983.
J C Decius and R M Hexter, *Molecular Vibrations in Crystals*, McGraw-Hill (New York), 1977.
J M Hollas, *Modern Spectroscopy*, John Wiley & Sons (Chichester), 1987.
D A Long, *Raman Spectroscopy*, McGraw-Hill (New York), 1977.
B P Straughan and S Walker (eds.), *Spectroscopy*, (3 vols.), Chapman & Hall (London), 1976.
E B Wilson, Jr., J C Decius and P C Cross, *Molecular Vibrations*, McGraw-Hill (New York), 1955 (the classical treatment of the applications of group theory to vibrational spectroscopy).
L A Woodward, *Introduction to the Theory of Molecular Vibrations and Vibrational Spectroscopy*, Oxford University Press (Oxford), 1972.

**Molecular orbitals**

In addition to the general texts listed on the previous page, see also:

J N Murrell, S F A Kettle and J M Tedder, *Valence Theory*, (2nd edn.), John Wiley & Sons (Chichester), 1975.

**Orbital symmetry and chemical reactions**

R E Lehr and A P Marchand, *Orbital Symmetry*, Academic Press (New York), 1972.

R B Woodward and R Hoffmann, *The Conservation of Orbital Symmetry*, Verlag Chemie (Weinheim), 1971.

# Index